Have you ever wanted to fly as fast as the wind to a land far away? Or to blast off in a rocket aimed for a distant star?

Or to dive as swiftly as a seal into the depths of the sea? Then turn the page!

Adventure lies just ahead in the pages of...

HOUGHTON MIFFLIN
The Literature Experience
READING

Cover, Introduction, and Title Page Illustrations from *The Weaving of a Dream* by Marilee Heyer. Copyright © 1986 by Marilee Heyer. Reprinted by permission of Toni Mendez, Inc. Published by Viking Kestrel.

Acknowledgments appear on page 493.

Printed in the U.S.A.

ISBN: 0-395-51924-1

ABCDEFGHIJ-VH-99876543210

FAST AS THE WIND

Senior Author
John J. Pikulski

*Senior Coordinating
Author*
J. David Cooper

*Senior Consulting
Author*
William K. Durr

Coordinating Authors
Kathryn H. Au
M. Jean Greenlaw
Marjorie Y. Lipson
Susan Page
Sheila W. Valencia
Karen K. Wixson

Authors
Rosalinda B. Barrera
Ruth P. Bunyan
Jacqueline L. Chaparro
Jacqueline C. Comas
Alan N. Crawford
Robert L. Hillerich
Timothy G. Johnson
Jana M. Mason
Pamela A. Mason
William E. Nagy
Joseph S. Renzulli
Alfredo Schifini

Senior Advisor
Richard C. Anderson

Advisors
Christopher J. Baker
Charles Peters

HOUGHTON MIFFLIN COMPANY   BOSTON
Atlanta   Dallas   Geneva, Illinois Palo Alto   Princeton   Toronto

BOOK 1

16 The Hey Hey Man
by Sid Fleischman

30 The Scarebird
by Sid Fleischman

46 McBroom Tells the Truth
by Sid Fleischman

THEME BOOK
The Whipping Boy
by Sid Fleischman

THE DANGER ZONE

BOOK 2

72 Ghost of the Lagoon
by Armstrong Sperry

86 The Lighthouse Keeper's Daughter
by Arielle North Olson

106 Where's Buddy?
from the book by Ron Roy

POETRY
127 Long Trip *by Langston Hughes*
Sea Calm *by Langston Hughes*

THEME BOOK
A Lion to Guard Us
by Clyde Robert Bulla

BOOK 3

136 Andy Bear: A Polar Cub Grows Up at the Zoo
from the book by Ginny Johnston and Judy Cutchins

157 Sterling: The Rescue of a Baby Harbor Seal
by Sandra Verrill White and Michael Filisky

169 Fly Away Free
by Joan Hewett

POETRY
152 Buffalo Dusk *by Carl Sandburg*
153 Eagle Flight *by Alonzo Lopez*
Hurt No Living Thing *by Christina Rossetti*
154 The Passenger Pigeon *by Paul Fleischman*
155 Bison *by Tonye Garter*

THEME BOOK
Saving the Peregrine Falcon
by Caroline Arnold

FICTION

191

SOLUTIONS, INC.

BOOK 4

194 The Pretty Pennies picket
from Philip Hall likes me. I reckon maybe.
by Bette Greene

216 The Streets Are Free
a play by Kurusa based on her book

232 The Doughnuts
from Homer Price
by Robert McCloskey

254 *Linking Literature to Social Studies*
Earth Is Our Address: A Textbook Selection

POETRY

212 Writing Limericks
by David McCord
A Young Lady of Crete
213 On Reading
by Myra Cohn Livingston
A Young Man from
Darjeeling

214 A Very Mean Man of
Belsize
A Chameleon
by Eve Merriam
215 A Mouse in Her Room
Woke Miss Dowd
A Flea and a Fly in a Flue

THEME BOOK
The Kid in the Red Jacket
by Barbara Park

LONG·AGO AND·FAR·AWAY

BOOK 5

266 The Weaving of a Dream
retold by Marilee Heyer

286 The Emir's Son
retold by Martin Ballard

304 Her Seven Brothers
retold by Paul Goble

POETRY
323 Reading's Enchanting Spell
by Leland B. Jacobs

THEME BOOK
Vassilisa the Wise: A Tale of Medieval Russia
retold by Josepha Sherman

NONFICTION
327

J O U R N E Y   I N T O   S P A C E

BOOK 6

332 To Space & Back
from the book by Sally Ride with Susan Okie

360 Mars
by Seymour Simon

378 Humans on Mars? Where Will the U.S.
Space Program Go Next?
by Renée Skelton

POETRY
391 Moon
by Myra Cohn Livingston

THEME BOOK
Space Challenger: The Story of Guion Bluford
by Jim Haskins and Kathleen Benson

To Be Continued...

BOOK 7

401 The Voyage of the *Dawn Treader*
from the book by C. S. Lewis

419 The Blossoms Meet the Vulture Lady
from the book by Betsy Byars

445 The Mouse and the Motorcycle
from the book by Beverly Cleary

THEME BOOK
The Mouse and the Motorcycle
by Beverly Cleary

GLOSSARY
476

AUTHOR

BOOK 1

·SID·

Fleischman

When it comes to writing, Sid Fleischman always has plenty of jokes and surprises up his sleeve. His homespun tales go from the serious to the downright silly.

In this book you will meet some of his unusual characters: the witty and sly Hey Hey Man, the sad Lonesome John, and the fast-talking Josh McBroom and his family.

Throughout this book are messages that Sid Fleischman wrote explaining how he got the ideas for each of the stories you will read.

Dear Houghton Mifflin Readers,

I have wonderful fun writing stories. If you were in my home office when I am writing at the computer, you would hear me burst out laughing from time to time.

I laugh when a funny scene pops into my head. I laugh at lines of dialogue. Often I don't know where the ideas come from. But sometimes I do.

A story almost never comes to the author with all its parts in place. Almost always it starts with a fragment. It's like a clue to a story, and the detective work begins for the missing parts.

CONTENTS

THE HEY HEY MAN   16

THE SCAREBIRD   30

McBROOM TELLS THE TRUTH   46

The Hey Hey Man

by Sid Fleischman

One night a thief, who fancied himself a handsome fellow, climbed a haystack to catch a wink of sleep. He stuffed his trouser legs and coat and sleeves with straw for added warmth. A black frost had already withered the Vermont farmlands.

Just after midnight he was awakened by sounds from the farmhouse. He saw a broad-shouldered man holding open the back door while a pack of dogs loped outside.

illustrated by John Littleboy

"Sh-h-h-h," the farmer called to the dogs. "This way, my lovely tail-waggers."

The farmer carried an old leather boot.

He picked up a shovel and headed for a lone chestnut tree. It stood huge against the starlit sky, ancient and tangle-branched. The seedling had come from the Old Country, and for generations folks had pointed it out as the Hey Hey Tree.

Some believed that a prankish tree spirit, a Hey Hey Man, had crossed the ocean with it.

At the base of the tree the farmer set the boot on the ground. He began to dig, then stopped. He peered up into the limbs and branches.

"Hey Hey Man," he called softly. "You up there, neighbor? Give us a peek at you."

The tree stood in stately silence.

"A shy one, you are," said the farmer, with a chuckle. "Or no one at all. Granny tales. How come my hounds can't sniff you out? Still, if you're watching, don't make off with my hard-earned savings, or I'll chop down your tree. No, I've nothing to fear from you, Mr. Hey Hey Man."

He finished digging the hole and turned to his dogs. "Put your noses to the boot. Don't forget the scent, my dear ankle-biters."

The dogs snuffed and sniffed the old jackboot, their tails whipping the chill air.

The farmer dropped the boot into the hole. It landed with a rattle of coins, and he covered it over with dirt and fallen leaves. "Come along, my pot-lickers," he said. "Before long the ground will freeze solid as rock. The gold'll be safe all winter."

The farmer and the dogs returned to the warmth of the house.

"What luck!" the thief muttered, laughing to himself. "A boot full of valuables, and not a single dog to guard it. The jabbering fool lets the old fleabags sleep with him!"

He rose from the haystack. Silent as a cat, step by step, he made for the chestnut tree. He dug up the jackboot, filled in the hole, and covered it again with leaves. Then, with the boot heaved over one shoulder, he moved as quietly as a shadow across the meadow.

Finally he began to run. With his clothing stuffed with straw he thought he must look like a scarecrow come to life. But soon, with treasure to spend, he'd be wearing ruffled shirts and velvet coats. What a dashing figure he'd cut!

He leaped a stone wall and sat down to catch his breath. For the first time, he reached into the boot, clutched up some coins, and examined them in the cold starlight. They shone like a handful of embers, and he yipped out a short, joyous laugh.

But the laughter caught in his throat. There on the wall stood a banty little man. He wore short leather breeches, green woolen knee socks, and an Alpine hat with a sprig of chestnut leaves tucked into the band.

"A chill in the air tonight," the man said pleasantly. He clutched a small whip under his arm.

"Stand where you are!" the thief shouted.

The little man clinked a few coins in his hands. "Yours? Yes, I think you must be dropping gold pieces like grain from a torn sack."

The thief looked at the sole of the jackboot. The farmer had worn a hole in it.

"I declare!" the little man remarked. "Is that Anton's old boot? I've seen it on his foot for many a year."

"One boot looks like another," the thief snapped. "Hand over my gold pieces."

"A pleasure," the man said, and poured the coins into the thief's palm.

Then the thief reached inside his sleeve for a wad of straw and plugged the hole in the boot.

"I'll walk with you for a piece," said the man.

The thief scowled. "I travel alone, stranger."

"As you wish."

And the thief took off toward the woods. He rushed along, deeper and deeper into the forest. By the time dawn broke, he couldn't find his way out.

And there, in the gray gloom, on a fallen log, sat the banty little man with chestnut leaves stuck in his hat.

"How did you get here?" the thief shouted. "Stop following me!"

"Only trying to be of service. You're lost, I see."

The thief's eyes darkened. "Where did you come from? Who are you?"

"Think of me as your obedient servant — the Hey Hey Man."

"Never heard of you!"

"It doesn't matter. You've been walking in circles. Never find your way out of the forest unless you follow your nose. That's my advice, sir. Follow your nose."

"Numbskull!" thundered the thief. "I can't see my nose to follow it."

"I can fix that," remarked the little man. He cracked his whip and said, "Hey! Hey!"

The thief's nose grew out as long and lumpy as a horseradish root.

"Always glad to oblige," said the Hey Hey Man amiably.

"Confound you!"

But the Hey Hey Man had vanished into the deep forest shadows.

The thief followed the end of his nose, like the jack staff of a ship, and it led him out of the woods.

He came to an unplowed cornfield and stopped to rest. "No need to footrace it," he told himself. "It'll be spring before the farmer and his curs discover the boot missing."

The dry cornstalks scraped and rustled in the wind. And there stood the Hey Hey Man with the whip under his arm.

"Temperature's dropping fast," he said.

The thief jumped to his feet, and his eyes shot fire. "You cussed little mongrel! Look at this tarnatious nose! Who are you, the devil?"

"No relation," said the Hey Hey Man.

"I'll maul the pinfeathers out of you!"

"No time, sir, no time." The Hey Hey Man cocked an ear. "Hear that? Listen."

"To what?"

"A pack of dogs. Sounds like they're on the hunt."

"Moonshine!" snarled the thief. "I don't hear a thing!"

"I declare!" remarked the little man. "Well, I can fix that." He cracked his whip and said, "Hey! Hey!"

Instantly the thief's ears grew as big as cabbage leaves.

The thief could now hear the distant baying of dogs. He turned dishwater-pale.

He fixed blazing eyes on the Hey Hey Man. "Blast your pesky hide! You didn't fetch me all the gold pieces!"

"I may have missed a few in the dark."

The thief picked up the jackboot and began to run. No doubt the farmer had found a trail of coins on the ground, discovered that the hole was empty, and turned his curs loose.

The thief went crashing through the dry cornstalks and came to a clearing. The bark and blather of the hounds was getting closer.

"They're following the sniff of the boot," he babbled to himself. "I'll have to get rid of the infernal thing."

He filled his pockets, but still he had coins left over. He cupped them in his hands, kicked the boot into a wild blackberry patch, and hurried away.

He ran for an eternity, but still the dogs howled in his ears. Still they pursued him. Once he looked back and saw the farmer and his ankle-biters leaping along the brow of a hill.

He waded across a shallow river. And there, on a stone, sat the Hey Hey Man with his legs crossed.

The jackboot lay beside him.

The thief snorted. "You meddling runt! Why didn't you leave that boot be? Sink it in the river!"

The Hey Hey Man looked hurt. "Dear me, I do apologize. But see here, you can't make strides with both hands clasping coins in front of you. You need a money sack."

He cracked his whip and said, "Hey! Hey!"

The jackboot turned into a cloth sack.

"Hang your sack!" the thief exclaimed. "What I need is a horse!"

"Wish I could oblige," said the Hey Hey Man. "But I need straw to make a horse. No, I can't help you there."

The thief's eyes lit up. "Straw! How do you think I've kept from freezing?"

He poured the coins from his hands into the sack. Then he shook his sleeves and straw fell to the ground. He pulled straw from inside his trouser legs. He plucked straw from all his clothing and threw it on the pile.

"Yes, that might do," remarked the Hey Hey Man.

"Hurry!" The thief could hear the hounds snorting. They'd soon be at his ankles. He emptied the gold from his pockets into the cloth sack and knotted the top.

The Hey Hey Man circled the pile of straw. He peered thoughtfully at it. Then he cracked his whip and said, "Hey! Hey!"

And there, nostrils breathing steam, stood a chestnut mare.

The thief jumped onto her back and rode away.

The horse galloped wildly across the countryside. She raced under the boughs of trees and the thief ducked low on her back. He held on for dear life. There was no holding or turning the beast.

She rattled along a pasture, over a covered bridge, and along a field. The wind blinded the thief. It whistled past his ears and turned his nose red.

The thief felt frozen to the bone. But he didn't care. Let the horse have her head, he thought. She was whisking him miles and miles from the farmer's tail-wagging, ankle-biting hounds.

Suddenly the mare hauled up short. The thief flew over her neck and into a stack of hay.

Still clutching the sack of gold, he looked up. He saw a farmhouse, and not far off, a chestnut tree.

On a lower limb sat the Hey Hey Man.

"I'm back where I started!" the thief cried out.

"You gave that galloping haystack her head," remarked the Hey Hey Man. "A horse always returns to the stable, so to speak."

The thief was shaking with anger and shivering with cold. "I'm off!" he chattered. "And keep out of my sight, I warn you!"

"But you're chilled to the bone." He cracked his whip and said, "Hey! Hey!"

A fire blazed up not far from where the thief stood.

"Warm yourself first," said the Hey Hey Man, putting away his whip.

The thief tried but couldn't resist the fire. He beat his arms and held out his hands to the flames. The tip of his nose began to scorch, and he reared back. What *did* he look like? Nearby stood a water trough, and the thief caught a first and awful glimpse of himself.

"I'm uglified!" he roared. "Look what you've done to me! My nose! My ears! Uglier'n mud! Uglier'n sin! I'll be recognized wherever I go!"

The Hey Hey Man sighed. "I was only trying to be of service."

"Idiot! I'll have to hide myself away in the mountains!"

"I expect so. But nothing to worry about. Seven years and the spell will pass."

"Seven years!" bellowed the thief. "You've the power — do something now!"

The man in the tree shrugged. "It's not so easy to undo the handiwork of a Hey Hey Man, sir. You would have to pass a test."

"What test? Get on with it!"

The banty little man scratched his chin. "Ah! I have it. Watch the bag. I'll go for a stroll. If everything you find in the bag is still there when I return, you pass the test."

"Go for the stroll," the thief laughed. "What a simple-minded test," he thought.

"Hey! Hey!" whispered the little man, with a soft snap of his whip, as he wandered off for a stroll.

The thief resumed rubbing his hands over the fire, and kept a sharp eye on the sack of coins. "But what if the farmer should return?" he thought. "I'd better move it out of clear sight."

When the thief lifted the sack it felt as light as air.

Surprise choked his breath. Quickly he opened the sack. It was full of fleas.

A groan of anguish burst from his lips. "Tricked! A sackful of fleas! That runt has *hey-heyed* the gold into vermin!"

The thief stood dazed. But when the fleas began leaping out of the sack he came to his senses. The test. He must not let a single jumper get away!

He fell to his hands and knees and pursued the insects. For every flea he captured, six others hopped away. He dove here and scrambled there, and began muttering to himself.

He lost track of time, and before long he was yelling out like a madman. "Got you! There's another! Hold still, you bloodsucking speck of nothing."

Suddenly he became aware of the farmer's voice.

"How do, stranger? Lose your watch or something? I declare if you don't look like a pig rooting in a potato patch."

The dogs loped forward and the thief reared back. "Hold your dogs!"

"My tail-waggers won't harm you," said the farmer.

The thief attempted to conceal his face behind his arm. "Fleas! They'll pick up fleas!"

"Won't be the first time," said the farmer. "You didn't notice a rascal about carrying an old jackboot, did you?"

"No," answered the thief, his voice muffled. By now, he knew, fleas were hopping far and wide. There'd be no refilling the sack with them. He was beaten.

"Our life savings gone, me and the dogs," said the farmer. "Do hate to think it was the little chunk of a man. Never heard that thievery was his line of trade. But my hounds would have caught anyone else." He looked up sadly at the Hey Hey Tree. It would pain him to chop it down. But all he had left of value was the lumber in it. "Might as well fetch my ax."

"I'll be on my way," said the thief.

"Stick to the main road," advised the farmer. "Otherwise you might meet up with a pint-size feller in leather breeches. Be on your guard. Infernally clever, that one. He leads travelers astray. Full of mischief."

The thief groaned and slouched away, still concealing his face.

The farmer went to the shed for a heavy ax and the dogs sniffed the sack and the ground around it. While he was gone, the stillness was broken by the snap of a whip and a whisper.

"Hey! Hey!"

The farmer returned to the chestnut tree and lifted his ax. He checked his swing in midair.

The dogs had begun to scratch themselves in a sudden, itching fury. The entire pack. Paws scraped away at necks and chins and chests. They nipped at their backs.

The farmer watched in bafflement. "As I'm alive!" he exclaimed. "My dear tail-waggers!"

It was hard to believe his own eyes.

The dogs were scratching and nipping gold pieces out of their fur. They were shedding coins as if they were fleas.

An Amazing Maze

If you had to retrace the thief's wild run through the woods, you'd probably get lost before you could say "Hey! Hey!" Draw a maze of the thief's run through the woods. Make sure you plot each of his encounters with the Hey Hey Man. When you're finished, swap mazes with a classmate.

F

The Hey Hey Man began when I stumbled across a folk saying: "It's easier to guard a sack of fleas than a young girl in love."

Guarding a sack of fleas! It made a picture in my mind. It began to excite my imagination *and* my sense of humor. I had a fragment, but no story yet. I began to ask myself questions. Why were all those fleas in a sack? Why would someone be guarding them?

Enter the Hey Hey Man, a wood spirit I had been reading about. He was full of tricks and mischief. What if he had changed something valuable into fleas? Then someone would need to guard it. Behold! I had a story.

The Scarebird

by Sid Fleischman

illustrated by Peter Sis

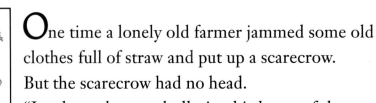One time a lonely old farmer jammed some old
clothes full of straw and put up a scarecrow.
But the scarecrow had no head.
"Just keep the cuss-hollering birds out of the corn
patch," said the farmer. "You don't need a head for that."

It was true. Crows and blackbirds circled the long-armed,
long-legged scarecrow and kept at a safe distance.

But as the first days of spring passed, the farmer — called

Lonesome John by the folks in town — grew uneasy. Every time he looked up from his chores, there stood that headless scarecrow.

And after supper, when he sat on the porch and played his nickel-plated harmonica, there against the fading sun stood the head-less scarecrow.

"If that's not the most fearsome sight I ever saw, it'll do," said Lonesome John in a loud voice. With his family gone and his old dog Sallyblue buried in the pasture, he had no one left to talk to but him-self. "That scarebird's enough to give a man the cold creeps."

The next morning Lonesome John hunted up an old pillowcase and stuffed it with straw. He used house paint to dab on a pair of yellow eyes. A hole in the pillowcase would do for a mouth.

He sauntered to the corn patch and fixed the head to the neck of the scarecrow.

"Does that face suit you, Scarebird? You look like sunshine on stilts with them yeller-paint eyes! Well, make yourself at home."

The next day, when Lonesome John went out to start up his tractor, he gave a wave. "Mornin', Scarebird! I slept like a pine log. How about you!"

And in the evenings, when he sat on the front porch playing his nickel-plated harmonica, he felt almost as if the scarecrow could hear every note.

"See you tomorrow, Scarebird!" he'd call out when he went in to bed.

Lonesome John was sleeping like a pine log when he was awakened by wind banging the barn door. He'd heard wind before, and went back to sleep. At daybreak, with the wind now howling and shrieking in his ears, he jumped out of bed.

The scarebird!

He looked out the window. There stood the scarecrow, face to the wind, holding his ground. Lonesome John grinned.

"I figured you were a goner, Scarebird!"

But when he squinted his eyes, he saw the wind was plucking straw from the scarecrow's cuffs and carrying off its hands and feet.

Lonesome John rushed outside with a pair of shoes and work gloves, and his pockets full of fresh straw. Within minutes he had replaced the straw in the cuffs, put the gloves on, and laced the shoes up tight.

"You're good as new, Scarebird, and a little better." And then he added, "Ain't you all dressed up! Those are my town shoes, but I hardly go to town anymore so you're welcome to them."

The wind whisked itself away. The days turned hot. Before long the sun was rising like a blowtorch at full blast.

"Mornin', Scarebird. Looks like another scorcher today."

Every time Lonesome John glanced up from his farm chores, there stood the scarecrow bareheaded under the flaming sun. He remembered how ol' Sallyblue used to head for the shade under the house on summer days like this.

"Scarebird, you need a hat," he called.

He picked out his wide-brimmed straw hat, his town hat, and set it on the scarecrow's head. He pulled the brim low over the sunflower yellow eyes.

"That's my bettermost hat, but you're welcome to it."

The hot spell passed, the evenings cooled off, and after supper Lonesome John sat on the porch playing old tunes on his nickel-plated harmonica.

"See you tomorrow, Scarebird."

But dark clouds tumbled in during the night, and when Lonesome John awoke he could smell rain. And he heard the windows chattering like baby rattles.

"It's going to rain blue thunderbolts!"

He rushed outside with his yellow slicker, pulled the arms of the scarecrow through the sleeves, and threw the hood over the wide-brimmed hat. When he had the rain gear buttoned, he looked up at the swollen clouds. "Yes sir, blue thunderbolts. Won't do to have you get soaked through and mold up, will it?"

The earth was drying out when Lonesome John hunted up his old checkerboard. He set an apple box in front of the scarecrow and opened the board.

"How about a game of checkers? I ain't played since the boys left home, so I'll be a mite rusty. You go first."

Lonesome John moved a checker for the scarecrow and then one for himself. Before long the game was far along and Lonesome John was in deep concentration.

"Your move, Scarebird."

Lonesome John hardly noticed the time pass. "King me, Scarebird! I ain't licked yet!"

Then a shadow fell across the checkerboard.

He looked up and saw a young man in worn jeans standing there, barefooted and bareheaded.

"Howdy, sir. Folks in town said you might need a hired hand."

"I get along by myself," answered Lonesome John.

"Yes, sir."

Lonesome John wanted to get back to the checker game, but the stranger looked foot-weary and hardly more than sixteen or so.

"You legged it all these miles? Didn't they tell you it's so far to my place that crows pack a lunch before setting out? If you're hungry, you'll find bread and sidemeat in the kitchen."

"Thanks."

"And open a can of peaches while you're at it."

Lonesome John resumed the checker game, though his mind was no longer on it.

The hired hand finished his meal. "I'll chop you some stove wood before I head back."

"Just a stick or two will be fine."

Lonesome John finished up the checker game, but felt foolish with a stranger looking on. He was careful not to talk aloud to the scarecrow, but he thought, "Seems like a nice enough lad, don't he, Scarebird?"

When he returned to the back porch, the hired hand was using a whetstone on the blade.

"The ax needs sharpening."

Lonesome John grinned a little. "It usually does. Wouldn't mind some help with the weeds, if you'd care to stay a day or so."

"Glad to. My name's Sam."

"There's a room off the barn. You can sleep there."

After supper Lonesome John sat on the porch, but he didn't play his nickel-plated harmonica. He'd feel uncomfortable with a stranger about the place. He gazed off at the scarecrow standing lonely under the darkening sky.

"See you tomorrow, Scarebird," he muttered softly.

Sam spent the morning with the hoe, working away steady as a clock.

"He's raising blisters on his hands," Lonesome John said to himself, and pulled the work gloves off the scarecrow.

"Put these on."

"Much obliged, sir."

"My name's John. John Humbuckle."

It took more than a day or so to catch up with the weeds. The hired hand stayed on, working under the hot sun without a hat on his head.

"Scarebird," said Lonesome John, "you won't mind if that young feller borrows your hat."

"Thank you kindly," said the hired hand.

"You from someplace?"

"Used to be."

"Where are your folks?"

"We graved and prayed 'em when I was a little kid."

When the weeding was done, Sam hung up the hoe and pulled off the gloves and hat. "I'll head back."

Lonesome John scratched his neck. "I've been meaning to clear that thornbush in the orchard, if you'd care to stay on a day or so."

"Sure thing."

"Them thorns are meaner'n fishhooks. You'd better wear shoes."

It was raining at first light. Lonesome John pulled the shoes off the scarecrow, then the yellow slicker.

"The boy'll be ever so grateful, Scarebird."

It was almost a week before they had the last of the thornbush grubbed out and burned.

After supper, the hired hand joined Lonesome John on the porch.
"I never saw a scarecrow with yellow-painted eyes. I had a dog once
with yellow eyes. He was a mighty good friend. I'll never forget him."

"That's the way it is with good friends."

"Job's done. Time for me to clear out tomorrow."

And then Sam pulled a harmonica out of his pocket and began to
play a joyful tune.

Lonesome John was silent for a long time, listening. Then he said, "It's time to start harvesting the crops, if you want to stay on a day or so, or a week or so."

"Yes, sir. Sure thing."

Lonesome John had been fingering the harmonica in his own hip pocket like an itch that needed scratching. Now he pulled it out and smiled broadly. "Do you know this tune?"

He began to play, working his right hand like a bird's wing to polish up the notes. When he was finished, Sam tapped his harmonica. "Do you know this one?"

They played, one after another, until full dark. When it was time to turn in, John Humbuckle looked over at the scarecrow for a long moment and then turned to Sam.

"Do you play checkers?"

A Tune in the Cornfields

With a few classmates, compose a song that tells the story of Lonesome John, the Scarebird, and Sam. Write as many verses as you need to tell the whole story. You might also set your song to music, perhaps to the tune of a familiar song such as "Yankee Doodle." Practice your song and sing it for your classmates.

I was reading in my Santa Monica home one afternoon when I came across the word "scarebird." I stopped, for the word caught my interest. I wondered what sort of story I could create about a scarebird.

A scarecrow is, after all, a figure of a person. What if someone very lonely began talking to a scarebird to keep from talking to himself? I'd call him Lonesome John. What would happen next?

I didn't know. A few weeks later a picture arose in my mind of the scarebird out in a strong wind. The straw was being plucked from its sleeves and legs. What would Lonesome John do? I was sure he would try to save the scarebird.

Suddenly, I could see the entire tale. And as you can see, the story of *The Scarebird* developed out of the word itself.

SHOO SHOO

Scarecrows have chased away crop-stealing birds for as long as people have farmed. Making a scarecrow can be as easy as stuffing an old shirt full of hay and hanging it on a post. But farmers of a hundred years ago might be amazed by some of the newfangled scarecrows that guard many fields of today.

This scarecrow jumps three feet into the air and spirals to the ground. When the scarecrow jumps, a cannon sounds.

This plastic scarecrow inflates when its radar picks up the motion of flying birds.

Every October, scarecrows from all over the country gather in Vacaville, California, for the Great Scarecrow Contest. Here are some award-winning scarecrows.

McBroom Tells
the Truth

by Sid Fleischman

illustrated by Stephen Osborn

There has been so much tomfool nonsense told about McBroom's wonderful one-acre farm that I had better set matters straight. I'm McBroom. Josh McBroom. I'll explain about the watermelons in a minute.

I aim to put down the facts, one after the other, the way things happened — exactly.

It began, you might say, the day we left the farm in Connecticut. We piled our youngsters and everything we owned in our old air-cooled Franklin automobile. We headed West.

To count noses, in addition to my own, there was my dear wife Melissa and our eleven red-headed youngsters. Their names were Will*jill*hester*chester*peter*polly*tim*tom*mary*larry*andlittle*clarinda*.

It was summer, and the trees along the way were full of birdsong. We had got as far as Iowa when my dear wife Melissa made a startling discovery. We had *twelve* children along — one too many! She had just counted them again.

I slammed on the brakes and raised a cloud of dust.

"Will*jill*hester*chester*peter*polly*tim*tom*mary*larry*andlittle*clarinda*!" I shouted. "Line up!"

The youngsters tumbled out of the car. I counted noses and there were twelve. I counted again. Twelve. It was a baffler as all the faces were familiar. Once more I made the count — but this time I caught Larry slipping around behind. He was having his nose counted twice, and the mystery was solved. The scamp! Didn't we laugh, though, and stretch our legs in the bargain.

Just then a thin, long-legged man came ambling down the road. He was so scrawny I do believe he could have hidden behind a flagpole, ears and all. He wore a tall stiff collar, a diamond stickpin in his tie, and a straw hat.

"Lost, neighbor?" he asked, spitting out the pips of a green apple he was eating.

"Not a bit," said I. "We're heading West, sir. We gave up our farm — it was half rocks and the other half tree stumps. Folks tell us there's land out West and the sun shines in the winter."

The stranger pursed his lips. "You can't beat Iowa for farmland," he said.

"Maybe so," I nodded. "But I'm short of funds. Unless they're giving farms away in Iowa we'll keep a-going."

The man scratched his chin. "See here, I've got more land than I can plow. You look like nice folks. I'd like to have you for neighbors. I'll let you have eighty acres cheap. Not a stone or a tree stump anywhere on the place. Make an offer."

"Thank you kindly, sir," I smiled. "But I'm afraid you would laugh at me if I offered you everything in my leather purse."

"How much is that?"

"Ten dollars exactly."

"Sold!" he said.

Well, I almost choked with surprise. I thought he must be joking, but quick as a flea he was scratching out a deed on the back of an old envelope.

"Hector Jones is my name, neighbor," he said. "You can call me Heck — everyone does."

Was there ever a more kindly and generous man? He signed the deed with a flourish, and I gladly opened the clasp of my purse.

Three milky white moths flew out. They had been gnawing on the ten dollar bill all the way from Connecticut, but enough remained to buy the farm. And not a stone or tree stump on it!

Mr. Heck Jones jumped on the running board and guided us a mile up the road. My youngsters tried to amuse him along the way. Will wiggled his ears, and Jill crossed her eyes, and Chester twitched his nose like a rabbit, but I reckoned Mr. Jones wasn't used to youngsters. Hester flapped her arms like a bird, Peter whistled through his front teeth, which were missing, and Tom tried to stand on his head in the back of the car. Mr. Heck Jones ignored them all.

Finally he raised his long arm and pointed. "There's your property, neighbor," he said.

Didn't we tumble out of the car in a hurry? We gazed with delight at our new farm. It was broad and sunny, with an oak tree on a gentle hill. There was one defect, to be sure. A boggy looking pond spread across an acre beside the road. You could lose a cow in a place like that, but we had got a bargain — no doubt about it.

"Mama," I said to my dear Melissa. "See that fine old oak on the hill? That's where we'll build our farmhouse."

"No you won't," said Mr. Heck Jones. "That oak ain't on your property."

"But, sir — "

"All that's yours is what you see under water. Not a rock or a tree stump in it, like I said."

I thought he must be having his little joke, except that there wasn't a smile to be found on his face. "But, *sir!*" I said. "You clearly stated that the farm was eighty acres."

"That's right."

"That marshy pond hardly covers an acre."

"That's wrong," he said. "There are a full eighty acres — one piled on the other, like griddle cakes. I didn't say your farm was all on the surface. It's eighty acres deep, McBroom. Read the deed."

I read the deed. It was true.

"*Hee-haw! Hee-haw!*" he snorted. "I got the best of you, McBroom! Good day, neighbor."

He scurried away, laughing up his sleeve all the way home. I soon learned that Mr. Heck was always laughing up his sleeve. Folks told me that when he'd hang up his coat and go to bed, all that stored-up laughter would pour out his sleeve and keep him awake nights. But there's no truth to that.

I'll tell you about the watermelons in a minute.

Well, there we stood gazing at our one-acre farm that wasn't good for anything but jumping into on a hot day. And that day was the hottest I could remember. The hottest on record, as it turned out. That was the day, three minutes before noon, when the cornfields all over Iowa exploded into popcorn. That's history. You must have read about that. There are pictures to prove it.

I turned to our children. "Will*jill*hester*chester*peter*polly*tim*tom*mary*larry*andlittle*clarinda*," I said. "There's always a bright side to things. That pond we bought is a mite muddy, but it's wet. Let's jump in and cool off."

That idea met with favor and we were soon in our swimming togs. I gave the signal, and we took a running jump. At that moment such a dry spell struck that we landed in an acre of dry earth. The pond had evaporated. It was very surprising.

My boys had jumped in head first and there was nothing to be seen of them but their legs kicking in the air. I had to pluck them out of the earth like carrots. Some of my girls were still holding their noses. Of course, they were sorely disappointed to have that swimming hole pulled out from under them.

But the moment I ran the topsoil through my fingers, my farmer's heart skipped a beat. That pond bottom felt as soft and rich as black silk. "My dear Melissa!" I called. "Come look! This topsoil is so rich it ought to be kept in a bank."

I was in a sudden fever of excitement. That glorious topsoil seemed to cry out for seed. My dear Melissa had a sack of dried beans along, and I sent Will and Chester to fetch it. I saw no need to bother plowing the field. I directed Polly to draw a straight furrow with a stick and Tim to follow her, poking holes in the ground. Then I came along. I dropped a bean in each hole and stamped on it with my heel.

Well, I had hardly gone a couple of yards when something green and leafy tangled my foot. I looked behind me. There was a beanstalk traveling along in a hurry and looking for a pole to climb on.

"Glory be!" I exclaimed. That soil was *rich!* The stalks were spreading out all over. I had to rush along to keep ahead of them.

By the time I got to the end of the furrow the first stalks had blossomed, and the pods had formed, and they were ready for picking.

You can imagine our excitement. Will's ears wiggled. Jill's eyes crossed. Chester's nose twitched. Hester's arms flapped. Peter's missing front teeth whistled. And Tom stood on his head.

"Will*jill*hester*chester*peter*polly*tim*tom*mary*larry*andlittle-*clarinda*," I shouted. "Harvest them beans!"

Within an hour we had planted and harvested that entire crop of beans. But was it hot working in the sun! I sent Larry to find a good acorn along the road. We planted it, but it didn't grow near as fast as I had expected. We had to wait an entire three hours for a shade tree.

We made camp under our oak tree, and the next day we drove to Barnsville with our crop of beans. I traded it for various seeds — carrot and beet and cabbage and other items. The storekeeper found a few kernels of corn that hadn't popped, at the very bottom of the bin.

But we found out that corn was positively dangerous to plant. The stalk shot up so fast it would skin your nose.

Of course, there was a secret to that topsoil. A government man came out and made a study of the matter. He said there had once been a huge lake in that part of Iowa. It had taken thousands of years to shrink up to our pond, as you can imagine. The lake fish must have got packed in worse than sardines. There's nothing like fish to put nitrogen in the soil. That's a scientific fact. Nitrogen makes things grow to beat all. And we did occasionally turn up a fish bone.

It wasn't long before Mr. Heck Jones came around to pay us a neighborly call. He was eating a raw turnip. When he saw the way we were planting and harvesting cabbage his eyes popped out of his head. It almost cost him his eyesight.

He scurried away, muttering to himself.

"My dear Melissa," I said. "That man is up to mischief."

Folks in town had told me that Mr. Heck Jones had the worst farmland in Iowa. He couldn't give it away. Tornado winds had carried off his topsoil and left the hardpan right on top. He had to plow it with wedges and a sledge hammer. One day we heard a lot of booming on the other side of the hill, and my youngsters went up to see what was happening. It turned out he was planting seeds with a shotgun.

Meanwhile, we went about our business on the farm. I don't mind saying that before long we were showing a handsome profit. Back in Connecticut we had been lucky to harvest one crop a year. Now we were planting and harvesting three, four crops a *day*.

But there were things we had to be careful about. Weeds, for one thing. My youngsters took turns standing weed guard. The instant a weed popped out of the ground, they'd race to it and hoe it to death. You can imagine what would happen if weeds ever got going in rich soil like ours.

We also had to be careful about planting time. Once we planted lettuce just before my dear Melissa rang the noon bell for dinner. While we ate, the lettuce headed up and went to seed. We lost the whole crop.

One day back came Mr. Heck Jones with a grin on his face. He had figured out a loophole in the deed that made the farm ours.

"*Hee-haw!*" he laughed. He was munching a radish. "I got the best of you now, Neighbor McBroom. The deed says you were to pay me *everything* in your purse, and you *didn't.*"

"On the contrary, sir," I answered. "Ten dollars. There wasn't another cent in my purse."

"There were *moths* in the purse. I seen 'em flutter out. Three milky white moths, McBroom. I want three moths by three o'clock this afternoon, or I aim to take back the farm. *Hee-haw!*"

And off he went, laughing up his sleeve.

Mama was just ringing the noon bell so we didn't have much time. Confound that man! But he did have his legal point.

"Will*jill*hester*chester*peter*polly*tim*tom*mary*larry*-
andlittle*clarinda*!" I said. "We've got to catch
three milky white moths! Hurry!"

We hurried in all directions. But moths are
next to impossible to locate in the daytime. Try it
yourself. Each of us came back empty handed.

My dear Melissa began to cry, for we were
sure to lose our farm. I don't mind telling you that
things looked dark. Dark! That was it! I sent the
youngsters running down the road to a lonely old
pine tree and told them to rush back with a bushel
of pine cones.

Didn't we get busy though! We planted a pine
cone every three feet. They began to grow. We
stood around anxiously, and I kept looking at my
pocket watch. I'll tell you about the watermelons
in a moment.

Sure enough, by ten minutes to three, those
cones had grown into a thick pine forest.

It was dark inside, too! Not a ray of sunlight
slipped through the green pine boughs. Deep in
the forest I lit a lantern. Hardly a minute passed
before I was surrounded by milky white moths —
they thought it was night. I caught three on the wing
and rushed out of the forest.

There stood Mr. Heck Jones waiting with the
sheriff to foreclose.

"*Hee-haw! Hee-haw!*" old Heck laughed. He was
eating a quince apple. "It's nigh onto three o'clock,

and you can't catch moths in the daytime. The farm is mine!"

"Not so fast, Neighbor Jones," said I, with my hands cupped together. "Here are the three moths. Now, skedaddle, sir, before both your feet take root and poison ivy grows out of your ears!"

He scurried away, muttering to himself.

"My dear Melissa," I said. "That man is up to mischief. He'll be back."

It took a good bit of work to clear the timber, I'll tell you. We had some of the pine milled and built ourselves a house on the corner of the farm. What was left we gave away to our neighbors. We were weeks blasting the roots out of the ground.

But I don't want you to think there was nothing but work on our farm. Some crops we grew just for the fun of it. Take pumpkins. The vines grew so fast we could hardly catch the pumpkins. It was something to see. The young-sters used to wear themselves out running after those pumpkins. Sometimes they'd have pumpkin races.

Sunday afternoons, just for the sport of it, the older boys would plant a pumpkin seed and try to catch a ride. It wasn't easy. You had to grab hold the instant the blossom dropped off and the pumpkin began to swell. Whoosh! It would yank you off your feet and take you whizzing over the farm until it wore itself out. Sometimes they'd use banana squash, which was faster.

And the girls learned to ride corn stalks like pogo sticks. It was just a matter of standing over the kernel as the stalk came busting up through the ground. It was good for quite a bounce.

We'd see Mr. Heck Jones standing on the hill in the distance, watching. He wasn't going to rest until he had pried us off our land.

Then, late one night, I was awakened by a hee-hawing outside the house. I went to the window and saw old Heck in the moonlight. He was cackling and chuckling and heeing and hawing and sprinkling seed every which way.

I pulled off my sleeping cap and rushed outside.

"What mischief are you up to, Neighbor Jones!" I shouted.

"*Hee-haw!*" he answered, and scurried away, laughing up his sleeve.

I had a sleepless night, as you can imagine. The next morning, as soon as the sun came up, that farm of ours broke out in weeds. You never saw such weeds! They heaved out of the ground and tumbled madly over each other — chickweed and milkweed, thistles and wild morning glory. In no time at all the weeds were in a tangle several feet thick and still rising.

We had a fight on our hands, I tell you! "Will*jill*hester*chester*peter*polly*tim*tom*mary*larry*andlittle*clarinda*!" I shouted. "There's work to do!"

We started hoeing and hacking away. For every weed we uprooted, another reseeded itself. We were a solid month battling those weeds. If

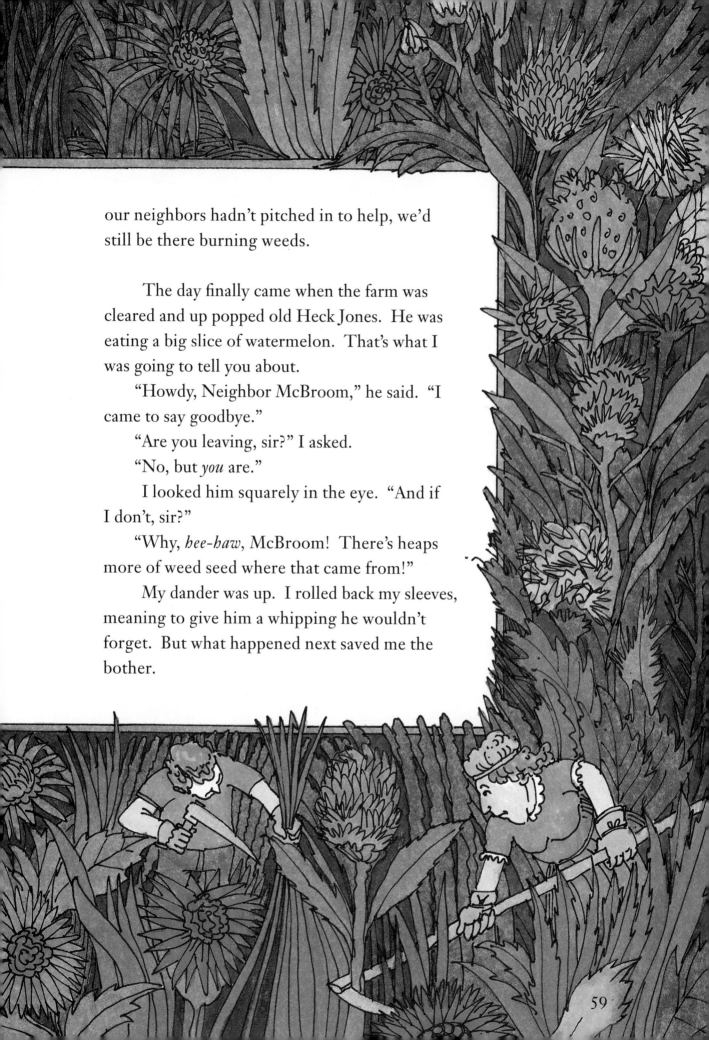

our neighbors hadn't pitched in to help, we'd
still be there burning weeds.

The day finally came when the farm was
cleared and up popped old Heck Jones. He was
eating a big slice of watermelon. That's what I
was going to tell you about.

"Howdy, Neighbor McBroom," he said. "I
came to say goodbye."

"Are you leaving, sir?" I asked.

"No, but *you* are."

I looked him squarely in the eye. "And if
I don't, sir?"

"Why, *hee-haw*, McBroom! There's heaps
more of weed seed where that came from!"

My dander was up. I rolled back my sleeves,
meaning to give him a whipping he wouldn't
forget. But what happened next saved me the
bother.

As my youngsters gathered around, Mr. Heck Jones made the mistake of spitting out a mouthful of watermelon seeds.

Things did happen fast!

Before I had quite realized what he had done, a watermelon vine whipped up around old Heck's scrawny legs and jerked him off his feet. He went whizzing every which way over the farm. Watermelon seeds were flying. Soon he came zipping back and collided with a pumpkin left over from Sunday. In no time watermelons and pumpkins went galloping all over the place, and they were knocking him about something wild. He streaked here and there. Melons crashed

and exploded. Old Heck was so covered with
melon pulp he looked like he had been shot
out of a ketchup bottle.

It was something to see. Will stood there
wiggling his ears. Jill crossed her eyes. Chester
twitched his nose. Hester flapped her arms like
a bird. Peter whistled through his front teeth,
which had grown in. Tom stood on his head.
And little Clarinda took her first step.

By then the watermelons and pumpkins
began to play themselves out. I figured Mr. Heck
Jones would like to get home as fast as possible.
So I asked Larry to fetch me the seed of a large
banana squash.

"*Hee-haw!* Neighbor Jones," I said, and pitched the seed at his feet. I hardly had time to say goodbye before the vine had him. A long banana squash gave him a fast ride all the way home. I wish you could have been there to see it. He never came back.

That's the entire truth of the matter. Anything else you hear about McBroom's wonderful one-acre farm is an outright fib.

Land for Sale

If the McBrooms had not come along,
what might Heck Jones have done to
try to sell his property? Make a billboard
to advertise Heck Jones's land.
Remember — if your billboard doesn't
sell Heck's land, nothing will.

Wisdom from the McBroom Family

Sid Fleischman wrote *McBroom's Almanac* for everyone who enjoys his tall tales about the McBroom family. Here are some useful tips from the *Almanac*.

To stop the hiccups, wrap your neck with an old stocking soaked in skunk oil.
-Tim McBroom

I'd rather have hiccups!
-Mary McBroom

One way to keep the crows out of the corn patch is to plant rhubarb instead.
Hester McBroom

If you lose your voice, kick a porcupine. Your voice will return instantly.
-Tom McBroom

Imagine soil so rich that when you planted a seed it grew so fast you had to jump out of the way. That's not a story. It has no characters. There is no drama in it, with the reader turning the pages to find out what happens next.

I wondered who might be living on such a tall tale farm. It would be a kindly man given to comic exaggerations, I decided. Farmers on the American frontier needed a lot of kids to help with the chores. So I gave Josh McBroom and his wife eleven children, and they came in handy.

It seemed to me that a villain might try to steal a farm with soil so rich. Aha, Heck Jones! Now I had a drama taking shape. But how would Heck Jones try to cheat the McBroom family out of the farm? And how would Josh McBroom foil him? The idea of moths saving the day occurred to me, and I burst out laughing.

Out of all of these questions and answers came *McBroom Tells the Truth*. And out of that super-rich, one-acre farm came nine additional McBroom stories.

You will have quickly noticed that in creating a story, the author asks and answers questions. Why? What if?

What if you were to write stories of your own? Then perhaps, in the years ahead, I will have the pleasure of reading books with *your* name on the covers. Good luck!

More stories to grow on you...

If you enjoyed the Sid Fleischman tales, you may enjoy these tales by Dick King–Smith and Alvin Schwartz. There's also another whopper by Sid Fleischman.

The Whipping Boy
by Sid Fleischman
Jemmy, a humble rat-catcher, has to outsmart two bumbling kidnappers to save Prince Brat. But does Jemmy really want to rescue the bratty prince?

The Fox Busters
by Dick King-Smith
Superman, move over. In this battle of wits, raids, and roosts, three wonder chicks challenge the vicious foxes.

The Queen's Nose
by Dick King-Smith
When Uncle Ginger gives her a magic coin, Harmony Parker finds that seven wishes can lead to all kinds of adventures.

Whoppers: Tall Tales and Other Lies
collected by Alvin Schwartz
Laugh, chuckle, and chortle as you read this collection of tall tales, fish stories, and narrow escapes.

Flapdoodle: Pure Nonsense from American Folklore
collected by Alvin Schwartz
Old and new tricks, rhymes, shaggy dog stories, and more fill this collection of fun from all over America.

SUSPENSE

BOOK 2

THE DANGER ZONE

THE DANGER ZONE

Tupa dragged the canoe right under the water — and the water boiled with white flame. The three fishermen in it were never seen again. . . .

from Ghost of the Lagoon

The wind howled around Miranda's ears. She clutched the icy railing. One slip and she would fall to the rocks below.

from The Lighthouse Keeper's Daughter

"Buddy! Are you in there? Buddy, Pete, answer me!" *Mike heard only the muffled sound of his own voice. And the roar of the Atlantic behind him.*

from Where's Buddy?

Ghosts, storms, rising tides! Time is running out for the characters in these stories. How will they face the dangers that lie ahead? Will they escape from THE DANGER ZONE? You'll find out when you read the stories in this book.

CONTENTS

Ghost of the Lagoon   *by Armstrong Sperry*   72

The Lighthouse Keeper's Daughter *by Arielle North Olson*   86

Where's Buddy?   *from the book by Ron Roy* 106

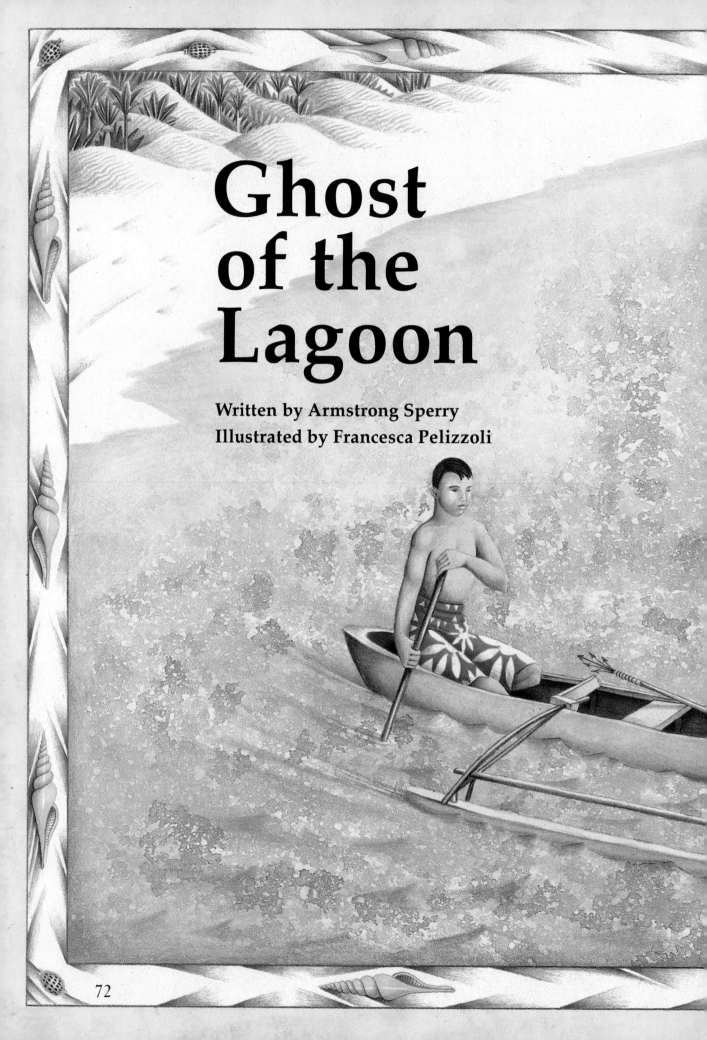

Ghost of the Lagoon

Written by Armstrong Sperry

Illustrated by Francesca Pelizzoli

The island of Bora Bora, where Mako lived, is far away in the South Pacific. It is not a large island — you can paddle around it in a single day — but the main body of it rises straight out of the sea, very high into the air like a castle. Waterfalls trail down the faces of the cliffs. As you look upward you see wild goats leaping from crag to crag.

Mako had been born on the very edge of the sea, and most of his waking hours were spent in the waters of the lagoon, which was nearly enclosed by the two outstretched arms of the island. He was very clever with his hands; he had made a harpoon that was as straight as an arrow and tipped with five-pointed iron spears. He had made a canoe, hollowing it out of a tree. It wasn't a very big canoe — only a little longer than his own height. It had an outrigger, a sort of balancing pole, fastened to one side to keep the boat from tipping over. The canoe was just large enough to hold Mako and his little dog, Afa. They were great companions, these two.

One evening Mako lay stretched at full length on the pandanus mats, listening to Grandfather's voice. Overhead, stars shone in the dark sky. From far off came the thunder of the surf on the reef.

The old man was speaking of Tupa, the ghost of the lagoon. Ever since the boy could remember, he had heard tales of this terrible monster. Frightened fishermen, returning from the reef at midnight, spoke of the ghost. Over the evening fires old men told endless tales about the monster.

Tupa seemed to think the lagoon of Bora Bora belonged to him. The natives left presents of food for him out on the reef: a dead goat, a chicken, or a pig. The presents always disappeared mysteriously, but everyone felt sure that it was Tupa who carried them away. Still, in spite of all this food, the nets of the fishermen were torn during the night, the fish stolen. What an appetite Tupa seemed to have!

Not many people had ever seen the ghost of the lagoon. Grandfather was one of the few who had.

"What does he really look like, Grandfather?" the boy asked for the hundredth time.

The old man shook his head solemnly. The light from the cook fire glistened on his white hair. "Tupa lives in the great caves of the reef. He is longer than this house. There is a sail on his back, not large but terrible to see, for it burns with a white fire. Once when I was fishing beyond the reef at night I saw him come up right under another canoe — "

"What happened then?" Mako asked. He half rose on one elbow. This was a story he had not heard before.

The old man's voice dropped to a whisper. "Tupa dragged the canoe right under the water — and the water boiled with white flame. The three fishermen in it were never seen again. Fine swimmers they were, too."

Grandfather shook his head. "It is bad fortune even to speak of Tupa. There is evil in his very name."

"But King Opu Nui has offered a reward for his capture," the boy pointed out.

"Thirty acres of fine coconut land and a sailing canoe, as well," said the old man. "But who ever heard of laying hands on a ghost?"

Mako's eyes glistened. "Thirty acres of land and a sailing canoe. How I should love to win that reward!"

Grandfather nodded, but Mako's mother scolded her son for such foolish talk. "Be quiet now, son, and go to sleep. Grandfather has told you that it is bad fortune to speak of Tupa. Alas, how well we have learned that lesson! Your father — " She stopped herself.

"What of my father?" the boy asked quickly. And now he sat up straight on the mats.

"Tell him, Grandfather," his mother whispered.

The old man cleared his throat and poked at the fire. A little shower of sparks whirled up into the darkness.

"Your father," he explained gently, "was one of the three fishermen in the canoe that Tupa destroyed." His words fell upon the air like stones dropped into a deep well.

Mako shivered. He brushed back the hair from his damp forehead. Then he squared his shoulders and cried fiercely, "I shall slay Tupa and win the king's reward!" He rose to his knees, his slim body tense, his eyes flashing in the firelight.

"Hush!" his mother said. "Go to sleep now. Enough of such foolish talk. Would you bring trouble upon us all?"

Mako lay down again upon the mats. He rolled over on his side and closed his eyes, but sleep was long in coming.

The palm trees whispered above the dark lagoon, and far out on the reef the sea thundered.

The boy was slow to wake up the next morning. The ghost of Tupa had played through his dreams, making him restless. And so it was almost noon before Mako sat up on the mats and stretched himself. He called Afa, and the boy and his dog ran down to the lagoon for their morning swim.

When they returned to the house, wide-awake and hungry, Mako's mother had food ready and waiting.

"These are the last of our bananas," she told him. "I wish you would paddle out to the reef this afternoon and bring back a new bunch."

The boy agreed eagerly. Nothing pleased him more than such an errand, which would take him to a little island on the outer reef half a mile from shore. It was one of Mako's favorite playgrounds, and there bananas and oranges grew in great plenty.

"Come, Afa," he called, gulping the last mouthful. "We're going on an expedition." He picked up his long-bladed knife and seized his spear. A minute later he dashed across the white sand where his canoe was drawn up beyond the water's reach.

Afa barked at his heels. He was all white except for a black spot over each eye. Wherever Mako went, there went Afa also. Now the little dog leaped into the bow of the canoe, his tail wagging with delight. The boy shoved the canoe into the water and climbed aboard. Then, picking up his paddle, he thrust it into the water. The canoe shot ahead. Its sharp bow cut through the green water of the lagoon like a knife through cheese. And so clear was the water that Mako could see the coral gardens, forty feet below him, growing in the sand. The shadow of the canoe moved over them.

A school of fish swept by like silver arrows. He saw scarlet rock cod with ruby eyes, and the head of a conger eel peering out from a cavern in the coral. The boy thought suddenly of Tupa, ghost of the lagoon. On such a bright day it was hard to believe in ghosts of any sort. The fierce sunlight drove away all thought of them. Perhaps ghosts were only old men's stories, anyway!

Mako's eyes came to rest upon his spear — the spear that he had made with his own hands — the spear that was as straight and true as an arrow. He remembered his vow of the night before. Could a ghost be killed with a spear? Some night when all the village was sleeping, Mako swore to himself, he would find out! He would paddle out to the reef and challenge Tupa! Perhaps tonight. Why not? He caught his breath at the thought. A shiver ran down his back. His hands were tense on the paddle.

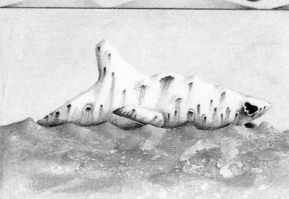

As the canoe drew away from shore, the boy saw the coral reef that above all others had always interested him. It was of white coral — a long, slim shape that rose slightly above the surface of the water. It looked very much like a shark. There was a ridge on the back that the boy could pretend was a dorsal fin, while up near one end were two dark holes that looked like eyes!

Times without number the boy had practiced spearing this make-believe shark, aiming always for the eyes, the most vulnerable spot. So true and straight had his aim become that the spear would pass right into the eyeholes without even touching the sides of the coral. Mako had named the coral reef "Tupa."

This morning as he paddled past it, he shook his fist and called, "Ho, Mister Tupa! Just wait till I get my bananas. When I come back, I'll make short work of you!"

Afa followed his master's words with a sharp bark. He knew Mako was excited about something.

The bow of the canoe touched the sand of the little island where the bananas grew. Afa leaped ashore and ran barking into the jungle, now on this trail, now on that. Clouds of seabirds whirled from their nests into the air with angry cries.

Mako climbed into the shallow water, waded ashore, and pulled his canoe up on the beach. Then, picking up his banana knife, he followed Afa. In the jungle the light was so dense and green that the boy felt as if he were moving underwater. Ferns grew higher than his head. The branches of the trees formed a green roof over him. A flock of parakeets fled on swift wings. Somewhere a wild pig crashed through the undergrowth while Afa dashed away in pursuit. Mako paused anxiously. Armed only with his banana knife, he had no desire to meet the wild pig. The pig, it seemed, had no desire to meet him, either.

Then ahead of him the boy saw the broad green blades of a banana tree. A bunch of bananas, golden ripe, was growing out of the top.

At the foot of the tree he made a nest of soft leaves for the bunch to fall upon. In this way the fruit wouldn't be crushed. Then with a swift slash of his blade he cut the stem. The bananas fell to the earth with a dull thud. He found two more bunches.

Then he thought, *I might as well get some oranges while I'm here. Those little rusty ones are sweeter than any that grow on Bora Bora.*

So he set about making a net of palm leaves in which to carry the oranges. As he worked, his swift fingers moving in and out among the strong green leaves, he could hear Afa's excited barks off in the jungle. That was just like Afa, always barking at something: a bird, a fish, a wild pig. He never caught anything, either. Still, no boy ever had a finer companion.

The palm net took longer to make than Mako had realized. By the time it was finished and filled with oranges, the jungle was dark and gloomy. Night comes quickly and without warning in the islands of the Tropics.

Mako carried the fruit down to the shore and loaded it into the canoe. Then he whistled to Afa. The dog came bounding out of the bush, wagging his tail.

"Hurry!" Mako scolded. "We won't be home before the dark comes."

The little dog leaped into the bow of the canoe, and Mako came aboard. Night seemed to rise up from the surface of the water and swallow them. On the distant shore of Bora Bora, cook fires were being lighted. The first star twinkled just over the dark mountains. Mako dug his paddle into the water, and the canoe leaped ahead.

The dark water was alive with phosphorus. The bow of the canoe seemed to cut through a pale, liquid fire. Each dip of the paddle trailed streamers of light. As the canoe approached the coral reef the boy called, "Ho, Tupa! It's too late tonight to teach you your lesson. But I'll come back tomorrow." The coral shark glistened in the darkness.

And then suddenly Mako's breath caught in his throat. His hands felt weak. Just beyond the fin of the coral Tupa there was another fin — a huge one. It had never been there before. And — could he believe his eyes? It was moving.

The boy stopped paddling. He dashed his hand across his eyes. Afa began to bark furiously. The great white fin, shaped like a small sail, glowed with phosphorescent light. Then Mako knew. Here was Tupa — the real Tupa — ghost of the lagoon!

His knees felt weak. He tried to cry out, but his voice died in his throat. The great shark was circling slowly around the canoe. With each circle it moved closer and closer. Now the boy could see the phosphorescent glow of the great shark's sides. As it moved in closer he saw the yellow eyes, the gill slits in its throat.

Afa leaped from one side of the canoe to the other. In sudden anger Mako leaned forward to grab the dog and shake him soundly. Afa wriggled out of his grasp as Mako tried to catch him, and the shift in weight tipped the canoe on one side. The outrigger rose from the water. In another second they would be overboard. The boy threw his weight over quickly to balance the canoe, but with a loud splash Afa fell over into the dark water.

Mako stared after him in dismay. The little dog, instead of swimming back to the canoe, had headed for the distant shore. And there was the great white shark — very near.

"Afa! Afa! Come back! Come quickly!" Mako shouted.

The little dog turned back toward the canoe. He was swimming with all his strength. Mako leaned forward. Could Afa make it? Swiftly the boy seized his spear. Bracing himself, he stood upright. There was no weakness in him now. His dog, his companion, was in danger of instant death.

Afa was swimming desperately to reach the canoe. The white shark had paused in his circling to gather speed for the attack. Mako raised his arm, took aim. In that instant the shark charged. Mako's arm flashed forward. All his strength was behind that thrust. The spear drove straight and true, right into the great shark's eye. Mad with pain and rage, Tupa whipped about, lashing the water in fury. The canoe rocked back and forth. Mako struggled to keep his balance as he drew back the spear by the cord fastened to his wrist.

He bent over to seize Afa and drag him aboard. Then he
stood up, not a moment too soon. Once again the shark charged.
Once again Mako threw his spear, this time at the other eye.
The spear found its mark. Blinded and weak from loss of blood,
Tupa rolled to the surface, turned slightly on his side. Was
he dead?

Mako knew how clever sharks could be, and he was taking no
chances. Scarcely daring to breathe, he paddled toward the still
body. He saw the faintest motion of the great tail. The shark was
still alive. The boy knew that one flip of that tail could overturn the

canoe and send him and Afa into the water, where Tupa could destroy them.

Swiftly, yet calmly, Mako stood upright and braced himself firmly. Then, murmuring a silent prayer to the Shark God, he threw his spear for the last time. Downward, swift as sound, the spear plunged into a white shoulder.

Peering over the side of the canoe, Mako could see the great fish turn over far below the surface. Then slowly, slowly, the great shark rose to the surface of the lagoon. There he floated, half on one side.

Tupa was dead.

Mako flung back his head and shouted for joy. Hitching a strong line about the shark's tail, the boy began to paddle toward the shore of Bora Bora. The dorsal fin, burning with the white fire of phosphorus, trailed after the canoe.

Men were running down the beaches of Bora Bora, shouting as they leaped into their canoes and put out across the lagoon. Their cries reached the boy's ears across the water.

"It is Tupa — ghost of the lagoon," he heard them shout. "Mako has killed him!"

That night as the tired boy lay on the pandanus mats listening to the distant thunder of the sea, he heard Grandfather singing a new song. It was the song that would be sung the next day at the feast that King Opu Nui would give in Mako's honor. The boy saw his mother bending over the cook fire. The stars leaned close, winking like friendly eyes. Grandfather's voice reached him now from a great distance, "Thirty acres of land and a sailing canoe . . ."

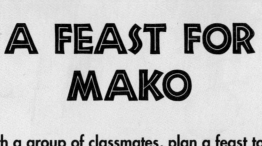

A FEAST FOR MAKO

With a group of classmates, plan a feast to cele-
brate Mako's victory over Tupa. Some members of your
group can write speeches for Mako, King Opu Nui,
Mako's grandfather, and his mother. Others can write a
song about the Great Shark, Tupa. When everyone is
ready, your group can present the menu, make the
speeches, and perform the song for the whole class.

The Lighthouse Keeper's Daughter

Written by Arielle North Olson
Illustrated by Elaine Wentworth

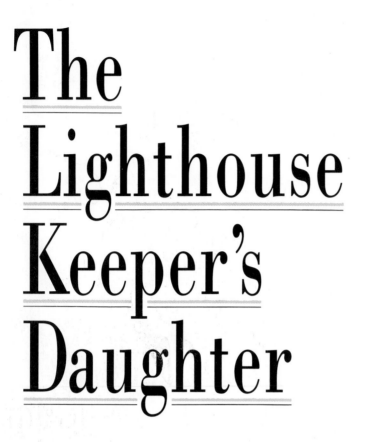

The wind howled around Miranda's ears. She clutched the icy railing. One slip and she would fall to the rocks below.

She watched the raging waves for a sign of her father, but there was no boat in sight.

Should I go inside? she wondered. She inched her way along the slippery catwalk, but when she reached the door, she hesitated. If Father were here, he would scrape every bit of ice off the lighthouse windows, no matter how hard the wind blew.

Miranda could almost hear his voice: "What if there's a ship out there? What if the sailors can't see the light? There might be a shipwreck."

And now Father needs the light, Miranda thought, to guide him safely home.

She held onto the railing with one hand and braced her body against the fury of the storm. Then she began to scrape off the ice. Her fingers grew numb and her arms ached, but she didn't stop. When she finally circled back to the lighthouse door, she barely had the strength to open it.

Miranda stumbled inside the lamp room, and the wind slammed the door shut behind her. She pulled off her mittens and rubbed her icy fingers. Then she lit one of the big lamps. She warmed her hands by it and breathed in the pungent smell of whale oil.

How long had Father been away? Two weeks? It seemed like years.

Miranda couldn't remember a stormier winter. For months, rough weather had kept the supply boat from making its regular stops at the lighthouse island. So Father had to brave the storm in their own boat.

"We're running out of food," he said before he left. "Keep the lamps burning tonight, and I'll be back tomorrow."

Did he reach shore safely, Miranda wondered, before the storm grew worse?

As soon as her fingers stopped aching, she worked her way around the circle of fourteen lamps, lighting them, one by one. They brightened the tower room and sent forth their warning to sailors at sea. BEWARE! ROCKY LEDGES BENEATH THE WAVES! LOW-LYING ISLAND AHEAD!

Miranda remembered how surprised she was last summer, the first time she saw the island. It was just a rock, miles and miles from shore. A huge gray rock, splashed by ocean waves. And perched on top were the lighthouse and a small stone cottage — their new home now that Father had become the keeper of the light.

As Father sailed the dory closer, Mother and Miranda could see that nothing grew on the rocky island. Not a tree. Not a bush. Not a flower.

Miranda could hardly believe it. She had packets of seeds in her skirt pocket, for bellflowers, sweet peas, and bouncing Bet. But where could she plant them?

Father lowered the sail and grabbed the oars. Then he rowed the boat in on the crest of a wave. It scraped bottom. Miranda's pet chickens fluttered and squawked in their crate. Father leaped onto the rocks and hauled the boat to safety. Then Mother and Miranda stepped ashore.

"We'll unload the rest later," he said.

They avoided the pools and puddles by the water's edge and followed the rocky path to the top. A fresh sea breeze pulled at their clothes. Gulls called overhead, and puffins waddled about. The summer sun sparkled on the waves.

Miranda watched for bits of greenery along the path to the lighthouse, but there was nothing there, not even a blade of grass. When they left Grandma's farm that morning, pink roses had been in bloom . . . would this barren island ever seem like home?

"Look," said Father. "Here's an old coop for your chickens." It was made of odds and ends. Not fancy, Miranda thought, but it would keep the hens safe.

They climbed the stone steps to the cottage and pulled open the heavy door. Miranda walked quickly through the kitchen and peeked into the parlor. Then she ran upstairs to see her bedroom. It looked sunny and cheerful. She took an old cushion from the chair by the bed and put it on the wide stone windowsill. This is where I'll read, she decided, where I can look up and see the waves.

Then Miranda hurried downstairs. She could hardly wait to explore the lighthouse.

"Come along," said Father. "It's right through this door."

Mother and Miranda followed him from the kitchen into the storeroom at the base of the tower. Mother took just one look at the long circular stairs. "I think I'll stay down here," she said.

But Father and Miranda climbed upward until they reached the room at the top, with its circle of lamps and its windows all around. They looked out at the ocean. It surrounded them on all sides and stretched beyond, as far as the eye could see. Small boats dotted the water as fishermen and lobstermen went about their daily work. And far off on the horizon, a great sailing ship came into view.

Miranda felt wild and free, like the sea gulls that swooped and hovered outside the lighthouse windows. One landed on the catwalk railing and tipped its head to look at her. She laughed.

"Mother should have come up too."

"Do you remember what happened that day we were up on the cliffs?" Father asked.

Miranda nodded. Mother had almost fainted when Miranda called her to the edge to see a wildflower.

"It's strange," Father said. "Most things don't scare her, but she's always been afraid of heights."

Miranda looked down at the island on which the lighthouse was built. I like being up high, she thought. But suddenly her mood changed. The rocks below looked so bleak.

"Why doesn't anything grow out here?" she asked.

"In winter storms," Father said, "waves wash right across this island and scour it clean."

Miranda stared at him. "Then how can I have a garden?"

Father patted her shoulder. "Don't fret," he said. "Let's go down and fix that coop for your chickens."

Miranda wanted to look for Father's boat one more time, but now it was too dark outside. She checked the lamps again, replaced the glass chimneys, and started down the tower stairs.

Father wouldn't try to come back in weather like this, she told herself. Such heavy seas would swamp a small boat.

But he knows we are almost out of food. He'll be so worried, he might start out when he shouldn't. Miranda shook away the thought.

Surely he's at Grandma's now, waiting out the storm. He's probably sitting at her kitchen table eating apple pie. Miranda's mouth watered. For a week now, she and Mother had eaten just a bowl of cornmeal mush and one egg a day. But now the cornmeal was running low.

When Father came back from Grandma's farm, he would bring potatoes from the root cellar, pumpkins, nuts, and dried apples. Miranda felt homesick just thinking about it.

"Miranda."

She looked over the edge of the curving stairs and saw her mother standing on the floor below.

"Coming," she answered.

"You've been up there so long, I was getting worried." They walked back to the kitchen together, arm in arm.

It was suppertime, but it took only a moment to eat. Miranda wondered how long they could last on so little food. They pulled their chairs close to the warm stove, and Mother picked up her knitting. But then she put it down again and stared across the room. Miranda knew she was worrying about Father.

Suddenly Miranda realized how seldom she saw her mother's hands still. There were always socks to knit, shirts to sew, or trousers to mend. Soap and candles had to be made, the wood stove tended, and bread baked. Remembering the smell of fresh-baked bread made Miranda ache with hunger. She threaded a needle and darned one of her father's socks.

Mother picked up a book and began to read out loud, but her voice soon grew hoarse. It was hard to speak above the roar of the surf. She put the book away.

Each day Miranda watched for her father's boat, but the gale continued to blow. It was three weeks now since he had left. Miranda continued to tend the lamps the way he had taught her. She carefully shined the reflectors, cleaned the glass chimneys, and filled the lamps with oil. Then she trimmed the wicks and lit them.

More ice froze on the lighthouse windows. When Miranda stepped out on the catwalk, she was buffeted by the wind. A sudden blast of frigid air pressed her skirt against her legs and whipped off her scarf, tossing it out to sea. Miranda's teeth chattered. By the time she finished scraping, her hair was stiff with frozen spray. She hurried down to the kitchen to get warm.

"Miranda," cried her mother. "You'll catch your death of cold! Dry your hair!" she said, thrusting a towel into Miranda's hands. "I'll make some tea."

The next afternoon, Miranda was coughing as she made the long climb up to the lamp room. Snowflakes were swirling past the tower windows. Everything was gray and white — the sky, the sea, and the rock itself. A much heavier snow was falling.

It was so dark, Miranda lit the lamps early. Then she cupped her hands around her eyes and peered outside. Where was Father now?

The blizzard grew more violent during the night. Miranda had no trouble waking up to check the lamps. Her cold was worse, and the booming waves and the wind made it almost impossible to sleep.

By morning, huge waves began to wash onto the island. Miranda heard water slapping against the house. She looked out the kitchen window.

"My hens!" she cried. When the sea fell back for a moment, she raced out to the coop, with icy water swirling around her knees.

"Hurry!" Mother shouted.

Miranda caught all four chickens quickly and thrust them into her basket. Then she ran back to the house. Mother slammed the door behind Miranda just before the next wave broke.

Miranda dumped the squawking hens in a little storeroom behind the kitchen, then rushed back to the window. The chicken coop was tumbling in the waves. She pulled off her wet shoes and stockings and warmed her legs by the wood stove.

Giant breakers began to surge right across the island. And water was coming in beneath the kitchen door.

"Help me!" Mother called. They both knelt on the floor and jammed strips of cloth into the crack. Then they pushed heavy wooden boxes against it to hold the cloth in place.

All day long the blizzard howled around the cottage. Huge boulders were washed from one side of the lighthouse rock to the other, cracking and crashing as they went. The booming surf was deafening.

Miranda knew that the lighthouse at Minot's Ledge had been toppled by heavy seas several years before. She shivered. But ours is well built, she told herself. Father said so.

Miranda kept the lamps burning all day. And each time she climbed the lighthouse steps, her cold seemed worse.

By evening she felt weak and her fever was high.

"You're too sick to climb that tower!" Mother insisted.

"What if the lamps go out?" Miranda asked angrily. "Father said there was a lighthouse that stood dark for just one night, and two ships crashed against the rocks. No one made it to shore alive."

Miranda started up the stairs. Mother hurried after her. She steadied her daughter, and step by step they went all the way to the top. Then Mother sank down on the floor, scarcely able to believe how high she had climbed.

Mother and Miranda looked at each other for a moment. Then they began to laugh uncontrollably . . . exhausted and close to tears, but triumphant.

By morning, Miranda knew the blizzard was letting up. Even
before she opened her eyes, she knew. She could tell from the sound
of waves and wind. The ocean was never still, but its wild roaring was
somewhat muted now.

She snuggled down into her warm featherbed, remembering the
dream she'd had moments before. She had been walking through

Grandma's garden.

Hollyhocks, roses, and poppies were in bloom, and Father was coming down the path. . .

Father! She bolted out of bed. She had to do his chores. Suddenly she realized she wasn't dizzy anymore. Her legs were weak, but she didn't feel feverish.

Miranda climbed the tower and snuffed out the flames in all fourteen lamps. Then she stepped out on the catwalk. Waves were no longer surging across the island, and she could see no planks or broken masts washed ashore. Despite the blizzard, the light must have been visible well beyond the dangerous rocks.

Miranda went down to the kitchen and gratefully accepted a cup of tea from Mother. She didn't feel quite as hungry with the warm liquid inside.

"Father will be home soon," Miranda said.

Mother half smiled, but her eyes looked misty.

Miranda knew she was fearing the worst.

That very afternoon, Miranda thought she could see a dark speck on the ocean, moving their way. She ran down the tower stairs to the kitchen. "A boat's coming!"

Mother climbed the lighthouse with her, too excited to be afraid. They stared at the tiny spot until they could see it was a dory . . . a blue one . . . their own.

"It's Father!" Miranda shrieked. She ran down the stairs with Mother close behind. They threw on coats and slipped and slid down to the water's edge.

Father had to use all his strength to avoid crashing the boat on the rocks or tipping it over in the cold sea. They caught the rope he tossed to them. Then they struggled for footholds on the ice and pulled his dory in. Father jumped onto the rocks and gave Mother and Miranda a bear hug.

"Are you all right?" he asked. For the first time, Miranda saw tears in her father's eyes.

"We're fine," Miranda said. "Mother even climbed the tower stairs."

Father smiled. "You did?"

"I've been half mad with worry about you," Mother said.

"As was I." Father drew them close again. "I didn't know if I could get back before you starved."

"I kept the lamps burning every night!" said Miranda.

"That's my girl," he said. "I knew I could trust you . . . but I didn't know I would be asking this much."

They climbed up the icy path, loaded with bags of potatoes, chicken feed, and flour.

When they reached the kitchen, Father handed dried apples to Mother and Miranda so they could eat something right away — and Mother made a cup of hot tea for Father.

"You must be chilled to the bone."

"Aye," he said, "but happy."

He reached into an inner pocket and pulled out a book for
Mother. Miranda could tell from the look on her face how much it
meant to her. Mother gently kissed his cheek.

Then Father fished around until he found a small oilskin bag.
He gave it to Miranda.

"Look inside. Grandma sent you something."

She untied the bag carefully and grinned when she saw what Father had brought to her.

"It's just enough dirt to start some seedlings," he said, "but I'll bring more. Your Grandma said there were gardens here years ago. Every spring fishermen brought dirt to the lighthouse keeper. The men would do it again if they knew you wanted it." He smiled at her. "I'll tell them how you tended the light."

Then he reached into his coat for small packets of flower seeds and gave them to Miranda. "Thought you might like these."

She read the handwritten labels out loud. "Columbine, larkspur, sweet William, candytuft, lupine, and Canterbury bells." She gave Father another hug.

"We'll have to see what grows best," said Mother. "I'll help you tend them."

By spring, the story about the girl who took care of the lighthouse had spread all along the Maine coast. Grateful seamen showed up almost every day with their gifts of rich, dark soil.

Miranda packed dirt into the cracks and crevices. She transplanted the seedlings, watered them every day and watched them grow.

Soon there were flowers blooming all over the rock, in patches of blue, pink, white, and red. There was even a bed of lettuce a few steps from the kitchen door — enough for the family, and some for the chickens.

Boats sailed close to the lighthouse, just to see the gardens. Grandma came to see them, too.

When Miranda and Father worked in the lamp room, Mother sometimes climbed the stairs to help them. Together, they looked down at the brightly colored flowers. Could this be the same barren rock they saw last summer? The same rock that was battered by gales and high seas during the terrible winter storms?

Miranda knew they'd never let their supplies run low again. They would stay safe on their small island while the blizzards howled — and await the return of spring, when fishermen would replenish the gardens the ocean had swept away.

Author's Note

Parts of this story actually happened at lighthouses along the Maine coast. At Matinicus Rock, a young girl kept the lamps burning for weeks while her father was held ashore by the monstrous storms of the mid-1850's — and she rushed into the waves to save her pet chickens from drowning. At Mount Desert Rock, summer gardens were swept out to sea each year by winter storms.

Stranded from my Family,
Far from Home

THE LIGHTHOUSE KEEPER'S
DAUGHTER

*is told from Miranda's point of
view. Imagine how Miranda's
father might have felt with
his family stranded far away.
Rewrite the story from the
father's point of view.*

BEWARE: Treacherous

**Gold Lifesaving Medal,
Awarded to Ida Lewis
in 1881**

Ida Lewis, 1905

Women have always played an important part in keeping the lighthouse lamps burning. Here are a few lighthouse heroines who faced danger and saved lives.

Lime Rock Lighthouse, 1869

Ida Lewis, one of America's most famous heroines, was the keeper of Lime Rock Lighthouse in Newport, Rhode Island, from 1879 to 1911. An expert sailor and a powerful swimmer, Ida Lewis made her first rescue when she was only sixteen. By the time she died in 1911, she had been credited with rescuing over a dozen people from the treacherous waters surrounding Newport.

Waters

The Scituate
Lighthouse

Rebecca and **Abigail Bates** knew they had to act quickly to save their town from attack! During the War of 1812, these two lighthouse keeper's daughters managed to scare a British warship out of Scituate Harbor in Massachusetts.

As the warship sailed past Scituate Lighthouse, Rebecca and Abigail hid in some bushes and played "Yankee Doodle" very loudly on an old drum and a cracked fife. The warship captain, mistaking the two teenage girls for an entire battalion, ordered his ship to turn around and sail out of the harbor as fast as the wind could take it.

**The drum and cracked fife
helped the Bates sisters
save the day!**

Where's Buddy?

FROM THE BOOK BY RON ROY   *ILLUSTRATED BY TROY HOWELL*

Buddy Sanders has disappeared. His older brother Mike is frantic because he was supposed to take care of Buddy in their parent's absence. Buddy is diabetic, and Mike needs to make sure he gets his daily insulin shots. If Mike doesn't find him within two hours, Buddy might die.

Buddy was last seen with his friend Pete Anderson. Mike and Pete's sister Loni have looked everywhere. Where could Buddy be?

♦♦♦

L oni looked up as Mike stepped onto the porch. His face was white. "Who was it?" she asked.

"My mom," Mike whispered. "I told her. They're coming home." He lowered himself to the steps on legs no longer able to support his weight. His mind had been a mess before the phone call. Now he couldn't think at all. He looked at Loni. "Did you have any luck?"

Loni stared at the ground and shook her head. "There were only a few kids at the playgrounds." She couldn't look at Mike. "No one has seen Buddy or Pete."

She scuffed a trench in the sand with the heel of her sneaker. The sand poured slowly back into the hole, and an ant scrambled for its life.

Mike stared at the insect. That's how he felt: trapped. At least the ant knew what to do.

"I can't stand this!" Loni cried. "They have to be somewhere!"

She turned to face Mike. "Help me think. They played with Pete's Indians and soldiers under the tree in our backyard. I sat near them reading. I went inside for a drink; when I came out they were

107

whispering. They stopped, but when they thought I wasn't listening they started again."

Loni closed her eyes to remember. "They were pretending to be real Indians. They were going to eat Indian food and talk Indian talk and . . . they mentioned a cave where they would sleep and . . ."

"There is a cave," Mike interrupted. "About half a mile from here. Buddy's not allowed to go there alone."

"Where is it?" Loni asked. "I never heard of any cave around here."

"It's at the bottom of Bald Head Cliff. My friend Chick showed it to me and Buddy last summer."

Mike and Loni looked at each other, each thinking the same thought. "They were whispering about it," Loni said. "I thought it was all make-believe."

Mike was already moving toward his bike. "Let's go. We can ride there in five minutes."

He pedaled across his yard toward the cliff. Loni caught up and they rode single file. Sixty feet below them, waves crashed over the rocky beach.

Mike slowed a little and yelled over his shoulder. "You'll see an old tree. That's Bald Head Cliff."

He had jogged this path a hundred times. He knew every rock, every patch of sun-browned grass and cliff-hugging bush. To his right the cliff dropped into the ocean, then there was nothing until you got to Spain. On his left were open fields of wild grass, blueberry bushes, and granite boulders the size of Volkswagens. A few people lived there, but their homes were beyond the fields.

On other days Mike liked to pretend he was an Olympic runner in training as he loped along this path. Today he thought only of his destination.

The wind from the ocean roared over the top of the ridge in sudden gusts. Mike hunched low over his handlebars and Loni copied him. This position changed her angle of vision so she was looking straight ahead instead of down. She never saw the stone on the path.

Mike heard the sound of metal slamming into rock and Loni's scream at the same time. He braked and whipped his head around. Loni's bike lay in the dirt. The rear wheel spun, humming like an angry hornet. The front half of the bike was resting on Loni's right arm and shoulder.

Mike jumped off his bike and let it drop to the ground. By the time he reached Loni, she was on her feet.

She was holding her right hand with her left. Both hands were shaking. Particles of dirt were imbedded in the flesh of her right palm. Blood oozed from the skin around the dirt.

Mike felt helpless. His own hands hung at his sides like anchors. "Does it hurt?"

"No, it feels terrific," Loni blurted. She was trying not to cry, but Mike saw her eyes water over and tears start to slide down her face. Her jeans were torn at one knee and the front of her T-shirt was covered with dirt. "Is my bike okay?"

Glad for something to do, Mike raised her ten speed. He held the handlebars and sighted with one eye along the bike's length. Nothing was bent. He walked the bike a few yards along the path, then back again.

"I think it's all right," he said. "But what about your hand?"

"It's just the palm," Loni said, carefully brushing at some of the imbedded dirt. "How much farther is the cave?"

"Can you ride?" Mike asked.

"Don't worry. I can make it," Loni answered.

Mike had his doubts. "Listen, I have an idea. You could go back to my house and wait. Maybe the kids . . ."

Giving no hint that she'd heard, Loni yanked her bike from Mike's hands, swung into the seat, and pedaled away. Toward Bald Head Cliff.

Mike stood with his mouth open. She's amazing, he thought as he retrieved his own bike from the dirt. He had to pump hard to catch up; Loni was yards ahead of him.

◆◆◆

The pine tree was the only living thing on Bald Head Cliff. Like most of the trees along the ridge, it was stunted and misshapen. Years of wind had twisted the branches, and salt, carried by the wind, had left them bare except for a few withered pine needles. The tree pointed away from the sea, as if in warning.

Two small bikes leaned against the trunk of the tree.

The relief of seeing the bikes propped there made Mike's eyes water. Buddy and Pete were here. In minutes the nightmare would be over.

Mike yelled to Loni, who, he guessed, hadn't noticed the bikes yet. "They're here!"

Loni's face burst into a smile. Mike felt his own grin spread as Loni dropped her bike and ran toward the tree. Then Mike remembered the cave, and his grin vanished.

Most of Mike's summer friends knew about the cave. At first they'd all thought Indians once lived in it, but they'd found no signs of early inhabitants: no arrowheads, no pottery, no wall pictures. Just a tunnel you had to crawl on your belly to get through and a medium-sized cave at the end.

Mike hated the cave. Ever since he could remember, any cramped dark place made him feel as if he were being smothered. Only Chick's persistent urging had persuaded Mike to crawl into the tunnel the first time. That had also been the last time.

The darkness was the worst part. Not knowing how much space was around him made him think he was running out of oxygen. Mike would never forget the sensation of suffocating.

Loni's voice broke into his thoughts. "Mike, come over here!" She was standing at the edge of the cliff, pointing at something on the beach.

Leaving his bike alongside hers, Mike ran to where she stood. When he looked down he understood why she had yelled. The beach was completely covered with water. And the beach was the only way to get into the cave.

Mike dropped to his hands and knees and moved to the very edge of the cliff. Just below where he crouched the rock bulged out; from the beach it looked like a giant forehead, bald except for the lone tree.

Mike couldn't tell how deep the water was on the beach. He tried to recall whether the tide had been high or low, incoming or

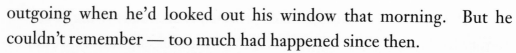

outgoing when he'd looked out his window that morning. But he couldn't remember — too much had happened since then.

He looked for a way down and saw what he wanted. Twenty yards away a small path left the ridge and zigzagged down to the water. With Loni right behind him, he began picking his way down.

The cliff was steep, but they found handholds and toeholds in the crumbly, eroding rock. Mike wondered if Buddy and Pete had climbed down this same path.

He couldn't take his eyes off the dark water below. Now that he was closer, it didn't look too deep. But it was coming in fast. Everyone, townies and summer people, knew about the Ogunquit tides.

Mike looked back at Loni. Her face was white, and she too had eyes on the water. He noticed that she was using both hands to keep herself from sliding.

Four feet from the bottom of the cliff, Mike jumped. The shock of the cold water made him clench his teeth. He knew the numbing pain would go away in a few minutes, but now he felt as if he were walking on needles. His sneakers didn't help a bit.

He was right about the depth of the water; it was just above his ankles. In a half hour it would be up to his waist.

Loni crouched at the spot from which Mike had jumped. She looked at Mike, then leaped into the water. Her eyes opened round when the impact hit her. "It's freezing!" she cried.

Mike backed away from the cliff until he was knee-deep in the swirling, sucking water. He flicked his eyes back and forth along the base of the cliff.

"There it is!" With arms flailing to help keep his balance, he splashed his way toward a black hole in the rock face about fifty feet away.

Loni followed. She kept her left hand on the cliff and held her right one against her stomach. Her eyes never left the water churning around her ankles.

Mike dropped to his knees at the tunnel entrance. He stuck one hand in the water and leaned the other against the rocks. He lowered his head and peered into the tunnel opening.

"*Buddy! Are you in there? Buddy, Pete, answer me!*" Mike heard only the muffled sound of his own voice. And the roar of the Atlantic behind him.

Loni leaned close to his ear. "What are you going to do?"

Mike felt her arm against his knee under the water. Her flesh felt cold, like the dead frogs in science class. "I'm going in."

Loni put her hand on his shoulder and shouted. "I can't hear you. What did you say?"

"I said I'm going in," Mike yelled back.

Loni lowered herself until the water slapped at her stomach and wet the ends of her hair. She peered into the dark hole. "I'm coming with you."

Mike stared at her. There was no way he could tell her the relief he felt at not having to face the tunnel alone.

"We'll have to crawl on our stomachs," he shouted. "The tunnel slopes up, so it should be dry most of the way. What about your hand?"

Loni held her palm up so Mike could see. "It got cleaned off in the water. It doesn't hurt anymore."

Mike swiveled on his knees and faced the ocean. Somewhere he'd heard that every seventh wave was bigger than the other six. To him they all looked the same.

Turning, he threw himself into the icy water and crawled into the mouth of the tunnel. He felt like one of the prehistoric lizards in Buddy's coloring book. The only part of him still dry was the top of his head. Everything else was soaked.

Suddenly he stopped. The tunnel was too narrow for his elbows and knees. He realized, lying in the dark and shivering, that he'd grown a lot since last summer. He and Chick had crawled in easily then.

Something touched Mike's leg. He jerked forward, then relaxed. It was Loni. He felt her breath on his ankles. Her wet hair tickled his skin.

"Can't you move in any farther?" she yelled. "My legs are still in the water!"

"I can't crawl," Mike yelled over his shoulder. "My stupid arms and legs are too long."

Loni didn't say anything for a few seconds. Then Mike heard a gasp and violent choking. Icy fingers grabbed his leg.

"*Mike!*"

"What's the matter?"

"A wave hit me," Loni said through chattering teeth. "I'm freez-ing. Can't you pull yourself along with your hands? I can't stay here."

Mike reached ahead and dug his fingers into the sand. Using his toes to push off with, he was able to move forward an inch at a time. He could hear Loni scraping along behind him.

Having her with him kept the panic away. He was scared, but he knew he wasn't going to smother. His breaths came easy. Somehow, knowing Buddy was waiting made a difference, too. He didn't want to scream and kick his way out as he had the other time.

Mike turned his head until his hair brushed the tunnel wall. "You okay?"

"I think I cut my knee on something," Loni answered. "But at least I'm out of the water. How about you?"

"I'm all right," Mike said. "Let's keep moving."

With Loni blocking out most of the sounds from the ocean, Mike heard only the noises their fingers and toes made digging into the sand. He established a system: stretch forward, dig in, pull, shove off . . . stretch forward again. His arms and shoulders began to ache. His muscles weren't used to this kind of exertion.

He stopped and laid his cheek in the cool sand. Loni's breathing told him she was getting a workout, too.

Something crawled over Mike's hand. He yelled, jerking it back.

"What's the matter?" Loni asked.

The back of Mike's neck felt as if it had been doused with ice water. He was sure his heart had stopped altogether. And all for nothing. He felt foolish.

"I think we've invaded a crab's home," he said. "One just walked over me."

"Crabs? Yuck! If one touches me I'll — "

"Shhh . . . quiet! I heard something." Mike's skin prickled all over. He held his breath.

He heard the sound again. "Didn't you hear it?" he asked Loni.

"I can hardly hear *you* back here," she said. "What is it?"

He waited till he heard the noise one more time. Then he was sure. He had heard the sound of someone crying.

"It's them. It's Buddy and Pete!"

♦♦♦

Mike cupped his hands and yelled into the darkness. "BUDDY, PETE . . . ARE YOU IN THERE?" He waited, but heard nothing except his own breathing.

"Maybe it was something else," Loni offered. Her voice sounded ghostly in the cold black space.

"Like what?" Mike asked.

"I don't know . . . a sea gull?"

At any other time Mike would have laughed at the thought of a sea gull living in a tunnel. But now he didn't even smile. "Let's go," he said. It *had* sounded like crying.

The short rest helped; Mike was able to hitch himself along more easily. He didn't forget Loni's remark about the sea gull. What if some animal *were* living in this cave? Why not? It was a perfect spot: away from the water and safe from enemies.

What lived in caves, he asked himself as he inched cautiously along. Bears? Yes, but they'd never fit in this tunnel. Skunks? Snakes? He drew his arms under his chest at the thought. He'd never been afraid of snakes, but putting his hand on one in the dark was a different matter.

Loni shoved his foot. "Why did you stop?"

Mike ignored her. He reached into the darkness, dug his fingers into the sand, and hiked himself forward. Look out snakes, here I come!

He realized that his head was no longer grazing the roof of the tunnel. One hand reached out but there was nothing to touch. He pulled his knees in under his rear and raised his arms over his head. He struck rock.

"What are you doing?" Loni whispered.

"The tunnel is wider here," Mike said. "I think we're close to the cave."

He heard a crunching noise, then felt Loni's hand on his back. She snuggled near him. "I wish I could see."

"I should have brought matches," Mike said. He reached down to check his pockets anyway. The only lumps he felt were the insulin and syringes.

"Come on," he muttered. Suddenly an explosion of light blinded him. He threw his hands up to protect himself. Loni screamed and grabbed his legs.

As fast as it had appeared, the light vanished. Mike heard a thumping, dragging noise. Something crashed into him and past him, making choking noises as it moved. Then Mike heard a cry from Loni.

"Petey! Petey, it's you!"

Loni's brother had crawled out of the darkness. She and he were both crying and trying to talk at the same time.

Mike groped until he found Petey's arm. "Pete, where's Buddy? Is he all right?"

Pete's sniffing and sobbing quieted. Mike smelled something familiar; it was peanut butter.

"Buddy fell asleep," Pete said. "I couldn't wake him up. I knew the tide was coming in and we had to leave, but he stayed asleep."

Mike's head began to spin. He squeezed Pete's arm tighter. *"Where is he?"*

"Back there," Pete answered. "I heard you guys talking and I . . ."

"Give me the flashlight," Mike snapped. He felt Pete's hand searching for his, then the metal touched his skin. Mike flipped the light on, and in the glow he saw Loni clutching Pete around his waist. Pete's face was black from playing in the cave; Loni's was white.

Mike turned and shone the light in the other direction. Ten feet ahead the tunnel sloped up and widened. Scrambling on all fours, he crossed the distance in seconds.

He knelt at the wider opening and flashed the light again. A backpack and the remains of a picnic lay in the beam. Two dozen toy Indians stood ready for battle; comic books were scattered in the sand. Mike moved the light and saw his brother.

Buddy was slumped against the cave wall. He looked like a stuffed doll that someone had forgotten to put away.

Mike crawled into the cave. His knee landed on something hard. He reached to remove the rock, but it wasn't a rock. It was an insulin bottle, partly empty.

Mike shook Buddy's shoulder, gently. His skin felt warm through the T-shirt.

"Buddy, wake up. Buddy, it's me, Mike — come on, wake up!"

Buddy's head rolled toward Mike. His mouth opened slightly, but his eyes stayed shut.

Mike turned and yelled back into the tunnel. "Loni, quick, I need you!" He heard her and Pete scuffling over the sand. Then they were in the cave, crossing to the light. Pete was first and Mike shone the light in his face.

"Did Buddy take his insulin shot in the cave?"

Pete nodded. "I helped him do it. He made me tell him when it was one-thirty."

Pete held up his wrist so Mike could see the red numbers glowing from the face of his watch. "Then he just went to sleep and I got scared." Pete started to cry again. "He stuck the needle into his leg and he was talking and he went to sleep."

Mike held Pete's arm up and looked closer at his watch. It said two-thirty-seven.

"What did he have to eat?" Mike asked. His voice was cracking.

"A banana, some potato chips, and peanut butter and crackers."

"Any soda?"

"No," Pete said. "We brought sodas, but Buddy never drank his. He was in a hurry to get his shot."

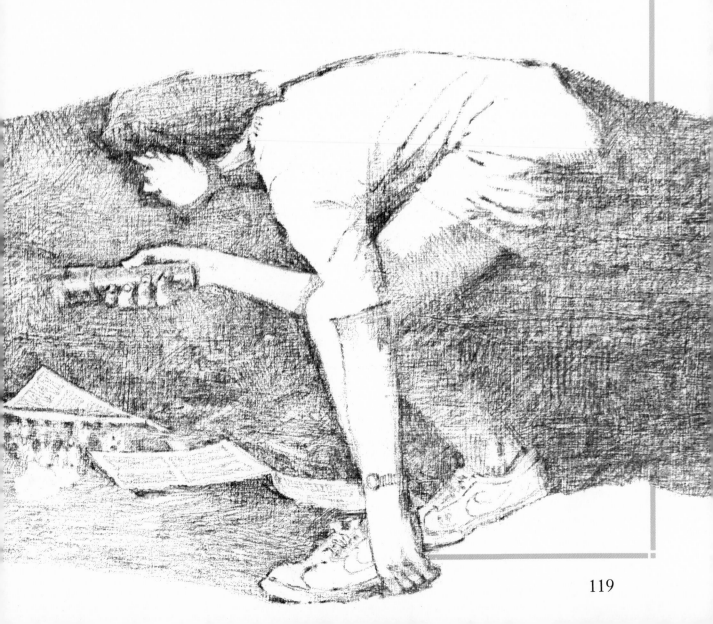

Mike spun around and found the pack; one soda can was un-opened. He yanked the top off and crawled back to Buddy. Thrusting the flashlight into Pete's lap, he slipped one hand behind Buddy's neck. His head felt heavy.

"Open his mouth," Mike said to Loni. She did, and he poured the warm foamy liquid between Buddy's lips. Buddy choked and spit up the soda. Mike repeated the pouring until he was sure his brother was swallowing more than he was spilling over his chin.

Mike stared at his brother's dirty face. Even with Loni and Pete kneeling next to him, he felt very alone.

♦♦♦

The next five minutes in the dank, close cave seemed like an hour to Mike. The hand supporting Buddy's head was numb, and his neck ached from holding it and his whole body in one position.

Loni knelt next to Mike with her fingers pressed under Buddy's ears where his jaw and neck bones came together. Buddy's mouth hung open as Mike poured small amounts of soda down his throat. Pete sat Indian style with the beam of the flashlight on Buddy's face.

Nobody spoke because there was nothing to say. Behind them, outside the tunnel, the ocean moaned as it closed in on Bald Head Cliff.

Then, as if he'd been napping and now it was time to get up, Buddy opened his eyes. He blinked and squinted at the light, then slowly recognized the faces above him.

"What's going on?" he asked.

Mike blinked back the tears that were trying to roll down his face. He felt as if he had been sucked into a whirlpool, but now he was floating on a calm lake; the whirlpool had vanished. It took a few seconds for him to realize that the nightmare was finally over.

"You had a reaction," he told Buddy. "How do you feel?"

"A little sleepy." Buddy sat up with Mike's help and looked around. "We're in the cave?"

Mike sat back on his heels; it felt good to move again. "Yes, but we aren't going to stay here talking about it." He took the light from Pete and trained it on Buddy again. "You sure you're okay? We have to get out of here right now."

"I'm okay, honest."

"Let me know if you start to feel funny or anything." Mike turned and used the light to find the Indians and soldiers. When he began stuffing them into the pack, he found a plastic bag half filled with cookies. He tossed the bag into Buddy's lap. "Eat a few of these," he ordered.

At school Buddy started to fall asleep once and the teacher poured grape juice down his throat. He was fine after the sugar got into his blood. Now, in the cave, Mike hoped for the same miracle.

Loni led them out. Pete came next, then Buddy. Mike followed Buddy so he could keep an eye on him.

They moved quickly. Being smaller, Buddy and Pete were able to scoot along on hands and knees. Mike had a harder time because of the flashlight he held in one hand. As he crawled, the light beam bounced from cave floor to ceiling to walls like a yellow bat.

After a few minutes Buddy stopped; Mike was forced to do the same. "What's the matter?" he called ahead to Loni.

"Water," she yelled back. "I don't know how deep it is. What should we do?"

Mike thought fast. They couldn't go back, that much was certain. They'd been in the cave about twenty minutes already. Mike knew the tide was slowly covering the mouth of the cave.

"The tunnel slopes down there," he yelled. "We'll have to swim out the last few feet."

"I can swim," Pete said.

"Me too," said Buddy.

Mike shone the light past Buddy until he saw Pete's face peering back at him like a raccoon's.

"Hold onto your sister's feet," Mike told him. "Crawl when she crawls, do everything she does, okay? And don't stop no matter what!"

Pete nodded, the excitement glowing in his eyes.

Mike put his hand on Buddy's back. "Listen, when we get to the end the water will be over our faces. That's because we'll be on our stomachs. Outside it'll only be up to your waist, so don't be afraid, all right?"

He could feel Buddy trembling with excitement and fear. He wondered if the little guy knew *he* was scared, too.

"When the water covers your head, hold your breath and start swimming underwater. I'll be right behind you and I'll push you along."

Mike looked into Buddy's trusting face. Right now he'd drink the ocean if I asked him to, Mike thought, sincerely hoping that wouldn't be necessary.

"We're only going to be underwater for a few feet," Mike added. "Okay?"

"I'm not scared," Buddy said. His voice sounded plenty scared to Mike. At Buddy's age he would have been terrified.

Mike shouted ahead to Loni: "Let's go." He prayed that he was right about how high the water had risen. But it was too late to do anything about that. They had to move on.

Mike stiffened as the cold water swirled around his chest and stomach. He put his hand out to touch Buddy. He knew his brother must be pretty panicky right now, no matter how brave he was acting.

"Don't stop!" Mike yelled ahead, but mostly for his brother. "I'm right behind you; keep going till you're outside."

The rest happened quickly. Mike was shoulder deep in water for an instant. The flashlight, still clutched in his hand, had gone out. One of Buddy's kicking feet smashed into his nose. Mike cried out and choked on a mouthful of salt water. He coughed it out, took a deep breath, and plunged. Now he was totally underwater.

It was black and cold down there. Mike opened his eyes and the salt bit into them; he saw only darkness and darker shadows. He released the dead flashlight and clawed his way forward. His back scraped the tunnel ceiling; he was floating.

Then the gray murk grew lighter. He knew he was seeing sunlight through the water. Kicking and scratching like a trapped animal, Mike shot the last few feet out of the tunnel.

His head smashed into someone's legs. Hands were all over him, yanking him to his knees, then his feet. He lost his balance, fell, was helped up again. The salt stung his eyes shut, but he knew he was outside and safe.

He spit out salt water and wiped his eyes. When he opened them Loni and Pete and Buddy were there with him. The water was at his waist, higher on the others. All around them it swirled, the waves smacking them, forcing them to hold on to each other.

"Come on," Mike cried. He grabbed Buddy under one arm and hurried him toward the cliff. Like seals, they left the water and climbed onto the rocks.

At the top, Buddy huddled against the tree trunk near his bike. Mike lay a few feet away with an arm over his eyes. Pete and Loni sat nearby, leaning against each other's backs.

No one spoke. The desperate swim out of the tunnel and the quick climb up the cliff path had left them drained. They shivered until the sun began to dry their hair and clothes.

"Mike? What made me fall asleep in the cave?" Buddy asked. He had lost one sneaker and was yanking a tube sock higher on his ankle.

Mike raised his head slowly. In only a few minutes the sun had begun to put him to sleep. He blinked and glanced around at the others. Another time he would have laughed. They all looked as if they'd just swum the English Channel.

"I think you needed sugar," Mike said, swinging his eyes to Buddy. "Either that or you got too much insulin in the needle back in the cave."

Mike sat up suddenly. "Where did you get the insulin, anyway?"

Buddy looked embarrassed. "I took it from the upstairs bathroom. When you didn't come home, Pete and me decided to come to the cave to play. He has a watch so I knew I could take my shot on time." He looked from his brother to Loni. "Didn't you see my note?"

"What note?"

"I wrote down where we were going and stuck it on the refrigerator," Buddy said.

Mike shook his head. "I was in the kitchen three times but I didn't see any note." He remembered how crazy he'd acted when he first found Buddy missing.

"It was still pretty stupid," Mike blurted, trying to keep his voice from showing how angry and scared he was. "You were told to wait, Buddy."

Buddy stared at his lone sneaker. "We left a note," he repeated, beginning to cry.

"I was looking for *you*, not a dumb *note*," Mike said, raising his voice. Pete looked as if he was going to start crying too.

"Let's go," Mike muttered.

Loni and Pete rode ahead. When he and Buddy were alone, Mike stopped his bike. "I'm sorry I wasn't home when you got there," he said. "The game took longer than I thought. I'm really sorry."

"That's okay." Buddy spun one pedal with the toe of his sneaker. When it stopped spinning he looked at Mike. "You going to tell Mom and Dad?"

"They already know," Mike answered. "Mom called home about an hour ago and I told her you were missing."

Buddy spun the pedal again.

"We've just got to face it," Mike said. "We messed up and they're going to be plenty mad and there's nothing we can do about it."

He watched Buddy's face working and tried to imagine what was going on inside his little brother's brain. "Look, don't worry about that now, okay? Let's just get home."

Buddy's face changed again. This time it grew solemn. He found his balance and pedaled furiously along the sandy path toward home. His bottom, high in the air, was still wet.

Mike yawned. He knew the day wasn't over yet by a long shot. His parents weren't going to be easy on him — or his brother. He pressed a tired foot onto its pedal and followed Buddy.

Overhead, a lone sea gull hovered, staring down at the procession of bikes.

◆◆◆

If you want to find out what else happens to Pete, Loni, Mike, and Buddy, read the rest of Where's Buddy?

RIGHT THERE
WITH YOU

Ron Roy's description of the tunnel makes you feel as if you were right there. Since the tunnel is dark, he relies on descriptions of sounds and feelings, such as "the *muffled* sound" and "her flesh felt *cold like . . . dead frogs.*"

Think of a place you know well. What would it be like in the dark? What sounds could you hear? What could you smell? What things could you touch? How would they feel? Write a description of the place. Make your readers feel as if they were there with you.

SEA POETRY

by Langston Hughes

Long Trip

The sea is a wilderness of waves,
A desert of water.
We dip and dive,
Rise and roll,
Hide and are hidden
On the sea.
   Day, night,
   Night, day,
The sea is a desert of waves,
A wilderness of water.

Sea Calm

How still,
How strangely still
The water is today.
It is not good
For water
To be so still that way.

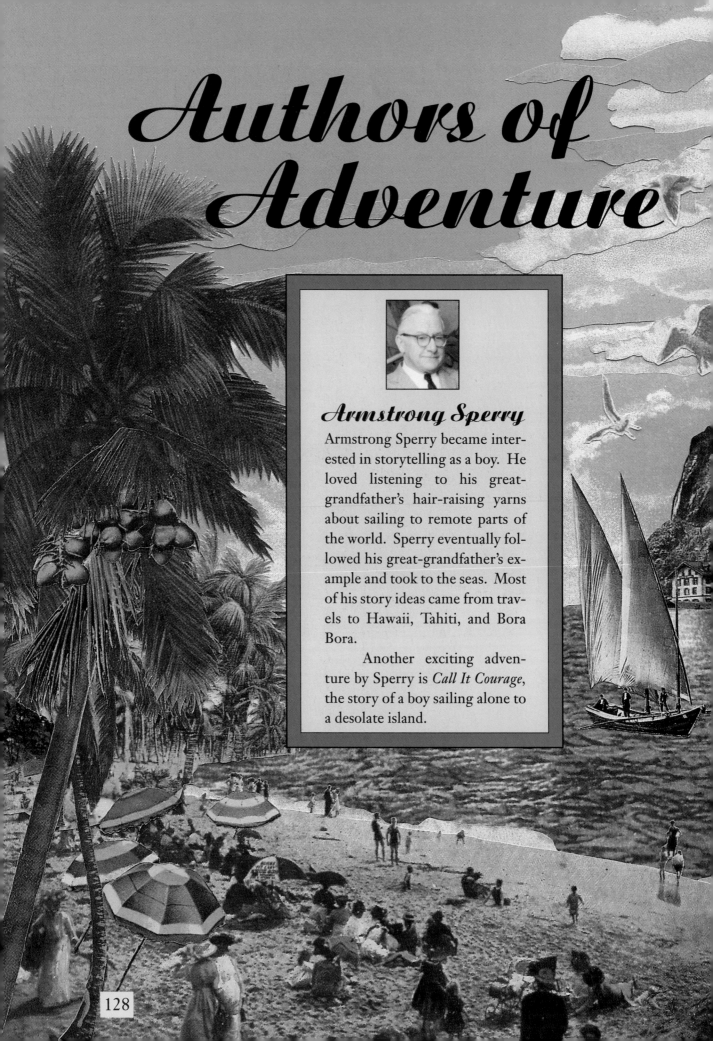

Authors of Adventure

Armstrong Sperry

Armstrong Sperry became interested in storytelling as a boy. He loved listening to his great-grandfather's hair-raising yarns about sailing to remote parts of the world. Sperry eventually followed his great-grandfather's example and took to the seas. Most of his story ideas came from travels to Hawaii, Tahiti, and Bora Bora.

Another exciting adventure by Sperry is *Call It Courage*, the story of a boy sailing alone to a desolate island.

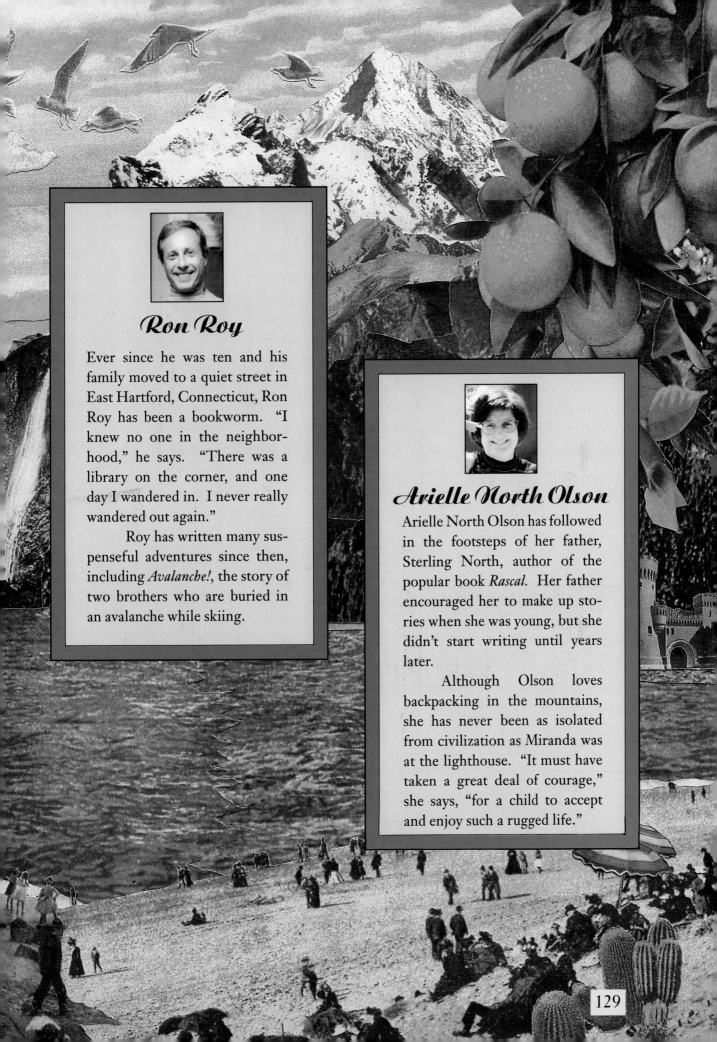

Ron Roy

Ever since he was ten and his family moved to a quiet street in East Hartford, Connecticut, Ron Roy has been a bookworm. "I knew no one in the neighborhood," he says. "There was a library on the corner, and one day I wandered in. I never really wandered out again."

Roy has written many suspenseful adventures since then, including *Avalanche!*, the story of two brothers who are buried in an avalanche while skiing.

Arielle North Olson

Arielle North Olson has followed in the footsteps of her father, Sterling North, author of the popular book *Rascal*. Her father encouraged her to make up stories when she was young, but she didn't start writing until years later.

Although Olson loves backpacking in the mountains, she has never been as isolated from civilization as Miranda was at the lighthouse. "It must have taken a great deal of courage," she says, "for a child to accept and enjoy such a rugged life."

WATCH OUT FOR THESE BOOKS!

A Lion to Guard Us
by Clyde Robert Bulla
Amanda, Jemmy, and Meg must brave a dangerous ocean crossing before they can make it to the New World.

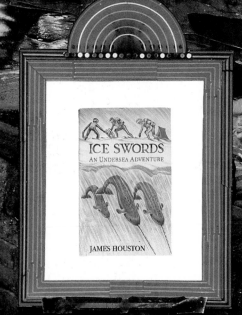

Ice Swords: An Undersea Adventure
by James Houston
In this exciting adventure story, Matthew, Kayak, and Jill swim for their lives in Arctic waters.

Help! I'm a Prisoner in the Library
by Eth Clifford
Two girls face a suspenseful night after they accidentally get locked in a library during a raging blizzard.

How Many Days to America?
A Thanksgiving Story
by Eve Bunting

A Caribbean family faces rough seas, engine trouble, and thieves on their dangerous voyage to America.

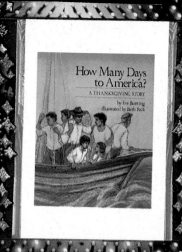

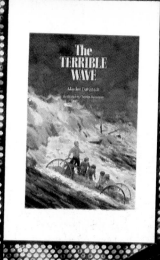

The Terrible Wave
by Marden Dahlstedt

During the 1889 Johnstown, Pennsylvania flood, Megan is swept along in the current on a swiftly sinking mattress.

NONFICTION

BOOK 3

Operation WILDLIFE

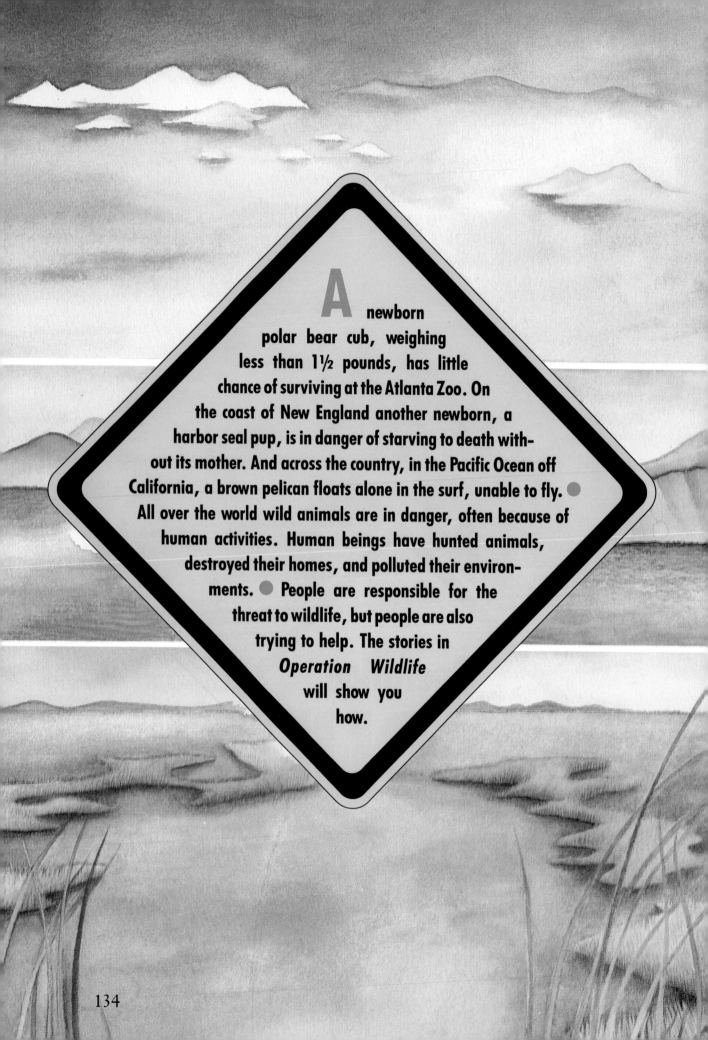

A newborn polar bear cub, weighing less than 1½ pounds, has little chance of surviving at the Atlanta Zoo. On the coast of New England another newborn, a harbor seal pup, is in danger of starving to death without its mother. And across the country, in the Pacific Ocean off California, a brown pelican floats alone in the surf, unable to fly. ● All over the world wild animals are in danger, often because of human activities. Human beings have hunted animals, destroyed their homes, and polluted their environments. ● People are responsible for the threat to wildlife, but people are also trying to help. The stories in *Operation Wildlife* will show you how.

CONTENTS

136

**Andy Bear:
A Polar Cub Grows Up at the Zoo**
*from the book by Ginny Johnston and Judy Cutchins
with photographs by Constance Noble*

157

**Sterling:
The Rescue of a Baby Harbor Seal**
by Sandra Verrill White and Michael Filisky

169

Fly Away Free
*by Joan Hewett
with photographs by Richard Hewett*

FROM THE BOOK

ANDY BEAR

A POLAR CUB GROWS UP AT THE ZOO
BY GINNY JOHNSTON & JUDY CUTCHINS

INTRODUCTION

Polar bears have been hunted for hundreds of years. Fifteen years ago, scientists began to study the great white bears in the Arctic. They estimated 20,000 polar bears were living there, but each year too many were being killed by hunters. In 1972, a law was passed in America to protect the polar bears. Four years later, an international agreement was signed by all the Arctic nations to limit the number of polar bears that could be killed each year. Now, the big bear is out of serious danger from hunters.

But the polar bear habitat is in danger from hunters of a different kind. People who are searching for oil and minerals beneath the Arctic ice threaten to destroy the polar bears' environment. Much more must be learned about the polar bears and their way of life in order to protect them.

Some zoos around the world are trying to help find out more about polar bears. They are breeding these beautiful animals in captivity and studying their habits. However, because people still know so little about the needs of polar bears, raising newborn cubs in zoos is very difficult. Most polar bear cubs in captivity do not survive.

Constance Noble in Atlanta, Georgia, is one of very few zookeepers in the world who has succeeded in keeping polar bear cubs alive. *Andy Bear* is the story of Constance and one of these rare cubs.

WITH PHOTOGRAPHS BY CONSTANCE NOBLE

ANDY BEAR

It was ten-thirty on Christmas morning and the Atlanta Zoo was closed to visitors. But, to the animals, Christmas was just like any other day. They were hungry and needed attention.

Most of the zookeepers had finished their work and gone home for the day. Only Constance Noble and one other keeper were still working. Constance loved her work at the zoo. She had cared for lions, bobcats, monkeys, sea lions, and bears for more than ten years. The animals seemed to know she was their friend.

"What a warm morning for December," Constance thought as she walked along the zookeeper's pathway behind the bear cages.

Grizzlies, Asiatic black bears, Malayan sun bears, Kodiaks, and polar bears all lived at the zoo. Each kind of bear had a cage with both indoor and outdoor areas. Inside each cage were two small "dens." These cavelike rooms allowed the bears some peace and quiet away from crowds of visitors. One of the dens in each cage opened into an outside yard with a swimming pool. In the yard the bears could exercise or sleep in the sunshine while visitors watched.

Climbing the ladder behind the polar bears' cage, Constance looked over the high rock wall into the yard below. She saw only Thor, the 1200-pound male bear, sleeping comfortably in the yard. Linda, the female polar bear, was inside the den. The two Siberian polar bears had shared a cage at the zoo for almost twenty years. Zookeepers had placed them together as playmates when they were very young. In the wild, male bears are loners, rarely having any contact with females. At the zoo, Thor and

Constance cleans the cage for Alice, an African lion.

Linda have developed an unusual polar bear relationship because they are constant companions.

In their cage, the sliding metal door between the inside dens and the outside yard was open so the bears could go in or out as they pleased. Constance tossed two pounds of chunky, dry food called "bear chow" into the yard. Seeing nothing unusual, she climbed down and went next door to feed the grizzlies, then the Kodiaks.

Just as she was finishing her work at the Kodiaks' cage, the quiet of the Christmas morning was shattered by ear-splitting screams and frightening howls. These terrifying sounds were coming from the polar bears!

Constance rushed behind the cages and looked through a small back door into the polar bears' den. She could see Thor. His head was lowered and he was snorting fiercely as he tried to come into the den. Inside, Linda was moaning and howling as she blocked the doorway with her 700-pound body. The screams were coming from a corner inside the dark den.

Constance knew immediately what was happening. During the night Linda had given birth to a cub and was protecting it from the powerful Thor. Now that he was awake, the father bear, with his extraordinary sense of smell, had discovered the new cub inside the den. If Thor got to the baby he would kill it.

A male polar bear will kill any newcomer, even his own cub. In the Arctic, polar bear mothers and newborn cubs live beneath the snow in large dens safely hidden from the male bears for several months. But, here at the zoo it was different. Zookeepers were afraid to move Thor away from Linda. She might be so lonely and upset she would not take care of her cub.

Thor smells the newborn cub and tries to come into the den.

The only way the baby bear could survive was for Constance to rescue it quickly. For the past few years, all of Linda's cubs had been killed before the zookeepers could get to them.

Constance knew how dangerous polar bears could be, especially at a time like this. These enormous white bears have more strength than gorillas. Constance would be killed if she went inside the den now. Somehow, she had to drive both bears out into the yard. Then she could close the sliding den door, lock them out, and go safely into the den. But how could she force them out?

Grabbing a bucket of bear chow, she rushed up the ladder and threw the food over the wall, hoping to attract Thor and Linda into the yard. It didn't work.

Hurrying down the ladder, she snatched up the hose and sprayed water through an opening in the door. But the bears didn't budge. They stood face to face, Thor growling, Linda moaning, and from deep inside the den, the newborn cub screaming.

Constance, a quiet and gentle zookeeper, was becoming desperate. She knew she was running out of time. Although Linda snapped and growled at Thor, she could not keep him away from the cub

If Constance throws bear chow over the wall, Linda might go into the yard with Thor.

much longer. Constance tried the last thing she could think of — she threw a screaming fit! She yelled at the bears, waved her arms, and banged on the door of the cage.

Thor was so surprised he backed out of the doorway. The startled Linda followed him into the yard. Constance couldn't believe her eyes. Quickly she ran to pull the handle that closed the den's sliding door. Both adult polar bears were locked out. At last, the cub would be safe.

Constance unlocked the zookeeper's doorway and crawled into the den. She stood up slowly and squinted in the darkness. At first she couldn't see anything. The cub was quiet now, making it even harder to find. Constance

To rescue the cub, Constance locks Thor and Linda in the outside yard.

141

shuffled her feet along the floor hoping not to step on the baby. When her foot bumped into the cub, it began to scream again. As her eyes adjusted to the dimness of the den, Constance could just about see the shape of the cub. It was no bigger than a guinea pig. She picked it up, gently snuggling its warm body to her chest, and headed for the zoo clinic.

By the time she arrived at the clinic, the cub was quiet. Constance examined the baby. It was a perfectly healthy boy!

The zookeepers had decided to name the next male cub born at the zoo Andrew, in honor of the city's mayor, Andrew Young. Later they gave the tiny cub a middle name, Nicholas, because he was born on Christmas morning. Andrew Nicholas Polar Bear was called Andy for short.

Andy weighed just under $1\frac{1}{2}$ pounds. He had a pink nose and his tiny ears were flat against his head. His eyes were closed and his wrinkled, pink body was covered with fine, white fur. Although Andy could already hold his head up, it would be weeks before he could walk.

Constance placed Andy in an incubator where he would be safe and warm. She made a formula of evaporated milk and water. Every hour and a half, she squirted a little of the mixture into Andy's mouth.

The newborn cub is the size of a guinea pig.

While the other zookeeper watched Andy, Constance left the clinic just long enough to check on Thor and Linda. Thor was resting quietly now on a large rock in the yard. But Linda was moaning and pacing around. She didn't understand why her cub was gone. Constance wished she could explain to the lonely mother bear that this was the only way her cub could survive at the zoo.

After the excitement, Thor rests quietly on a rock.

Zoo officials were excited about the birth of Andy and the miraculous rescue by Constance. They knew this rare baby polar bear would need attention twenty-four hours a day. Constance was placed in charge of the new cub. Since she could not live at the small zoo clinic, Constance took Andy home with her. While Constance cared for Andy at her apartment, another zookeeper would do her zoo chores until she returned.

For the next few months, Constance would have to become a mother polar bear—comforting, warming, and feeding the baby bear night and day. Constance knew that the biggest problem would be mixing a formula identical to real polar bear milk. The milk of the mother polar bear is very different from any milk Constance could buy. It is much thicker and creamier.

Linda misses her cub.

Constance watched Andy closely and kept a diary of each change in the little bear as he grew. When Andy was

143

 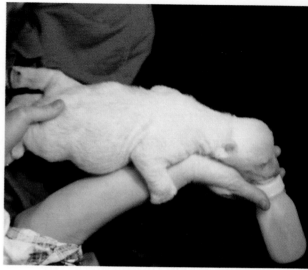

Constance
has to feed
Andy every
1½ hours.
The little
cub
changes
as he grows.
At one
week, Andy
weighs 2½
pounds . . .

just three days old, Constance noticed that his soft, pink nose and pink foot pads were starting to turn black. This was good news; it meant the cub was growing normally. She was still feeding him every hour and a half. After the first week, Andy had gained one pound. Now, he weighed 2½ pounds!

One stormy evening, Constance sat in her bedroom jotting notes in her diary about Andy's tenth day. Nearby, Andy was crawling around in his playpen. He couldn't walk yet, because his little legs would not hold him up. Suddenly, a flash of lightning and a crash of thunder startled the bear cub, and he began to cry.

Over the next few days, Constance noticed that Andy was very sensitive to loud noises. The ring of the telephone scared him and caused him to whimper. Constance asked her friends not to call. She stopped using her noisy dishwasher. Even the television and radio had to be turned down so low they could hardly be heard.

Andy was changing in other ways, too. When he was twenty-eight days old, his shiny, dark eyes opened for the first time. Thicker fur was beginning to cover his body.

Constance had been working so hard, she had not had time to notice what a beautiful animal little Andrew Nicholas was becoming. He was less like a furry ball and more like a polar bear. He was developing the long muscular neck that makes polar bears look so different from other bears.

Although the first four weeks had not been easy, the next four were even harder. By the end of January, Andy was becoming very sick. Just as Constance had feared, the milk formula was the cause of his problems. His delicate digestive system was not working properly. Constance knew if Andy got any sicker, he could die. Polar cubs are so rare in captivity that neither Constance nor the zoo veterinarian knew exactly what to do for Andy. They tried several "people" medicines, hoping to find the one that would save Andy's life.

To make matters worse, Andy was cutting his baby teeth, and his gums were very sore. The doctor gave him mild painkillers to make the teething easier. Constance wondered how this tiny bear that weighed just 5 pounds could possibly survive. It seemed hopeless, but she would not give up.

and when he is four weeks old, his eyes open.

Hour after hour, day after day, Constance sat with the sick little bear until the medicines finally began to work. Andy at last rested more comfortably. Constance was using a different formula consisting of cream and water, and Andy was feeling much better. His digestive problems were finally over and his baby teeth were all in place. By the last week in February, Constance could relax a little. Now two months old, Andy was gaining weight again, and his eyes were shining brightly.

Constance watched one morning as Andy stretched, yawned, and rolled onto his stomach after a long nap. On unsteady but determined legs, he took his first steps. Nine-week-old Andy was walking! Now Constance would have to watch him even more closely.

Andy began to suck on everything he came near. He sucked on his blanket and on Constance's arm. His sharp little teeth caused a painful bite, but when she pulled away, Andy screamed. Constance solved the problem by giving Andy a baby bottle nipple to use as a pacifier.

One afternoon in late March, Constance sat relaxing by her window watching a rare southern snowfall gently

After one month, Andy gets sick. He finally begins to get stronger and feel better as the medicine begins to work.

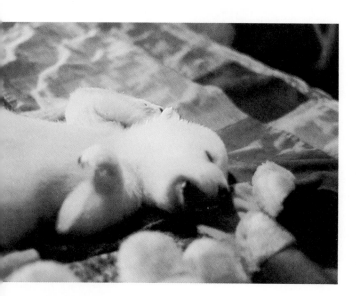

Healthy
and curi-
ous, the
polar cub
is eager to
explore,
indoors
and out.

Andy bites
everything
within
reach with
his sharp
teeth.

Andy
"helps"
Constance
with her
flower
garden.

cover the ground. She decided to give Andy a taste of what "real" Arctic polar bear life might be like.

She bundled herself up with a coat and gloves and opened the back door. Andy stepped uncertainly onto the soft white blanket of snow. Suddenly, out he went! He looked like a running, sliding snowball of fur. A squirrel scurried to the warmth of its nearby nest. Constance knew Andy wouldn't be cold because polar bears have thick fur and layers of fat to keep them warm. Even the bottoms of their feet are covered with fur. In the Arctic, temperatures drop to forty degrees below zero.

Constance and her friends enjoyed romping with Andy Bear, but they were always careful of the frisky cub's teeth. Constance had already lost a fingernail because of his powerful bite. Even three-month-old polar bears have very strong jaws. Constance knew that although she had rescued Andy and raised him from a tiny cub, he was not a pet. In just a few months he would weigh over 100 pounds and be a strong and unpredictable polar bear.

By spring, Andy was becoming more curious and playful. He climbed on the kitchen counters and chewed on the furniture. Andy was wrecking Constance's apartment. Outdoors, he splashed in the water, dug in the garden, and explored in the yard. At 25 pounds, Andy was becoming a problem around the house. His claws were over an inch long and his teeth were very sharp. It was time for Andy to return to the zoo.

How will Andy adjust to the zoo after months of apartment living? You can find out by reading the rest of *Andy Bear*.

A lot of time, money, and care was spent to save Andy's life. Some people might think it wasn't worth it, just to save one polar bear. What do you think — and why? Discuss this question with a partner or a small group. Then plan a way to convince the rest of the class that you are right. For example, you might make a poster, present a skit, or make an announcement.

Ginny Johnston and Judy Cutchins

Ginny Johnston and Judy Cutchins describe themselves as "educators first and writers second." In their work as instructors at the Fernbank Science Center in Atlanta, they quickly discovered the great interest children have in learning about animals. This awareness led them to write several books for children on wildlife and conservation. Says Cutchins, "We do not just look for subjects for the sake of writing another book. We want to share with young readers some of the fascinating things we discover in the worlds of wildlife, museums, and zoos."

If you enjoyed reading about Andy Bear's experiences at the Atlanta Zoo, you may also be interested in these other books by Johnston and Cutchins:

- *Are Those Animals Real?* shows how museums prepare their wildlife exhibits.
- *Windows on Wildlife* tells about six outstanding zoo and aquarium exhibits from all around the country.
- *The Crocodile and the Crane: Surviving in a Crowded World* describes the efforts to save several endangered species.

Poems About WILDLIFE

Buffalo Dusk

The buffaloes are gone.
And those who saw the buffaloes are gone.
Those who saw the buffaloes by thousands and
    how they pawed the prairie sod into dust
    with their hoofs, their great heads down
    pawing on in a great pageant of dusk,
Those who saw the buffaloes are gone.
And the buffaloes are gone.

Carl Sandburg

Eagle Flight

An eagle wings gracefully
    through the sky.
On the earth I stand
    and watch.
My heart flies with it.

Alonzo Lopez

Hurt No Living Thing

Hurt no living thing:
Ladybird, no butterfly,
Nor moth with dusty wing,
No cricket chirping cheerily,
Nor grasshopper so light of leap,
Nor dancing gnat, no beetle fat,
Nor harmless worms that creep.

Christina Rossetti

153

The Passenger Pigeon

(a poem for two voices)

We were counted not in	
	thousands
nor	
	millions
but in	
billions.	*billions.*
	We were numerous as the
stars	stars
	in the heavens
As grains of	
sand	sand
at the sea	
	As the
buffalo	buffalo
	on the plains.
When we burst into flight	
	we so filled the sky
that the	
sun	sun
was darkened	
	and
day	day
	became dusk.
Humblers of the sun	Humblers of the sun
we were!	we were!
The world	
inconceivable	inconceivable
	without us.
Yet it's 1914,	
and here I am	
alone	alone
	caged in the Cincinnati Zoo,
the last	
	of the passenger pigeons.

Paul Fleischman

Bison

Where has he gone?
The great shaggy beast.
The wild one.
The provider,
The warmth from cold.
The food to drive away hunger.
The robe and moccasins for my feet.
The leather for my shirt.
The skin for my tent.
The bones for my tools.
The sinew for my bowstring.
The horn for my spoon and cups.
The stomach for a bag to carry my things in.
The rawhide.
I look for him on the plains and he is not there.
I look for him in the meadows and the valleys
     and at the water and
he is not there either.
I cannot live without him.

Tonye Garter
Sioux/Senior, Cheyenne-Eagle Butte High School

Sandra Verrill White's fascination with seals began several years ago, when she started working as a volunteer for the Animal Care Program at the New England Aquarium in Boston, Massachusetts. Seals, she discovered, crave attention even more than food. Although they are wild animals, they are extremely curious about people. Her work on Sterling's story gave White a chance to observe the release program and to study how released seals interact with seals that have remained in the wild.

White is currently the Assistant Curator for Education at the Aquarium and is involved in the production of other New England Aquarium Books.

Michael Filisky wrote *Sterling: The Rescue of a Baby Harbor Seal* with Sandra Verrill White as an answer to children's questions about what goes on behind the scenes at the New England Aquarium. While working on this book, Filisky learned how complicated the care of wild animals is and how little is known about the ways in which animals get along with each other.

Formerly the manager of the New England Aquarium Books series, Filisky is currently writing more nature books for children.

Sterling

The Rescue of a Baby Harbor Seal

by SANDRA VERRILL WHITE
& MICHAEL FILISKY

In the cold ocean off the coast of New England, an animal has come to the surface. What kind of animal is it? It is a seal. In fact, it is the most common kind of seal found in New England. It is a harbor seal.

Harbor seals are different from other northern seals. Gray seals like this fuzzy pup have much longer, horselike faces.

Hooded seals are much larger than harbor seals. Hooded seal pups have a beautiful dark back and cream-colored belly.

Harp seals, which are dark as adults, give birth to snow-white pups.

But only the harbor seals live in New England in large numbers. Several thousand of them make their homes off the coast of Maine.

A harbor seal hunts in the water and rests on the rocks by the shore. Its earholes and nostrils close tight to keep out icy waters; its large eyes and sensitive whiskers help it search the rocks for signs of food.

The harbor seal shares its underwater habitat with many kinds of animals and plants. Dense mats of rockweeds sway in the current. Periwinkle snails and prickly sea urchins graze on the seaweeds, while starfish search for tasty mussels. None of these tempt harbor seals.

Schools of small, silvery fish swim among the rocks and seaweeds. Usually, harbor seals try to catch slower-swimming fish than these.

A seal decides to come out of the water. Carefully, it hauls itself out onto the rocks that have been exposed by the outgoing tide.

This seal is a female, heavy with her first pup. She has come out of the water to give birth.

Away from other seals, the new pup comes into the world. Mother and pup touch noses and call to each other, learning each other's smells and sounds. Briefly, the pup nurses on her mother's rich milk and sleeps by her side.

The newborn follows her mother into the ocean. Newborn harbor seal pups have little insulating fat, so they cannot stay long in the chilly water. The pup returns to the beach to wait in the sun while her mother feeds in the sea. . . .

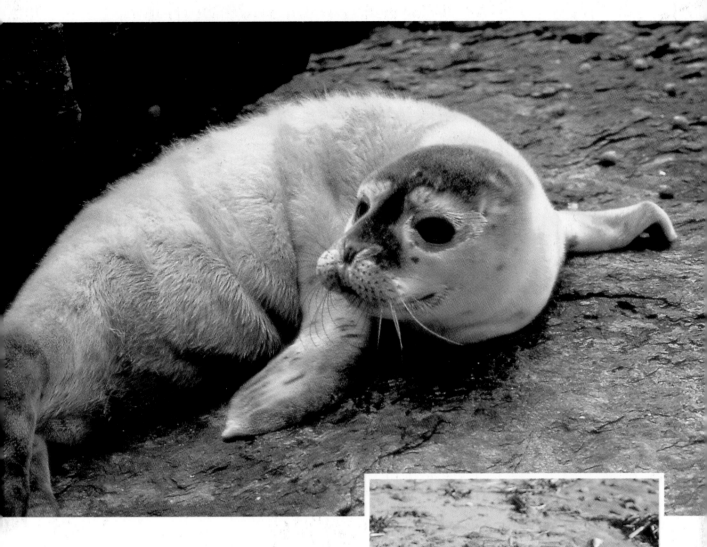

After several hours alone, the pup becomes hungry. She looks expectantly toward the sea, but there is no sign of her mother. Soon the harbor seal pup becomes distressed and calls softly.

By morning the pup is frantic for food.

Several days later the mother seal has still not appeared. Dazed and weak, the pup wanders from the rocks to the beach.

Seal pups rest on shore.
Do not disturb them!
It's the law.

Report animals in distress to
LOCAL POLICE
or
NATIONAL MARINE FISHERIES SERVICE
LAW ENFORCEMENT DIVISION
or
NEW ENGLAND AQUARIUM
BOSTON, MASSACHUSETTS

Every spring on the coast of New England people find baby seals. Some of the pups have been orphaned, but most mother seals have just gone on short fishing trips. Fortunately, people also find signs like this one.

Someone from the Marine Mammal Stranding Network must determine that the little seal has really been abandoned.

The Marine Mammal Stranding coordinator sees how thin the pup is and knows this means the pup is probably a real orphan. The pup is immediately brought to the Animal Care Facility at the New England Aquarium.

At the New England Aquarium the pup is placed on a steel examining table in a clean, bright room. Animal-care specialists check her temperature, weigh her, test her reflexes, and note her activity. The pup watches but is too weak to move.

Everything about the harbor seal pup is recorded on her own chart. To identify her a temporary tag is glued to

the hair on her head. Every orphaned pup is given a name. Like most pups, she lost her very pale newborn coat a few days after birth. But because she still has a silvery sheen to her fur, she is called Sterling.

Sterling is placed in the holding area, where other pups snooze under the warm lamps. She nuzzles up to them and falls asleep.

Waking up, Sterling hears the voices of the keepers as they prepare infant seal formula. Making formula is messy work. Pounds of herring are filleted, then pureed in a blender. This fish mush is added to heavy cream, vegetable oil, vitamins, and minerals until it is the consistency of a thin milk shake. A portion is measured out for each pup and warmed before feeding.

Sterling is so thin that the keepers are very worried. If they can't get plenty of the nourishing formula into her stomach, Sterling will not live long. Sick seal pups find it

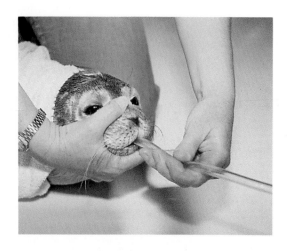

difficult to nurse from a bottle. To feed Sterling, a flexible tube is inserted into her mouth and gently guided into her stomach. In only minutes her stomach is full.

After the feedings, the keepers make notes about each pup and clean the pen with antiseptics. Their hunger satisfied, the pups sleep contentedly.

Later in the day, most of the pups follow the keepers around, begging for food and attention. Exercise is impor-

tant for recovering seal pups, but when Sterling is introduced to the seal pup "swimming pool," she is too weak to play or swim. She flops out and wriggles onto a keeper's lap.

In several weeks, Sterling has put on weight and grown teeth. If the keepers aren't careful, they can get nipped. After all, Sterling is still a wild harbor seal.

As the pups get stronger, they become more independent of the keepers. The little seals sleep and play together as a group. A daily swim helps prepare them for life in the ocean.

One day the keepers place some thawed fish in the pool to interest the pups in solid food. The pups nudge the fish around, biting at them. They are great playthings.

The seal pups play with the fish for several days. Then, one afternoon the pups are especially hungry. Sterling takes a fish into the water. She holds it briefly in her mouth and then swallows it whole. Sterling has "caught" her first meal.

It doesn't take the other pups long to catch on to feeding and, when they learn how to eat fish, it seems they enjoy eating better than anything.

After two months, most of the pups have tripled their birth weight. They are swimming and eating just like adults. The time has come for their release into the wild.

Two pups are ready for release. One of them is Sterling. They are taken by van to the coast of Maine, where a colony of harbor seals has been spotted.

When the cages are opened Sterling dashes right into the water. The other pup is timid and carefully slides into the waves. In a few days the seals will lose their tags in the water.

Eventually both pups are so far away the keepers can't tell them apart from the wild seals. The rescued orphans are on their own.

There are many dangers in the sea for a young harbor seal. Sharks and other predators are always a threat. In recent years, however, dangers made by man have become very serious: chemical pollution, crowded harbors, garbage dumped in the sea.

People can cause problems for seals, but people can help, too. At the New England Aquarium, the Marine Mammal Stranding Network learns important facts about wild seals and their rehabilitation. This kind of knowledge could someday help save endangered seal species, such as the Hawaiian monk seal. The rescue of Sterling and the other baby harbor seals helps ensure there will always be wild animals in the waters of the world.

"People can help, too."

Near the end of the selection, the authors say, "People can cause problems for seals, but people can help, too."

This is true for other animals as well. With a small group, choose a wild animal that lives in your area or an animal that interests you. Make a list of problems that people might cause for this animal. For each problem, try to think of a way in which people can help.

Joan Hewett says, "I always wanted to write and I always loved animals, all kinds of animals, but I never thought about combining these two interests." Her husband, Richard, a professional photographer, suggested that she start writing books about animals for children. Now they work as a team: Joan writes the stories and Richard takes the photographs.

You might enjoy reading the Hewetts' second book. *Watching Them Grow: Inside a Zoo Nursery* traces in words and photographs a four-month period in the animal nursery at the San Diego Zoo.

Fly Away Free

by Joan Hewett

Photographs by Richard Hewett

The chill air felt good. Veterinarian Joel Pasco, surfboard under one arm, strode across the deserted beach. The waves weren't high, but they were breaking just right for surfing. The water nipped his ankles.

Daybreak was Joel's favorite time to surf. He often surfed for an hour or more before his day's work at the animal hospital began.

Joel was on his board, making his way through the surf when he spotted the bird. It was hard to see clearly. Its brownish gray feathers blended with the ocean. Its wings were stretched as though ready for flight, but it made no move to fly. Joel paddled closer. It was a pelican. Joel had seen pelicans flying two or three together off the California coast, but he couldn't remember ever having seen a lone pelican. Certainly he had never seen a lone pelican floating in the surf. Joel paddled closer and closer. The bird could see him now. It would fly away, if it could. Something was wrong.

Joel brought his surfboard up directly behind the pelican. He leaned forward, put an arm firmly about the bird, and lifted it onto the board.

The pelican barely struggled. Poor frightened bird, Joel thought. He talked to it in a soothing tone of voice as he carried it across the wide beach, across the parking lot, and into the hospital.

Joel turned on the bright lights over the examining table. Pelicans often get tangled up in fishline when they fish close to shore. Perhaps this pelican wasn't sick or injured; perhaps it was just caught. Joel's fingers probed gently. He searched for the transparent, thin, hard-to-see fishline. He didn't find any. It was almost time to open the hospital doors. He still had to shower and change. Joel put the pelican in a pen.

Joel was on his board, making his way through the surf when he spotted the bird.

171

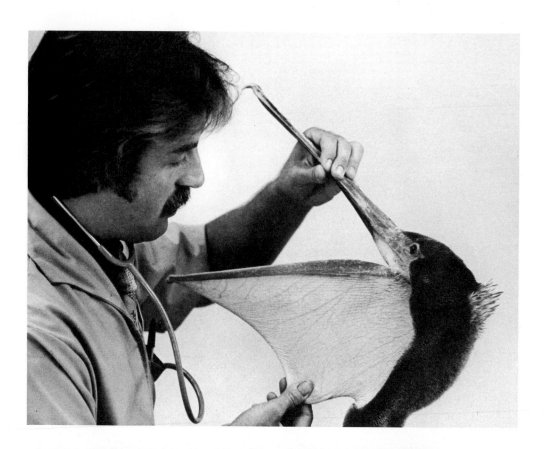

"What's that funny awful smell?" his nurse asked as she walked in.

"That's Rusty our pelican," Joel said. He told her about the rescue. Then he added, "I named him Rusty because his rusty old wings don't work well, and also it just seems like a good pelican name."

"Can we bathe Rusty?" his nurse asked.

"Sure," Joel said, "but I want to examine him first."

Joel weighed Rusty. He listened to his heart, to his breathing. He pulled his wings open as he looked for fractures. He examined Rusty's pouch, his bill. Then he opened the pelican's bill and looked at his pink, fleshy throat. There was no fishhook buried there. His throat looked just fine. Rusty did not seem nervous. He appeared to trust Joel. Joel examined Rusty's eyes, then raising his hand slightly and brushing the feathers aside, he examined the pelican's ears. He checked the bird's webbed feet. Then he X-rayed his wings to see if the X-rays would show a break. "Rusty," he said finally, "you have me stumped. We'll just see what some food, vitamins, and rest will do for you." He put a tube down Rusty's throat, then gave him liquid food and vitamins through the tube. He gave Rusty an antibiotic too, just to be on the safe side. Then he put Rusty back in his pen.

Then he opened the pelican's bill and looked at his pink, fleshy throat.

How old was Rusty? Joel wondered. If he was young, he would have a better chance of recovering than if he was old. Joel called up a scientist friend, an ornithologist who knew a lot about seabirds. He told him that Rusty weighed seven pounds, then he described his coloring: grayish rusty brown, with an almost white belly.

"Your bird's a California brown pelican," his friend said, "but are you sure it's his belly that's off-white, not his head?"

"I'm sure," Joel answered.

"Measure his wingspan, from the tip of one wing to the tip of the other," his friend instructed.

Joel measured. "Seven feet," he reported back.

"Rusty's a young pelican," his friend said. "He has reached his full growth, but he doesn't have his adult coat yet. I'd say he's about a year old."

Rusty slept for several hours, his head tucked under his wing. When he woke up, Joel fed him. Rusty seemed very calm. He looked at Joel steadily. "I like you, you're a nice bird," Joel said. Everyone else at the Sun and Surf Animal Hospital, the nurses and the attendants, liked Rusty too, but nobody liked the way he smelled. It was time for that bath.

It was time for that bath. Rusty perked up right away.

Rusty perked up right away; his feet churned the water, he spread his wings. Joel could see that the tub was a perfect playpen.

Four times a day Rusty was fed, and twice a day he was bathed. Each day he got stronger. By the fourth day Rusty was eating fish, cut up into big chunks. By the fifth day he was flapping his wings, but making no effort to fly. When Rusty had been in the hospital for a week, Joel decided that Rusty needed more exercise to make his wings stronger. But how could he get a bird to exercise its wings if it could not fly?

The next day Joel tied the end of a long rope around one of Rusty's legs, put Rusty on his shoulder, and set out for the surf.

The next day Joel tied the end of a long rope around one of Rusty's legs, put Rusty on his shoulder, and set out for the surf. Sherlock, his dog, went with them.

Rusty rode along. He seemed to be enjoying the whole world from his moving perch. When Joel put Rusty down, Rusty made no attempt to get away. He waddled along right behind Joel. When they reached the water's edge, Joel picked him up, carried him out aways, and set him on the board.

174

There was no doubt, Rusty loved to surf. In no time at all he seemed to understand what it was all about. Riding a wave, he would lose his balance sometimes and fall off the board. Then he'd swim about for a few minutes and scraggle back up. But what Rusty seemed to enjoy most was riding out into the ocean, wings outstretched toward the incoming breeze.

When they got out of the water, Joel took off his wet-suit and stretched out lazily on the sand. Rusty flapped his wings several times. Then he held them open to the warmth of the sun to dry.

After that, every time Joel went surfing, Rusty went too. They surfed early mornings or evenings before the sun went down. Sometimes they went surfing during Joel's lunch break.

Rusty was at the hospital for ten days. He was beginning to feel very much at home. In fact, Rusty was fast becoming the hospital bully. He did not want to be cooped up in his pen. He wanted to poke about. He seemed to delight in frightening Cedar the cat. A snap of Rusty's bill would send Cedar scurrying off in the opposite direction.

One afternoon Joel worked late. He had to care for a sick animal. So Rusty and Joel didn't go surfing. The next morning Joel was busy, too busy to go surfing. Rusty was out of sorts. Flapping his wings, he waddled about. He squawked if anybody got close — a very little squawk, for pelicans have very little voices.

When Joel walked into the examining room, Rusty seemed glad to see him. Joel looked Rusty over, then he weighed him. Rusty now weighed seven and a half pounds.

The bathtub, which just a short time ago had seemed like a perfect play place, now seemed very small. Rusty's feet made paddling motions, but there was no place to

paddle to. Now and then he'd duck his bill underwater, but there were no fish to spear. After a few minutes Rusty had had enough of the tub. He climbed out, perched on the edge, and started beating his wings.

"Poor Rusty," Joel said, "I don't think I'd like being cooped up either if I were a pelican. But it shouldn't be long. Those wings are looking pretty good."

That afternoon Joel took Rusty to the beach. He had a new idea he wanted to try out. A good breeze was blowing in across the ocean. The waves were two to three feet high. Perfect, Joel thought. We're going to combine a little flying with this swim.

Pelicans, like airplanes, take off against the wind. The wind helps lift them. "Here we go," Joel said. He held Rusty up above the water. Then he tossed him in the air as a wave came close. Joel ducked under the wave so he wouldn't get caught in it. As he came up, he saw Rusty come gliding down.

Wings flapping, Rusty soared above each oncoming wave. Sometimes Joel got thrown by a wave. There wasn't always time to dive under. Joel and Rusty swam and hopped the waves for quite a while. Then they dried out, rested, and went back in again.

Pretty soon Rusty was going for short test flights. Joel would pitch the pelican and unwind the rope giving him room enough to fly. Following along, Joel would run down the beach. He would pull Rusty in when he seemed to tire.

Flying, swimming, surfing, or just waddling across the sand, Rusty became a familiar sight to the people who lived at the beach. But visitors could hardly believe their eyes. "What is it?" they'd ask. There was always someone near who would tell them about Rusty and the veterinarian who had saved him. Joel always made sure to tell people that Rusty was not a pet. He was a wild creature who would soon be set free.

Pelicans, like airplanes, take off against the wind.

Pretty soon Rusty was going for short test flights.

179

Sometimes Joel could scarcely believe how quickly Rusty had gotten used to people. Children liked to see him close up. They'd reach out and stroke his feathers. Rusty never seemed to mind.

Each day Rusty's flying got better.

Each day Rusty's flying got better. His wingbeat became stronger. Now when they were going down the beach, it was Joel who tired first. When Rusty could catch a wind, he'd turn into it, spiraling upward. Only the rope was keeping him from soaring on high. Tomorrow would be Rusty's big day.

The day dawned bright and clear. With Rusty perched on his shoulder, Joel set out across the beach. It was early, the sand was still cool. "How's Rusty doing?" a few people asked. "Fine," Joel answered. Joel was busy counting. Sixteen, only sixteen days had passed since he had found Rusty in the surf, helpless and frightened. And now he couldn't possibly think of Rusty as just a pelican. He was Rusty.

They swam and they surfed. Joel was happy, but he was also a little sad. He'd miss Rusty, he knew. He'd miss him every time he went surfing.

One final test flight, then Joel untied the rope around Rusty's leg and set him on his shoulder. Rusty didn't move. "You're free now, Rusty," Joel said. Rusty didn't stir. Joel swallowed hard. He thrust the bird into the air. Rusty flapped his wings. Slowly he circled above Joel's head. Round and round he flew, gaining height, gaining speed. Now suddenly swerving, he headed toward the open sea.

Joel watched. He watched till Rusty was just a speck on the horizon. "Good-bye, friend," Joel said softly. Then he turned around and walked across the beach.

About Pelicans

Do you think Rusty is remarkable? If so, you won't be surprised to learn that people have long been intrigued by this odd-looking bird. Pelicans were nesting and caring for their young thirty or even forty million years ago. Scientists can tell this from the fossil remains they've found.

Pelicans are large fish-eating birds. Each one has a very long bill with a pouch hanging from it. There are two types of pelicans in this hemisphere: the white pelican and the brown pelican. The browns, which are more common, live on islands along both coasts of the southern United States, Mexico, Central America and parts of South America. Rusty is a brown pelican.

Brown pelicans breed in colonies. Hundreds, often thousands, come together to court, mate and nest. The female usually lays three eggs. When the chicks hatch, they are wrinkled, almost hairless and very weak. Mother and father birds fish for their young. Spotting a fish from the air they dive towards it bill first. They trap the fish, along with a great deal of water, in their pouch. Then they surface, drain the water, and swallow the fish. Returning to the nest they regurgitate, or bring it back up into their pouch. The hungry chicks thrust their bills into the parent's pouch and eat the partly digested, cut-up fish. By the time the chicks are ten to eleven weeks old, they are ready to leave the nest. They may live for twenty or thirty years.

Suddenly, in the late 1960's, naturalists realized that the pelican was vanishing. Colonies in Louisiana, Texas and California, once teeming with chicks, were almost bare of new life.

Pesticides, poisons that kill insects and other pests, were the cause. Because the water was polluted by these pesticides, the fish became contaminated. When the pelicans ate the fish, the chemicals stayed in their bodies. This caused the birds to lay eggs with unnaturally thin shells. The eggs were crushed while being laid, or gave way while the mother or father bird was trying to keep them warm till they hatched. DDT, a widely used pesticide, was banned. Pelicans were listed as an endangered species, making it illegal to harm them.

Almost ten years passed. Then one mating season large numbers of California brown chicks were born. The next season more chicks were born. Young adult California brown pelicans, like Rusty, are becoming more common. If we care enough to guard our environment, these graceful-awkward, dignified-comical, remarkable birds will once again thrive.

● ● ●

I don't believe it!

People at the beach got used to seeing Rusty surfing and swimming with Joel, but newcomers couldn't believe their eyes. With a partner, act out a conversation between a beach "regular" and a surprised visitor.

Since
the days of the
dinosaur, animals have
been disappearing from the
earth. In recent times, however, the
decline in animal populations increased so
much that people became alarmed. ● In 1973,
the United States Congress passed the Endangered Species
Act. Under this law, a species of animal or plant may be officially
listed as "endangered" (in danger of becoming extinct) or "threatened"

Endangered
S P E C I E S

(likely to become endangered in the near future). ● Once an animal is
listed, it becomes illegal for anyone to harm it, hunt it, catch it, or
sell it, without special permission. ● The U.S. Fish and
Wildlife Service enforces the Endangered Species Act
and coordinates groups that are working
to save endangered and threatened
wildlife. The following suggestions tell how you
can be part of
this effort.

What can you do?

You can show your concern for wildlife by learning more about endangered and threatened species and how they are protected.

Find out

Find out what species in your area are endangered or threatened by writing the state fish and game or conservation department.

Write

Write the U.S. Fish and Wildlife Service for a list of federally protected endangered and threatened species.

Visit

Visit a National Wildlife Refuge near you, where specialists describe resident wildlife and their needs. Help out with the annual population count of birds during breeding season or the mid-winter bald eagle count.

Join

Join a local conservation group.

Don't buy

Don't buy products without checking the law first.

Report

Report violations of wildlife laws to your local game warden.

Be informed

Be informed on wildlife and conservation issues in your area.

From the pamphlet Endangered Species, *Department of the Interior, U.S. Fish and Wildlife Service.*

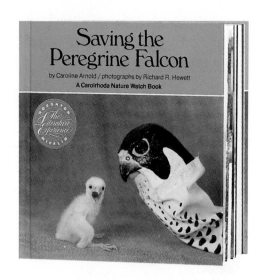

Saving the Peregrine Falcon
by Caroline Arnold
This colorful book describes the work of scientists who raise peregrine falcon chicks in captivity to assure their survival in the wild.

Wildlife, Making a Comeback: How Humans Are Helping
by Judith E. Rinard
Dramatic episodes and color photographs show what people are doing to prevent the extinction of various animals around the world.

Reynard: The Story of a Fox Returned to the Wild
by Alice Mills Leighner
Meet Reynard, a young red fox rescued by Wildcare, an organization that cares for injured wildlife and returns them to their natural habitat.

The Way of the Grizzly by Dorothy Hinshaw Patent
A grizzly bear may weigh 900 pounds and roam over an area of 190 square miles. Read how researchers are trying to learn more about the mighty grizzly.

WILDLIFE

Information Center

Turtle Watch
by George Ancona
In a Brazilian conservation project, the townspeople cooperate with scientists to save the loggerhead turtle. Even the children help.

Rescue of the Stranded Whales
by Kenneth Mallory and Andrea Conley
Tag, Notch, and Baby, three young pilot whales, were stranded on a beach on Cape Cod, Massachusetts, in 1986. This is the story of their rescue.

189

FICTION

BOOK 4

SOLUTIONS, INC.

SOLUTIONS, INC.

Case #1: Young customers are cheated by a mean storekeeper.

Case #2: Children in a crowded city have no place to play.

Case #3: A doughnut machine goes haywire in a local diner.

Where can solutions to these problems be found? Right here, in **Solutions, Inc.**

In **Solutions, Inc.,** you'll meet characters with the brains and patience to think of solutions to these problems.

Solve any problem in a blink.
Pick up the phone —
Call Solutions, Inc.

CONTENTS

The Pretty Pennies picket
from Philip Hall likes me. I reckon maybe.
by Bette Greene   194

The Streets Are Free
a play by Kurusa based on her book   216

The Doughnuts
from Homer Price
written and illustrated by Robert McCloskey   232

SOLUTIONS,
INC.

THE PRETTY PENNIES PICKET

From *Philip Hall likes me. I reckon maybe.*
by Bette Greene
illustrations by Floyd Cooper

Even though Beth Lambert and Philip Hall have worked together to catch turkey thieves and run a vegetable stand, they compete with each other in everything else.

After Philip organizes the all-boys Tiger Hunters club, Beth decides Pocahontas, Arkansas, needs an all-girls club too. Beth and her friends—Susan, Esther, Bonnie, and Ginny—form the Pretty Pennies Girls Club. Beth's role as club president is about to be tested as the Pretty Pennies come to order.

I no sooner set the ice-cold pitcher of lemonade on the porch when I saw the Blakes' green pickup truck stirring up the dust as it traveled down our rutty road. "Ma," I called through the screen door. "Bring out the cookies! The Pretty Pennies are a-coming."

Right away the door opened, but it wasn't Ma. It was Luther wearing a fresh white dress shirt and the blue pants from his Sunday suit. While Susan, Esther, and Bonnie jumped off the truck's back platform, Luther didn't hardly pay no never mind. It wasn't until Ginny the gorgeous climbed down that Luther, wearing a very pleasant expression, took a couple of giant steps toward her and asked, "How y'all getting along, Ginny?"

Ginny didn't get a chance to answer 'cause the one girl who folks say was born into this world talking answered my brother's question. "Fried to a frizzle," said Bonnie Blake. "And that lemonade yonder looks mighty refreshing."

After the lemonade was drunk and the cookies eaten, I performed my duties by rapping on the floor of the porch and saying, "This here meeting of the Pretty Pennies Girls Club is now called to order."

"Trouble with this club," said Bonnie without waiting until we got to new business, "is that we never do nothing but drink lemonade and talk about the boys in the Tiger Hunters' Club."

Heads bobbed up and down in agreement.

Bonnie smiled as though she was onto something big. "What this club needs is somebody with new ideas about things that are fun doing."

Then Ginny did something unusual. She found that one sliver of a moment which Bonnie wasn't cramming with words and said, "We just go from one meeting to the next meeting without ever doing anything. Reckon we could use a new president."

Even before Ginny's words were being applauded, I knew there was some truth to be found in them. We do just sit around gabbing — which is fun — but it was the same amount of fun before I got the idea that we had to become a club. "Philip Hall and the Tiger Hunters ain't the only ones can be a club!" And it was also me that told them how it was a known fact that clubs have more fun than friends. Suddenly I felt ashamed of myself for having promised more than I delivered, but mostly I felt angry with the Pretty Pennies, who were fixing to dump their president without as much as a "begging your pardon."

I looked up at the porch ceiling, looking for something like a good idea waiting to bore through my brain. Well, I looked, but I didn't see nothing but ceiling paint. So I closed my eyes and sure enough something came to me. I waved my hands for quiet. "It so happens that I do have a wonderful idea, but I was waiting to tell y'all about it."

Bonnie began, "Is it fun? 'Cause I got me plenty of chores to do at home so if it's — "

I broke right in. "Quiet! Now next month the Old Rugged Cross Church has their yearly picnic, and I've been thinking that we oughta challenge the Tiger Hunters to a relay race."

"Five of them," said Bonnie. "Five of us."

"Yes siree," I agreed. "But they is going to be something special about our five 'cause we're going to be wearing a special uniform which we ourselves made."

Right away I noticed how all the girls came alive when I mentioned the uniform, so I went on to describe it. "With the money we got in our club treasury, we're going to buy big T-shirts and some different-colored embroidery thread for each Pretty Penny. And then" — my finger traced a crescent across my chest — "we could all embroider the words: THE PRETTY PENNIES GIRLS CLUB OF POCAHONTAS, ARKANSAS." I said, really beginning to feel my presidential powers, "And if we were of a mind to, we could also embroider on the names of all the folks we like."

"You going to embroider on the name of Mister Phil Hall?" asked Bonnie in that cutesy-pooh voice of hers.

I laughed just as though I had nary a worry in this world. Oh, sometimes I think that Philip Hall still likes me, but at other times I think he stopped liking me the moment he stopped being the number-one best everything.

But he wouldn't do that, would he? Stop liking me just because I'm smarter than him? I can't help it and, anyway, Miss Johnson herself said that if I'm going to become a veterinarian I'm going to have to become the best student I know how to be.

On Saturday afternoon all us Pennies went into the Busy Bee Bargain Store for white T-shirts big enough to get lost in. After a lot of discussion, we dropped five T-shirts, fifty skeins of embroidery thread, five embroidery hoops, and five packages of needles onto the wrapping counter in front of Mr. Cyrus J. Putterham.

After taking our money, he pulled one tan sack from beneath the counter and began shoveling everything into it.

"Oh, no, sir," I corrected. "We each need our own bags."

His bushy eyebrows made jumpy little elevator rides up and then down. "Don't you girlies have any feeling? Five sacks cost me five times as much as one."

"But we need them," I explained. " 'Cause we're not even related."

He pulled out four more. "Costs me money, each one does. But you wouldn't care nothing about that. Kids never do!"

As we Pretty Pennies embroidered our shirts on the following Wednesday evening, we drank Bonnie Blake's strawberry punch, ate her potato chips, and gabbed on and on about those Tiger Hunters.

We even sent them a letter saying that they ought to get busy practicing their relay running 'cause we Pretty Pennies were aiming to beat them to pieces.

The next meeting was at Ginny's house, where we all sat in a circle on the linoleum floor and talked about our coming victory over the boys while we munched popcorn from a cast-iron skillet and embroidered away. Then from outside: *Bam . . . bam . . . bam-my . . . bam . . . bam!*

Our embroidery dropped to our laps as we grabbed onto one another. Bonnie pointed toward the outside while, for the first time in her life, her mouth opened and closed and closed and opened without a single sound coming out.

Finally, Esther, who almost never had a word to say, said, "Wha — What was that?"

"Let's see," I said, moving cautiously and pulling Esther along with me toward the door. I peeked out just in time to see two figures (both less than man size) race deeper into the halflight before disappearing from sight.

Bonnie, Ginny, and Susan were still sitting like frozen statues.

"It's OK," I told them. "Whoever they were — and I think I know who they were — have already ran away."

Esther followed me out on the porch, where there was a rock the size of a crow's nest and sticking to this rock was a sheet of wide-lined paper. I pulled off the paper, which had been stuck on with a wad of gum, and read aloud:

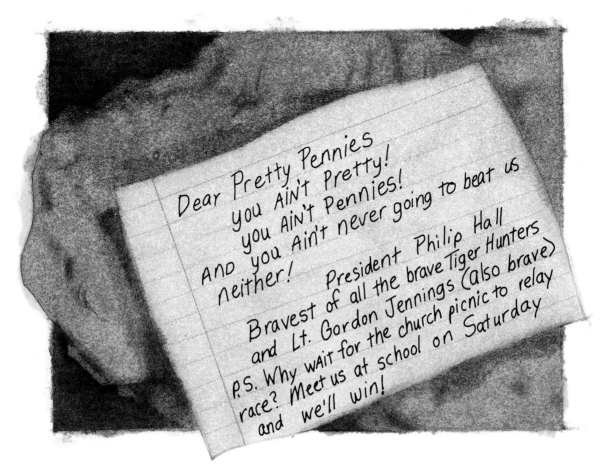

Dear Pretty Pennies
you Ain't Pretty!
you Ain't Pennies!
And you Ain't never going to beat us neither!

Bravest of all the brave Tiger Hunters President Philip Hall
and Lt. Gordon Jennings (also brave)
P.S. Why wAit for the church picnic to relay race? Meet us at school on Saturday and we'll win!

Everybody was really mad and we all began talking at once about those Tiger Hunters who run around scaring the wits out of a person. Bonnie thought we ought to teach them a lesson. "Specially that Phil Hall."

I'd have liked nothing better, but probably for a different reason. It wasn't the scare so much as what he said about not being pretty that ruffled my feathers. Did he mean nobody was pretty? Or was nobody but me pretty? Or . . . or was everybody pretty excepting me? Next thing I knew I was shouting, "We're going to get those low-down polecats!" Then while I had everybody's attention, I gave them their final instructions: "Next Saturday we'll race. Finish embroidering on our club name, front and back. Then everybody wash your shirts so our club name will be clean easy reading. All the folks in Pocahontas is going to know just who it was that beat them Tiger Hunters."

The next morning Philip didn't show up for work at The Elizabeth Lorraine Lambert & Friend Veg. Stand. Well, he's probably just mad or practicing up his relay running. Or maybe Mr. Hall has him doing chores. But that's the unlikeliest explanation of them all.

Without him there ain't no games or giggles, but today there's not a speck of boredom either 'cause I'm just too busy embroidering my T-shirt and running my business. And with every sale my college money grows. I'm going to become a veterinarian yet.

It was just before bedtime on Friday night that I stitched the last beautiful stitch on my shirt. I held it out for better viewing. Even with the soil from two weeks of handling along with Baby Benjamin's mashed-in, smashed-in sweet potato, it was beautiful. Just beautiful!

As I began to draw the wash water, Ma told me to get to bed 'cause I'd be needing my strength for the big race tomorrow. She took the shirt from my hand as she gave me a light shove toward the bedroom. "Reckon I can do the washing if you can do the resting."

When the morning sky came again to Pocahontas, I woke wide awake just as though I hadn't been sleeping at all but only resting up before the big race.

At the kitchen table Ma sat in front of a bowl of peas needing shelling, but her hands sat unmoving in her lap. I tried to remember the last time I had seen my mother just sitting without actually doing anything. All I said was "Morning, Ma," but it was enough to make her look as though she was staring at a ghost.

"Reckon I'm going to have to tell you," she said, holding tight to the bowl. "But I don't know how to tell you . . . It's about your shirt. Done shrunk to midget size. Sure did."

As Pa drove down Pocahontas's Main Street, I spotted the rest of the Pennies leaning up against a yellow fireplug. A block away Pa turned his car and angle-parked in front of the E-Z Cash & Carry Market. When the Pennies saw me walking toward them, they all shook their heads just like I was doing something wrong. What does that mean? That I'm not wearing my uniform? No, but I'm carrying it wrapped like a fish in an old newspaper to show them what they'd never believe without seeing. Anyway, they're not wearing theirs either. Too lazy to finish their embroidery probably.

Bonnie began by saying that it was an ordinary washing powder, one of those kinds that they're always talking about over the radio. Then Esther, who would never interrupt anybody, interrupted to say that her water was barely warm.

I was losing patience with everybody talking, everybody understanding but me. "What are you all babbling about mild soap and barely warm water for?"

Suddenly Ginny whipped from a grocery bag a white T-shirt so shrunk that the embroidery's lettering was no longer readable. "We is talking about this."

First we talked about our wasted efforts and then we talked about our wasted money and then we talked about what nobody could understand: what caused the shrinkage.

"Listen here," I said suddenly. "We bought something in good and honest faith that didn't turn out to be a bit of good. Well, if we all go down to the Busy Bee and explain the situation to Mr. Putterham, then he'll give us back our money. Probably even apologize that he can't pay us for our trouble."

"What Mr. Putterham is you talking about?" asked Bonnie, cocking her head like a trained spaniel. "The only Mr. Putterham I know wouldn't apologize to his ma if he ran her down in the broad daylight."

I told her right off. "Trouble with you, Miss Bonnie, is that you ain't got no faith in human nature."

Still, the thought that old bushy eyes ever had a mother was surprising. Reckon I just couldn't see Mr. Putterham having anything that couldn't turn a profit.

Even though I walked into the Busy Bee as slow as I could possibly walk, the others carefully managed to walk even slower. They stayed behind me, pushing me on toward the wrapping counter and the awesome presence of Cyrus J. Putterham. As I watched him tying a piece of

string around a shoe box, I got to wishing that one of the other girls had replaced me as president of the Pennies; then they'd be standing here on the firing line instead of me.

The merchant lifted his eyebrows at me, which was a kind of a cheapskate way of asking what I wanted without actually bothering to ask.

"Well, uh . . . Mr. Putterpam — ham! Mr. Putterham, it's uh . . . about what happened two Saturdays ago when we all bought T-shirts from your store. We washed them like we wash anything else," I said, removing the newspaper from my shirt to hold it up. "And they all five shrunk up like this."

He stretched his lips into a hard straight line. "How much you pay for that shirt?"

"Eighty-nine cents."

"See?"

What did he want me to see? "Sir?"

A short blast of air rushed through his nostrils and I came to understand that his patience zipped off on that blast of air. "Something you girls paid only eighty-nine cents for isn't going to last forever. Why, eighty-nine cents for a T-shirt is mighty cheap."

"Oh, no, sir," I corrected him. "Paying eighty-nine cents for something that ain't never been worn is mighty expensive."

He waved his hand as though he was shooing a fly. "All right, I was nice enough to listen to you girls and now y'all get on out of here. I got me a store to run."

"Yes, sir," I said pleasantly. "We appreciate your attention, sure do. But what we really want is for you to refund us our money 'cause a shirt that ain't fit to be washed ain't fit to be sold."

"Get on out of here!" Both his hands went flapping in the air. "Now get!"

We may have left the store like scared chicks, but once outside we became more like mad wet hens. Esther kept saying, "Imagine!" Or sometimes she'd vary it with "Would you imagine that!"

Then, as if we didn't have enough trouble, the Tiger Hunters led by the bravest of all the brave Tiger Hunters came up to say that we were going to be beaten so bad that it would be a long time before we showed our face in Pocahontas again.

"Don't fret about it," I told him. " 'Cause I don't think I want to show my face anymore, anyway." A warm tear had begun to worm its way down my cheek.

Philip looked uncomfortable. What's the matter? Hadn't he ever seen a tear before? "We don't have to relay race today," he was saying. "We can put it off until the Sunday of the Old Rugged Cross Church picnic."

We shook hands on it, but I was not able to say any more. Talking took too much effort. So Bonnie explained while Ginny showed Philip and his Tiger Hunters what happened to our shirts. Right away Philip said, "We don't have to let Mr. Putterham get away with that. That's robbery!"

Philip's comment about its being a robbery struck me like one of God's own revelations!

At the far end of Main Street, sitting on a square of grass, is the old red brick courthouse where Sheriff Nathan Miller has a narrow office and two barred cells. As the Pennies and Hunters strode up the court-house walk, old men sitting out on sunny park benches looked up.

The sheriff told us all to crowd on in. "I'll never forget what good police work you and Phil did in capturing those fowl thieves. You know, no farmer has reported any livestock missing since they left town."

His words encouraged me to tell him about our "robbery" at the hands of the merchant Putterham. I watched the sheriff's face grow more and more thoughtful. Finally he said, "I'm sorry, but there ain't no way I can help you out."

". . . But why?"

With his booted feet, the sheriff pushed his chair from his desk. "Follow me," he said, already walking with strong strides from his office.

Outside, the men on the benches now seemed doubly surprised to see us kids half-running in order to keep up with Randolph County's long-legged lawman. A block down Main Street and then two blocks down School Street to the last house at the end of the block. The sheriff walked up the driveway and into the backyard. At a backyard sandpile a little boy dressed in diapers and pullover shirt toddled over, saying, "Dadadadada."

The sheriff picked him up and then asked me, "What do you think of my boy's shirt?"

Surely eleven folks didn't walk all the way over here just to look at a tight-fitting baby shirt. It seemed silly, but he really did want my opinion. "I reckon it's a nice enough baby shirt," I told him.

"Uh-hun!" answered the more than six feet of sheriff as though he had suddenly struck gold. "Uh-hun," he repeated. "For a baby shirt it's mighty fine, but it wasn't bought to be no baby's shirt. No Sir! It was bought for me. Last Saturday I paid eighty-nine cents for that T-shirt at the Busy Bee Bargain Store."

"You too!! — Then why don't you — "

"Because selling bad merchandise," he said, "can get a merchant in trouble with his customers without getting him in trouble with the law."

We Pretty Pennies walked with the Tiger Hunters back toward Main Street like a bunch of beaten soldiers. No reason for hurrying.

No good left in the day nohow. Then it struck me like a pie in the face. Why are we defeated? Ten of us and only one of them Putterhams. "Stop!" I said, whirling around like a general of the army. "We ain't giving up this battle!"

"We ain't?" asked Philip.

I was the fightingest president the Pretty Pennies would ever have. "No, we ain't, 'cause if we all stood out in front of the Busy Bee Bargain Store showing off our shrunken shirts, then old Mr. Putterham would be so embarrassed he'd have to refund our money."

I broke into a run, followed by Philip Hall, followed by the rest of them. In front of the Busy Bee, we all formed a loose line — a Penny, a Hunter, a Penny, and so forth. "Pretty Pennies and Tiger Hunters. When we're working together we'll call ourselves the great Penny Hunters," I said.

Since Philip Hall didn't look exactly thrilled by my suggestion, I said, "Well, would you rather be called the Pretty Tigers?" His groan gave me his answer.

When a heavy woman with three chilluns slowly made her way toward the Busy Bee door, Bonnie approached her. A moment later she was spreading out her doll-size shirt across her chest while the woman shook her head and said, "I'm going to do my trading at Logan's."

The very next person who was persuaded not to spend money at the Busy Bee was my sister, Anne. She said she could buy fingernail polish at the dime store just as well.

After Anne, there was our preacher, the Reverend Ross, who was going to buy some white handkerchiefs from Putterham, but the Reverend said he'd "be happy to respect your picket line."

"Respect our what?" I asked.

"Folks who is standing like some of God's own soldiers against the world's injustices is," said the Reverend Ross, "a picket line."

Never before in my whole life had I ever felt so important, but then never before had I been on special assignment for God.

Just then a family of five reached for the Busy Bee's door and I called out, "Don't you folks go buying things in there unless" — I held up my shirt — "you don't object to shrinking."

"Lordy," said the wife, coming right over to get a closer look. "Now ain't that a pity?"

Mr. Putterham stepped outside the door. "What's this? What's going on here?"

I turned to watch Philip Hall 'cause I didn't want to miss seeing him speak right up to that old man merchant. But the only thing I saw was the bravest Tiger Hunter of them all with his mouth flung open, looking for all the world like he would never again be able to speak.

The proprietor's eyes now swept past Philip and were looking down the long picket line. "Don't tell me that all you kids have been struck speechless? Somebody better tell me what's going on!"

I took one step forward. "I reckon you oughta know that we is picketing your store, Mr. Putterdam — ham! Mr. Putterham."

His big, bushy eyebrows jumped up and down as though they were skipping rope. "You is doing WHAT? And to WHOM?"

"We is" — my mouth felt too dry for stamp licking — "picketing you," I said, grateful that the words actually sounded.

"Now you listen here, you," he said. "Nobody pickets Cyrus J. Putterham, Pocahontas's leading merchant. Know that?"

"Yes, sir."

"Good," he said, smiling a pretend smile. "Then y'all get on out of here."

"Uh . . . no, sir," I said, trying to remember the Reverend Ross's words about being one of God's own soldiers.

"What do you mean No, sir?" he asked, allowing his voice to rise into a full shout. "You just got through saying Yes, sir."

"Uh, well, sir, that was my answer to your question."

Mr. Putterham blinked as though my words were being spoken in a strange new language. I tried again. "What I was saying, Mr. Putter-

jam . . . ham! Mr. Putterham, was yes, sir, I know all about you being Pocahontas's leading merchant. But no, sir, we ain't moving from our picket line. Not until we get our money back."

His eyes told me how much he wanted me to understand. "But if I give you folks your money back, then everybody who ever bought bad merchandise from me will be wanting their money back too."

From the picket line a single voice called, "Give back the money!" Then more voices, more Pennies and Hunters together calling, "Give back the money!" And I joined my voice with the Penny Hunters and even some folks on the street who were now chanting, *"Give back the money!"* And taken together the voices sounded as though they were doing a lot more demanding than asking.

The shopkeeper threw up his hands. "All right, all right." He smiled, but it wasn't what you'd call a sincere smile. "Making my customers happy is the only thing that's ever been important to Cyrus J. Putterham. Take your shirts back to the wrapping counter for a full and courteous refund."

After all the shirt money was safely back in the hands of our treasurer, Bonnie Blake, I spoke again to the merchant. "There is one more thing, Mr. Putterpam — ham! Mr. Putterham."

"As long as you girls are satisfied — well, that's thanks enough for me. Why, my very business is built on a foundation of square and fair."

"Yes, sir," I agreed. "Would you mind giving us back our embroidery money?"

"Your what?"

I presented him with the cash register receipt. "Two dollars and fifty cents worth of embroidery thread, ruined when our shirts shrunk."

For a moment I thought his face was growing angry, but then he sighed and placed the additional two-fifty on the counter.

"Thanks, Mr. Putterham."

He smiled and this time it didn't look all that insincere. "You called me Putterham. Finally you did it right."

I smiled back at him. "And finally, Mr. Putterham, so did you."

You can read more stories about Beth Lambert and Philip Hall in the book Philip Hall likes me. I reckon maybe. *by Bette Greene.*

Why We're Picketing Putterham

Write a flier that the Pretty Pennies might have handed out while they picketed. The flier should explain what Mr. Putterham has done and why people should not shop at his store. You might want to include a drawing or a slogan.

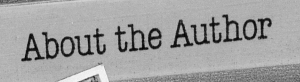

Bette Greene

Bette Greene grew up in a small Arkansas town similar to the hometown of Beth Lambert and Philip Hall. During the days of World War II, when sugar was being rationed, Greene was considered "the luckiest girl in town" because her parents owned a general store full of gum and candy.

Greene looks back on those childhood experiences to help her write. "Without the memory of childhood sights and feelings and events," she says, "I'd be a writer with nothing to say."

Greene has written a sequel to her Philip Hall book called Get on out of here, Philip Hall.

Silly Solutions

Writing Limericks

The limerick's lively to write:
Five lines to it — all nice and tight.
  Two long ones, two trick
  Little short ones; then quick
As a flash here's the last one in sight.

David McCord

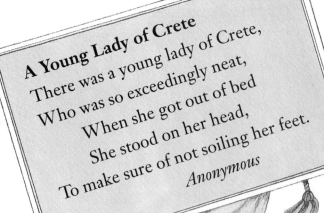

A Young Lady of Crete

There was a young lady of Crete,
Who was so exceedingly neat,
  When she got out of bed,
  She stood on her head,
To make sure of not soiling her feet.

Anonymous

to Pesky Problems

On Reading
If you don't know the meaning of *snook*
Or of *snaffle* or *rhombus* or *rukh,*
     If you're curious how
     To tell *dhoti* from *dhow,*
Get yourself up — and go find a book!
Myra Cohn Livingston

A Young Man from Darjeeling
There was a young man from Darjeeling,
Who got on a bus bound for Ealing;
     It said at the door:
     "Don't spit on the floor,"
So he carefully spat on the ceiling.
Anonymous

A Very Mean Man of Belsize
There's a very mean man of Belsize,
Who thinks he is clever and wise.
And, what do you think,
He saves gallons of ink
By simply not dotting his "i's."
Anonymous

A Chameleon
A chameleon, when he's feeling blue,
Can alter his glum point of view
By changing his hue
To a color that's new:
I'd like to do that, wouldn't you?
Eve Merriam

214

A Mouse in Her Room Woke Miss Dowd
A mouse in her room woke Miss Dowd;
She was frightened and screamed very loud,
   Then a happy thought hit her —
   To scare off the critter,
She sat up in bed and meowed.

Anonymous

A Flea and a Fly in a Flue
A flea and a fly in a flue
Were caught, so what could they do?
   Said the fly, "Let us flee."
   "Let us fly," said the flea.
So they flew through a flaw in the flue.

Anonymous

216

A play by Kurusa based on her book
illustrated by Brian Pinkney

The
STREETS
Are
FREE

In the hills above the city of
Caracas, Venezuela, thousands of
people live crowded together in
neighborhoods called *barrios*.
The children of the barrio of San
José de la Urbina had a problem.
More than anything else they
wanted a place to play. *The
Streets Are Free* is the true story of
how they worked to make their
wish come true.

CHARACTERS

Carlitos	Mayor
Cheo	Reporter
Camila	Cheo's Father
Neighbor	Camila's Mother
Librarian	Cheo's Mother
Guard	Carlitos's Father

(Children, Officials, Police Officers, Mayor's Aide, *and* Photographers)

SCENE 1

(The play takes place in the barrio of San José, a neighborhood at the edge of the city of Caracas, Venezuela. The play opens on a street in the barrio with the sound of a loud truck horn. Carlitos, Cheo, and Camila look to the right at an imaginary truck that has just passed by.)

CARLITOS: *¡Caray!*[1] That was close!

CHEO: That truck nearly ran us over!

CAMILA *(Yelling to driver)*: *¡Epa!*[2] Why don't you watch where you're going?

CHEO: I guess we can't play in the street.

CARLITOS: I thought the streets were supposed to be free.

CAMILA: Not for us, they aren't.

CHEO: Well, where else can we play?

CAMILA: Don't ask me.

---

[1] **¡Caray!** (kah•RYE): Gee or gosh!
[2] **¡Epa!** (AY•pah): Hey!

CARLITOS: How about flying kites up on the hill?

CAMILA: Impossible. If we go up there, on the hill, the kites will get tangled in the power lines.

CHEO: And I don't feel like getting electrocuted.

CARLITOS: How about playing catch right here? Hey, Cheo! Catch! (*He throws a ball to* Cheo, *but it lands in a* Neighbor's *laundry basket.*) Uh-oh. (*He goes to get ball, and gets in the* Neighbor's *way.*)

NEIGHBOR: You kids get out! Go on! Scram! You're always getting in my way!

CAMILA: We can't help it! There's nowhere else to go!

NEIGHBOR: That's not my problem. I have my laundry to do! And after that I've got to go shopping at the market or I'll never get supper on the table! And after that . . .

CHEO: Come on, Camila. Let's just leave her alone.

(*The* Children *sit down on the steps of the library.*)

CARLITOS (*Gloomily*): There must be somewhere we can play.

CHEO: Maybe we can go to City Hall and ask the Mayor.

CAMILA (*Sarcastically*): Oh, sure. Do you really think the Mayor's going to listen to a bunch of kids?

CARLITOS: We can ask our parents to come with us.

CHEO: My parents are working.

CAMILA: So are mine. They're always busy.

CARLITOS: I guess mine are, too.

CAMILA: So much for that idea.

(*They sigh and sit in silence.* Librarian *comes out.*)

LIBRARIAN: Why all the sad faces?

CHEO: There's no place to play.

LIBRARIAN: Hmmm. You're right. (Librarian *sits down next to them.*) Did you know that this entire hillside, was once covered with forests, streams, and trails? The trouble is, our city grew up so fast that the streets and buildings just took over. No one had time to plan a playground.

CAMILA: Well, why doesn't somebody plan one now?

219

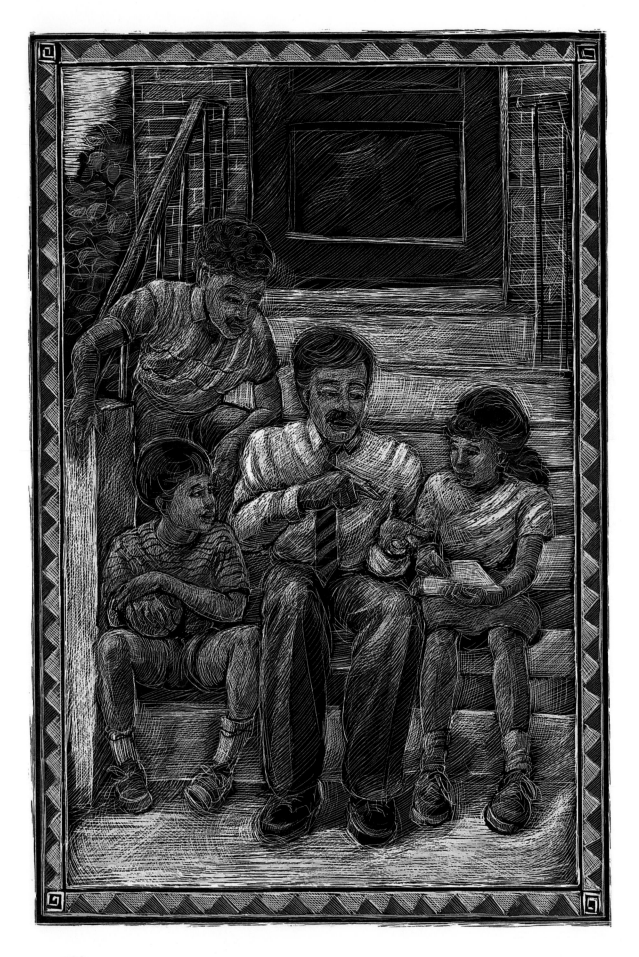

CHEO: I know a great place — that empty lot near the bottom of the hill.

CAMILA: That one with all the garbage and broken glass? Who would want to play there?

CARLITOS: If someone fixed it up it wouldn't be bad.

LIBRARIAN: What would *you* do to fix it up, Carlitos?

CARLITOS: Who, me? I don't know. Maybe if we planted those tall *apamate*[3] trees and some shrubs . . .

LIBRARIAN: Wait! You should write this down! I'll get a pencil and a pad of paper.

(Librarian *runs into the library.*)

CAMILA: What's the use of writing it down? Who's going to read it?

CARLITOS: Maybe the Mayor will!

CAMILA: Here we go with the Mayor again.

(Librarian *returns with paper and pencil.*)

LIBRARIAN: Here, Camila. I appoint you official list-maker.

CAMILA (*Sighing and taking the pencil and paper*): Fine. Go ahead.

CARLITOS: Our playground should have swings and slides!

CHEO: And room to play baseball and volleyball and soccer.

CARLITOS: And tag, and hide and seek, and places to fly kites, and run around!

CHEO: And benches for our parents to sit and visit.

CAMILA: Slow down!

CARLITOS: And don't forget the *apamate* trees and shrubs.

LIBRARIAN: Don't you have any suggestions, Camila?

CAMILA: Yes. I suggest we forget the whole thing. What good is planning a park if we can't get our parents to help us?

CARLITOS (*Boldly*): We don't need their help. We'll go to City Hall by ourselves. We can round up all our friends . . .

CHEO (*Caught up in the spirit*): And we can make a banner!

CARLITOS: Right! It can say, "Give us a playground or else!"

---

[3]**apamate** (ah•pa•MAH•tay): A tree found in Venezuela.

LIBRARIAN: Maybe something a little less threatening would be better.

CHEO: What about, "We have nowhere to play. We need a playground"?

LIBRARIAN: Perfect. You can use the paint and crayons I have in the library.

CHEO *(Enthusiastically)*: Great! Come on, Camila. You're good at making posters.

CAMILA *(Reluctantly standing up)*: Fine, I'll help, but I'm telling you, you're wasting your time.

▣ SCENE 2 ▣

(The setting is in front of City Hall. Carlitos, Cheo, Camila, and their friends are marching in a circle. They are carrying the banner they made.)

CHILDREN *(Chanting)*: We need a playground! We need a playground!

GUARD *(Gruffly)*: I told you before. No one gets in to see the Mayor. Especially not a bunch of kids off the street. Go home!

CAMILA: We need somewhere to play.

GUARD: Then go somewhere to play. But not here!

CHEO: The streets are free! We're not leaving until we see the Mayor.

GUARD *(Losing his patience)*: That does it. I'm calling the police!

(The Guard *blows a whistle. The* Children *continue to shout. Five* Police Officers *enter. The* Children *stop chanting.)*

CARLITOS: The police!

CAMILA: *¡Qué bueno!*[4] Now we'll have our playground in jail.

GUARD: Arrest these kids!

(Police Officers try to grab the Children, *who run around trying to avoid them. In the middle of the confusion the* Librarian *and several worried* Parents *rush in.)*

LIBRARIAN: There they are!

CHEO'S FATHER: What is going on here?

---

[4]*¡Qué bueno!* (KAY BWAY•no): Great!

CHEO (*Pointing at the* Guard): He won't let us talk to the Mayor about our playground!

GUARD: These kids are disturbing the peace! (*To* Police Officers) Take them away!

(Police Officer *takes hold of* Camila's *arm*.)

CAMILA'S MOTHER (*Stepping forward*): Oh, no you don't. If you put a hand on these children, you'll have to arrest me, too.

CARLITOS'S FATHER: And me!

LIBRARIAN: And me!

(Children *and* Parents *cheer*. Police Officers *stand there, uncertain*. Children *begin to chant,* "We want a playground!" *The* Mayor, Mayor's Aide, *a* Reporter, *and* Photographers *appear at the door of City Hall*.)

MAYOR: What's all this ruckus? What is going on out here?

CARLITOS: It's the Mayor!

GUARD: Your Honor, these people are starting a riot.

CHEO'S FATHER: They're trying to arrest our children!

CHEO: We need a playground!

MAYOR: ¡Un momento!⁵ Wait a minute! One at a time!

LIBRARIAN: Let the children speak first.

REPORTER: Yes, I would be very interested to hear what they have to say. (Reporter *takes out notebook and pen*.)

CHEO: We came to ask you for a playground.

CAMILA: The barrio of San José is too crowded!

CARLITOS: The streets are dangerous. There are too many cars and trucks.

CAMILA: But the streets are the only place we have!

CARLITOS: We just want a place to play baseball and volleyball and soccer and fly kites.

CHEO (*Cheerfully*): That's all.

MAYOR: A playground. Hmmmmm. (*To* Aide) Is there a space for them to have a playground?

---

⁵¡**Un momento!** (OON moe•MEN•toe): Just a minute.

CARLITOS: *¡Sí!* [6] We know the perfect place!

CHEO: It's an empty lot at the bottom of the hill.

CARLITOS: It's beautiful!

CAMILA (*Amazed*): You think that empty lot is *beautiful*?

CHEO: Well, with a little work, it could be beautiful.

CARLITOS: We even made a list. (Carlitos *begins reading from the list.*) It should have *apamate* trees and shrubs and flowers and benches and a field for playing.

REPORTER (*While writing in pad*): You children have been doing your homework.

MAYOR: Hmmmm. "Mayor Builds Playground For City Children." (*The* Mayor *smiles.*) I like the sound of that. *¡Sí!* I'll look into it first thing tomorrow. Remember, I am always here to serve you. Now, line up and I'll let you shake my hand. Then you can leave.
(*The* Mayor *shakes everyone's hand and leaves, along with* Aide.)

REPORTER: I'd like to take a look at this playground of yours.

CHEO: Come on! We'll take you there!
(Cheo, Reporter, *and* Photographers *leave.*)

CARLITOS: Isn't it great, Camila? We've practically done it!

CAMILA: I'll bet nothing happens. Just you wait and see.
(Carlitos *and* Camila *follow after* Cheo.)

▣ SCENE 3 ▣

(*The setting is the vacant lot at the bottom of the hill. It is one week later. The lot is scattered with garbage. Carlitos, Cheo, and Camila are standing at the edge of the lot.*)

CAMILA: I told you nothing would happen. Check it out. This lot is the same ugly garbage dump that it was one week ago.

---

[6]**¡Sí!** (SEE): Yes.

CHEO (*Discouraged*): And after all that work we did. The banner, the list, the marching . . .

CARLITOS: Maybe we should have made the banner bigger.

(The Librarian *rushes in, waving a newspaper.)*

LIBRARIAN: Hey, you three! Take a look at this!

CARLITOS: *¿Qué pasa?*[7]

CAMILA: What is it?

LIBRARIAN: Today's newspaper. Read the front page.

CHEO (*Reads from newspaper*): "Children of San José take on City Hall. They demand park, but Mayor doesn't budge."

CHEO: The children of San José! That's us!

CARLITOS: We're famous!

CHEO (*Laughing*): Look at this picture of the Mayor. He looks as if he just swallowed an *arepa*.[8]

CARLITOS: And there's me, right behind him. Look, Camila.

CAMILA (*Glancing at the paper and speaking sarcastically*): Ah, *sí*. That's a nice picture of the back of your head, Carlitos.

CARLITOS: At least the back of my head is in the newspaper.

CHEO: We're all in the newspaper! They'll have to take us seriously now.

CAMILA: Come on, Cheo, wake up. They're still not going to do anything.

LIBRARIAN: You may be wrong, Camila. Look who's coming.

(The Mayor *enters, wearing a new suit. He carries a huge pair of scissors. His* Aide, Officials, *the* Reporter, *and* Photographers *are with him. The* Aide *carries a sign and a long red ribbon.)*

CARLITOS: *¡Buenos días!*[9] Mr. Mayor.

MAYOR (*To* Photographers): Stand over there so you can get the whole picture. Hurry up now, we don't have all day.

CARLITOS (*Craning his neck*): What does that sign say? I can't see!

CAMILA: "This Site Reserved for the Children's Park of San José."

CHEO: You see, Camila? Everything's working out fine!

---

[7]*¿Qué pasa?* (KAY PAH•sah): What's going on?

[8]*arepa* (ah•RAY•pah): A cornmeal cake, typical of Venezuela.

[9]*Buenos días* (BWAY•nose Dee•ahs): Good day.

226

(The Officials *unwind the red ribbon and hold it in front of the* Mayor. *The* Mayor *takes out a piece of paper, clears his throat, and reads.*)

MAYOR: *Señoras y señores.*[10] The children of San José are unhappy. And when the children are unhappy, I am unhappy.

CAMILA (*Rolling her eyes*): Oh, give me a break.

MAYOR: My friends, the barrio of San José has become too crowded! The streets are dangerous. But the streets are the only place the children have to play!

CAMILA: Wait a minute. Haven't I heard this somewhere before?

MAYOR: They need a place to play baseball and volleyball and soccer and fly kites.

CAMILA: He's saying the exact same things *we* said!

MAYOR: *Señoras y señores,* the children need a playground. And I intend to give them one.

(*Light applause, mostly from* Aide *and* Officials.)

MAYOR (*Holding hands up modestly*): Thank you. My friends, I have come up with a wonderful idea. I am reserving this vacant lot for the children of San José. A playground will make the future brighter for you — and you — and you. (Mayor *points to the three* Children.) Now, turn around and smile for the cameras, children.

CAMILA (*Smiling a fake smile*): This is so dumb.

(Mayor *cuts the ribbon with the giant scissors. The cameras flash.*)

MAYOR: How about another shot of me with the children? (*To* Children, *as he poses*) Well, my young friends, are you happy with your new playground?

CHEO AND CARLITOS: Very happy, Mr. Mayor.

MAYOR: What about you, little girl?

CAMILA: New playground? (*Scornfully*) It still looks like a garbage dump to me. It just has a pretty new sign, that's all. You can't fool me. There's an election coming up. I'll bet after this ceremony you don't do anything.

---

[10]**Señoras y señores** (seh•NYOR•ahs EE seh•NYOR•ess): Ladies and gentlemen.

MAYOR (*Embarrassed*): *¡Qué va!*[11] You have it all wrong, little girl! I'm always here to serve you! Now, line up and I'll shake your hands, and then you'll have to leave. I'm very busy!

(*The* Mayor *hastily shakes some hands and then walks off with* Photographers, Aide, Reporter, *and* Officials.)

LIBRARIAN: Well, children, it looks as if your hard work has finally paid off.

CARLITOS: Yes! We're going to get a playground!

CAMILA: Don't count on it.

🔲 SCENE 4 🔲

(*It is four weeks later. The sign the* Mayor *left has faded in the sun. The letters are barely visible. The lot is even dirtier than before.* Camila *kicks a can across the stage.*)

CAMILA: I told them, I warned them, but they didn't believe me. Maybe they'll believe me now. It's been over a month. Where are the swings? Where are the playing fields? Where are the flowers? There's more garbage and junk in this lot than there was before our march! It's hopeless!

(Carlitos *enters.*)

CARLITOS: No, it's not, Camila!

(Cheo, *the* Librarian, *the* Children *and* Parents *of San José enter behind* Carlitos *carrying hammers, wood, trees, flowers, shrubs, paint buckets, and shovels.*)

CAMILA: What's going on?

CHEO'S MOTHER: We had a meeting last night.

CARLITOS'S FATHER: We decided to build the playground ourselves!

CHEO: Who needs City Hall?

CARLITOS: All it takes is a little teamwork!

CAMILA: Teamwork? Come on! No one ever cooperates in San José, not even to clean the sidewalks.

---

[11]*¡Qué va!* (KAY VAH): Not at all!

CAMILA'S MOTHER: Well, that's going to change. I brought some wood I had lying around.

CARLITOS'S FATHER: I have some flowers and a few saplings.

LIBRARIAN: I brought my shovel and some tools.

CHEO: And I made a brand new sign to put up over the old one.

(Cheo *and* Carlitos *and some of the* Parents *hammer the new sign up. It says, "San José Playground. Everybody Come and Play."*)

LIBRARIAN: *Bueno,*[12] what do you say now, Camila?

CAMILA: What do I say? I'll tell you what I say. (*Pause.*) I say — that I always knew we could do it!

(*Everyone cheers. People begin digging, planting, painting, and cleaning up as the curtain closes.*)

 **THE END**

---

[12]**Bueno** (BWAY•no): Well.

THEY MADE A DIFFERENCE

With a partner, make a plaque to be placed at the entrance of the San José playground. The plaque should briefly tell the story of how the children of San José got their playground and how it changed life in their crowded barrio. Place the story in the center of the plaque, and display it for the rest of your class.

About the Author
Kurusa

Kurusa is from Caracas, Venezuela. She has spent over twelve years working with children, including starting an experimental library and a publishing house for children's books. Kurusa's book *The Streets Are Free (La Calle Es Libre* in Spanish) is based on her experiences with the children who attend the library in San José de la Urbina, a barrio on the edge of Caracas.

In addition to being a writer, Kurusa is the director of an organization that promotes reading, library services, and children's literature in Venezuela.

The Doughnuts

From Homer Price ◆ *Written and illustrated by Robert McCloskey*

One Friday night in November Homer overheard his mother talking on the telephone to Aunt Agnes over in Centerburg. "I'll stop by with the car in about half an hour and we can go to the meeting together," she said, because tonight was the night the Ladies' Club was meeting to discuss plans for a box social and to knit and sew for the Red Cross.

"I think I'll come along and keep Uncle Ulysses company while you and Aunt Agnes are at the meeting," said Homer.

So after Homer had combed his hair and his mother had looked to see if she had her knitting instructions and the right size needles, they started for town.

Homer's Uncle Ulysses and Aunt Agnes have a very up and coming lunch room over in Centerburg, just across from the court house on the town square. Uncle Ulysses is a man with advanced ideas and a weakness for labor saving devices. He equipped the lunch room with automatic toasters, automatic coffee maker, automatic dish washer, and an automatic doughnut maker. All just the latest thing in labor saving devices. Aunt Agnes would throw up her hands and sigh every time Uncle Ulysses bought a new labor saving device. Sometimes she became unkindly disposed toward him for days and days. She was of the opinion that Uncle Ulysses just frittered away his spare time over at the barber shop with the sheriff and the boys, so, what was the good of a labor saving device that gave you more time to fritter?

When Homer and his mother got to Centerburg they stopped at the lunch room, and after Aunt Agnes had come out and said, "My, how that boy does grow!" which was what she always said, she went off with Homer's mother in the car. Homer went into the lunch room and said, "Howdy, Uncle Ulysses!"

"Oh, hello, Homer. You're just in time," said Uncle Ulysses. "I've been going over this automatic doughnut machine, oiling the machinery and cleaning the works . . . wonderful things, these labor saving devices."

"Yep," agreed Homer, and he picked up a cloth and started polishing the metal trimmings while Uncle Ulysses tinkered with the inside workings.

"Opfwo-oof!!" sighed Uncle Ulysses and, "Look here, Homer, you've got a mechanical mind. See if you can find where these two pieces fit in. I'm going across to the barber shop for a spell, 'cause there's somethin' I've got to talk to the sheriff about. There won't be much business here until the double feature is over and I'll be back before then."

Then as Uncle Ulysses went out the door he said, "Uh, Homer, after you get the pieces in place, would you mind mixing up a batch of doughnut batter and putting it in the machine? You could turn the switch and make a few doughnuts to have on hand for the crowd after the movie . . . if you don't mind."

"O.K." said Homer, "I'll take care of everything."

A few minutes later a customer came in and said, "Good evening, Bud."

Homer looked up from putting the last piece in the doughnut machine and said, "Good evening, Sir, what can I do for you?"

"Well, young feller, I'd like a cup o' coffee and some doughnuts," said the customer.

"I'm sorry, Mister, but we won't have any doughnuts for about half an hour, until I can mix some dough and start this machine. I could give you some very fine sugar rolls instead."

"Well, Bud, I'm in no real hurry so I'll just have a cup o' coffee and wait around a bit for the doughnuts. Fresh doughnuts are always worth waiting for is what I always say."

"O.K.," said Homer, and he drew a cup of coffee from Uncle Ulysses' super automatic coffee maker.

"Nice place you've got here," said the customer.

"Oh, yes," replied Homer, "this is a very up and coming lunch room with all the latest improvements."

"Yes," said the stranger, "must be a good business. I'm in business too. A traveling man in outdoor advertising. I'm a sandwich man, Mr. Gabby's my name."

"My name is Homer. I'm glad to meet you, Mr. Gabby. It must be a fine profession, traveling and advertising sandwiches."

"Oh no," said Mr. Gabby, "I don't advertise sandwiches, I just wear any kind of an ad, one sign on front and one sign on behind, this way . . . Like a sandwich. Ya know what I mean?"

"Oh, I see. That must be fun, and you travel too?" asked Homer as he got out the flour and the baking powder.

236

"Yeah, I ride the rods between jobs, on freight trains, ya know what I mean?"

"Yes, but isn't that dangerous?" asked Homer.

"Of course there's a certain amount a risk, but you take any method a travel these days, it's all dangerous. Ya know what I mean? Now take airplanes for instance . . ."

Just then a large shiny black car stopped in front of the lunch room and a chauffeur helped a lady out of the rear door. They both came inside and the lady smiled at Homer and said, "We've stopped for a light snack. Some doughnuts and coffee would be simply marvelous."

Then Homer said, "I'm sorry, Ma'm, but the doughnuts won't be ready until I make this batter and start Uncle Ulysses' doughnut machine."

"Well now aren't *you* a clever young man to know how to make *doughnuts!*"

"Well," blushed Homer, "I've really never done it before but I've got a receipt to follow."

"Now, young man, you simply must allow me to help. You know, I haven't made doughnuts for years, but I know the best receipt for doughnuts. It's marvelous, and we really must use it."

"But, Ma'm . . ." said Homer.

"Now just *wait* till you taste these doughnuts," said the lady. "Do you have an apron?" she asked, as she took off her fur coat and her rings and her jewelry and rolled up her sleeves. "Charles," she said to the chauffeur, "hand me that baking powder, that's right, and, young man, we'll need some nutmeg."

So Homer and the chauffeur stood by and handed things and cracked the eggs while the lady mixed and stirred. Mr. Gabby sat on his stool, sipped his coffee, and looked on with great interest.

"There!" said the lady when all of the ingredients were mixed. "Just *wait* till you taste these doughnuts!"

"It looks like an awful lot of batter," said Homer as he stood on a chair and poured it into the doughnut machine with the help of the chauffeur. "It's about *ten* times as much as Uncle Ulysses ever makes."

"But wait till you taste them!" said the lady with an eager look and a smile.

Homer got down from the chair and pushed a button on the machine marked, "*Start.*" Rings of batter started dropping into the hot fat. After a ring of batter was cooked on one side an automatic gadget turned it over and the other side would cook. Then another automatic gadget gave the doughnut a little push and it rolled neatly down a little chute, all ready to eat.

"That's a simply *fascinating* machine," said the lady as she waited for the first doughnut to roll out.

"Here, young man, *you* must have the first one. Now isn't that just *too* delicious!? Isn't it simply marvelous?"

"Yes, Ma'm, it's very good," replied Homer as the lady handed doughnuts to Charles and to Mr. Gabby and asked if they didn't think they were simply divine doughnuts.

"It's an old family receipt!" said the lady with pride.

Homer poured some coffee for the lady and her chauffeur and for Mr. Gabby, and a glass of milk for himself. Then they all sat down at the lunch counter to enjoy another few doughnuts apiece.

"I'm so glad you enjoy my doughnuts," said the lady. "But now, Charles, we really must be going. If you will just take this apron, Homer, and put two dozen doughnuts in a bag to take along, we'll be on our way. And, Charles, don't forget to pay the young man." She rolled down her sleeves and put on her jewelry, then Charles managed to get her into her big fur coat.

"Good night, young man, I haven't had so much fun in years. I *really* haven't!" said the lady, as she went out the door and into the big shiny car.

"Those are sure good doughnuts," said Mr. Gabby as the car moved off.

"You bet!" said Homer. Then he and Mr. Gabby stood and watched the automatic doughnut machine make doughnuts.

After a few dozen more doughnuts had rolled down the little chute, Homer said, "I guess that's about enough doughnuts to sell to the after theater customers. I'd better turn the machine off for a while."

Homer pushed the button marked *"Stop"* and there was a little click, but nothing happened. The rings of batter kept right on dropping into the hot fat, and an automatic gadget kept right on turning them over, and another automatic gadget kept right on giving them a little push and the doughnuts kept right on rolling down the little chute, all ready to eat.

"That's funny," said Homer, "I'm sure that's the right button!" He pushed it again but the automatic doughnut maker kept right on making doughnuts.

"Well I guess I must have put one of those pieces in backwards," said Homer.

"Then it might stop if you pushed the button marked '*Start*,'" said Mr. Gabby.

Homer did, and the doughnuts still kept rolling down the little chute, just as regular as a clock can tick.

"I guess we could sell a few more doughnuts," said Homer, "but I'd better telephone Uncle Ulysses over at the barber shop." Homer gave the number and while he waited for someone to answer he counted thirty-seven doughnuts roll down the little chute.

Finally someone answered "Hello! This is the sarber bhop, I mean the barber shop."

"Oh, hello, sheriff. This is Homer. Could I speak to Uncle Ulysses?"

"Well, he's playing pinochle right now," said the sheriff. "Anythin' I can tell 'im?"

"Yes," said Homer. "I pushed the button marked *Stop* on the doughnut machine but the rings of batter keep right on dropping into the hot fat, and an automatic gadget keeps right on turning them over, and another automatic gadget keeps giving them a little push, and the doughnuts keep right on rolling down the little chute! It won't stop!"

"O.K. Wold the hire, I mean, hold the wire and I'll tell 'im." Then Homer looked over his shoulder and counted another twenty-one doughnuts roll down the little chute, all ready to eat. Then the sheriff said, "He'll be right over. . . . Just gotta finish this hand."

"That's good," said Homer. "G'by, sheriff."

The window was full of doughnuts by now so Homer and Mr. Gabby had to hustle around and start stacking them on plates and trays and lining them up on the counter.

"Sure are a lot of doughnuts!" said Homer.

"You bet!" said Mr. Gabby. "I lost count at twelve hundred and two and that was quite a while back."

People had begun to gather outside the lunch room window, and someone was saying, "There are almost as many doughnuts as there are people in Centerburg, and I wonder how in tarnation Ulysses thinks he can sell all of 'em!"

Every once in a while somebody would come inside and buy some, but while somebody bought two to eat and a dozen to take home, the machine made three dozen more.

By the time Uncle Ulysses and the sheriff arrived and pushed through the crowd, the lunch room was a calamity of doughnuts! Doughnuts in the window, doughnuts piled high on the shelves, doughnuts stacked on plates, dough-nuts lined up twelve deep all along the counter, and dough-nuts still rolling down the little chute, just as regular as a clock can tick.

"Hello, sheriff, hello, Uncle Ulysses, we're having a little trouble here," said Homer.

"Well, I'll be dunked!!" said Uncle Ulysses.

"Dernd ef you won't be when Aggy gits home," said the sheriff.

"Mighty fine doughnuts though. What'll you do with 'em all, Ulysses?"

Uncle Ulysses groaned and said, "What will Aggy say? We'll never sell 'em all."

Then Mr. Gabby, who hadn't said anything for a long time, stopped piling doughnuts and said, "What you need is an advertising man. Ya know what I mean? You got the doughnuts, ya gotta create a market . . . Understand? . . . It's balancing the demand with the supply . . . That sort of thing."

"Yep!" said Homer. "Mr. Gabby's right. We have to enlarge our market. He's an advertising sandwich man, so if we hire him, he can walk up and down in front of the theater and get the customers."

"You're hired, Mr. Gabby!" said Uncle Ulysses.

Then everybody pitched in to paint the signs and to get Mr. Gabby sandwiched between. They painted "SALE ON DOUGHNUTS" in big letters on the window too.

Meanwhile the rings of batter kept right on dropping into the hot fat, and an automatic gadget kept right on turning them over, and another automatic gadget kept right on giving them a little push, and the doughnuts kept right on rolling down the little chute, just as regular as a clock can tick.

"I certainly hope this advertising works," said Uncle Ulysses, wagging his head. "Aggy'll certainly throw a fit if it don't."

The sheriff went outside to keep order, because there was quite a crowd by now — all looking at the doughnuts and guessing how many thousand there were, and watching new ones roll down the little chute, just as regular as a clock can tick. Homer and Uncle Ulysses kept stacking doughnuts. Once in a while somebody bought a few, but not very often.

Then Mr. Gabby came back and said, "Say, you know there's not much use o' me advertisin' at the theater. The show's all over, and besides almost everybody in town is out front watching that machine make doughnuts!"

"Zeus!" said Uncle Ulysses. "We must get rid of these doughnuts before Aggy gets here!"

"Looks like you will have ta hire a truck ta waul 'em ahay, I mean haul 'em away!!" said the sheriff who had just come in. Just then there was a noise and a shoving out front and the lady from the shiny black car and her chauffeur came pushing through the crowd and into the lunch room.

"Oh, gracious!" she gasped, ignoring the doughnuts, "I've lost my diamond bracelet, and I know I left it here on the counter," she said, pointing to a place where the doughnuts were piled in stacks of two dozen.

"Yes, Ma'm, I guess you forgot it when you helped make the batter," said Homer.

Then they moved all the doughnuts around and looked for the diamond bracelet, but they couldn't find it anywhere. Meanwhile the doughnuts kept rolling down the little chute, just as regular as a clock can tick.

After they had looked all around the sheriff cast a suspicious eye on Mr. Gabby, but Homer said, "He's all right, sheriff, he didn't take it. He's a friend of mine."

Then the lady said, "I'll offer a reward of one hundred dollars for that bracelet! It really *must* be found! . . . it *really* must!"

"Now don't you worry, lady," said the sheriff. "I'll get your bracelet back!"

"Zeus! This is terrible!" said Uncle Ulysses. "First all of these doughnuts and then on top of all that, a lost diamond bracelet . . ."

Mr. Gabby tried to comfort him, and he said, "There's always a bright side. That machine'll probably run outta batter in an hour or two."

If Mr. Gabby hadn't been quick on his feet Uncle Ulysses would have knocked him down, sure as fate.

Then while the lady wrung her hands and said, "We must find it, we *must*!" and Uncle Ulysses was moaning

about what Aunt Agnes would say, and the sheriff was eye-
ing Mr. Gabby, Homer sat down and thought hard.

Before twenty more doughnuts could roll down the
little chute he shouted, "SAY! I know where the bracelet is!
It was lying here on the counter and got mixed up in the
batter by mistake! The bracelet is cooked inside one of
these doughnuts!"

"Why . . . I really believe you're right," said the lady
through her tears. "Isn't that *amazing*? Simply *amazing*!"

"I'll be durn'd!" said the sheriff.

"Ohh-h!" moaned Uncle Ulysses. "Now we have to break up all of these doughnuts to find it. Think of the *pieces*! Think of the *crumbs*! Think of what *Aggy* will say!"

"Nope," said Homer. "We won't have to break them up. I've got a plan."

So Homer and the advertising man took some cardboard and some paint and printed another sign. They put this sign in the window, and the sandwich man wore two more signs that said the same thing and walked around in the crowd out front.

THEN . . . The doughnuts began to sell! *Everybody* wanted to buy doughnuts, *dozens* of doughnuts!

And that's not all. Everybody bought coffee to dunk the doughnuts in too. Those that didn't buy coffee bought milk or soda. It kept Homer and the lady and the chauffeur and Uncle Ulysses and the sheriff busy waiting on the people who wanted to buy doughnuts.

When all but the last couple of hundred doughnuts had been sold, Rupert Black shouted, "I GAWT IT!!" and sure enough . . . there was the diamond bracelet inside of his doughnut!

Then Rupert went home with a hundred dollars, the citizens of Centerburg went home full of doughnuts, the lady and her chauffeur drove off with the diamond bracelet, and Homer went home with his mother when she stopped by with Aunt Aggy.

As Homer went out of the door he heard Mr. Gabby say, "Neatest trick of merchandising I ever seen," and Aunt Aggy was looking sceptical while Uncle Ulysses was saying, "The rings of batter kept right on dropping into the hot fat, and the automatic gadget kept right on turning them over, and the other automatic gadget kept right on giving them a little push, and the doughnuts kept right on rolling down the little chute just as regular as a clock can tick — they just kept right on a comin', an' a comin', an' a comin', an' a comin'."

In the book Homer Price *by Robert McCloskey, Homer comes across more sticky situations, and as always, Homer has clever solutions up his sleeve.*

OF THE NEWS

Doughnut Machine Runs Amuck

Centerburg Bugle

Jubilant Crowds Mob Lunch Room

125th Year   No. 246

Price Pinpoints Priceless

A Celebration On the Streets Of Centerburg

It was mayhem on the streets in front of Uncle Ulysses' lunch room when a large crowd gathered to look through the front window at an automatic doughnut machine that would not stop making doughnuts.

Residents feel that they have been

When the editors at the *Centerburg Bugle* heard what was going on at Uncle Ulysses' doughnut shop, they sent a reporter to check on all the commotion. Write a newspaper article as if you were the *Bugle* reporter. Tell how the diamond bracelet was lost and how Homer Price thought of a plan to find it. Include interviews with Homer, the wealthy lady, and Rupert Black.

About the Author

Robert McCloskey

Although Robert McCloskey has written many books, he says that he is mainly an artist. He attended art school in Boston, Massachusetts, but never studied writing. "I think in pictures," he says, "and I fill in between the pictures with words." In fact, McCloskey wrote his first book, *Lentil*, so that he would have something to illustrate.

Of all his characters, Homer Price is perhaps his favorite. McCloskey still receives fan mail about the book, even though it was first published in 1943.

McCloskey has also written *The Centerburg Tales*, another collection of Homer Price's adventures.

Further Reading From Our Files

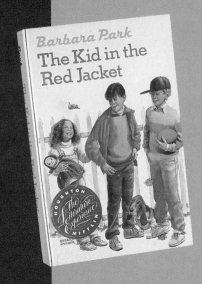

The Kid in the Red Jacket
by Barbara Park
Moving to a new home is hard for Howard Jeeter. Six-year-old Molly Vera Thompson, who follows him everywhere, only makes things worse.

Oliver Dibbs and the Dinosaur Cause
by Barbara Steiner
Oliver Dibbs organizes the whole fifth grade to get the stegosaurus named as the official Colorado state fossil.

From the Mixed-up Files of
Mrs. Basil E. Frankweiler
by E. L. Konigsburg
Feeling misunderstood at home, Claudia and her younger brother take all their savings and go to live in New York's Metropolitan Museum of Art.

SOLUTIONS, INC.

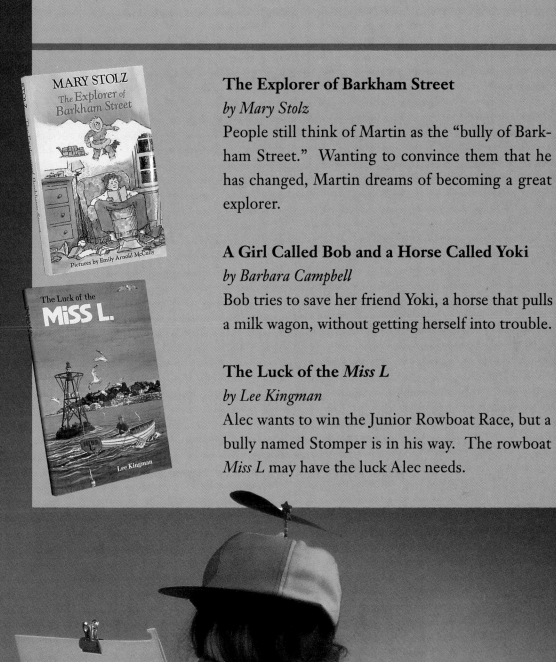

The Explorer of Barkham Street
by Mary Stolz

People still think of Martin as the "bully of Barkham Street." Wanting to convince them that he has changed, Martin dreams of becoming a great explorer.

A Girl Called Bob and a Horse Called Yoki
by Barbara Campbell

Bob tries to save her friend Yoki, a horse that pulls a milk wagon, without getting herself into trouble.

The Luck of the *Miss L*
by Lee Kingman

Alec wants to win the Junior Rowboat Race, but a bully named Stomper is in his way. The rowboat *Miss L* may have the luck Alec needs.

Linking Literature To Social Studies

Literature is often based on real-life experiences, and one of the most common of these is solving problems. In the stories you just read, characters worked together to solve a variety of problems, large and small, serious and humorous.

In real life, too, people work together every day to find solutions to a variety of problems. The article that follows was taken from a social studies textbook chapter. It describes two major problems facing the world today and the solutions that have been attempted to solve them.

Earth Is
Our Address

Working to Make Earth Better

READING FOCUS

What are some ways in which people around the world are cooperating to solve problems?

Key Terms

- catch basin
- silt
- people-to-people
- committee

People everywhere have hopes for a better world. But many of Earth's people are doing more than hoping for a change in the future. They are working *now* to make this planet a better place to live. Very often they are cooperating with others to solve problems.

This article will focus on two examples of cooperation to solve problems. These cases are typical of what is happening across the globe.

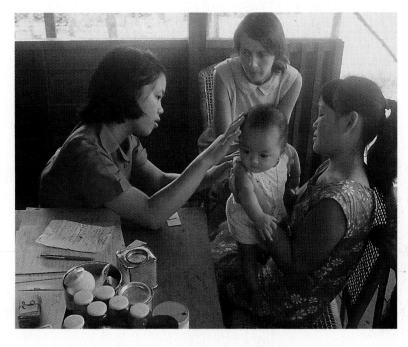

People of many nations around the world help each other. Here an American nurse and a nurse from Maylasia care for a Maylasian baby.

Working to Restore the Land

More than a third of the people on Earth use wood to cook their food and to warm themselves. Wood is also used to build homes and furniture. To meet the need for wood, people are chopping down more and more of the world's forests. Stripping the land of trees has badly damaged many areas of our planet. The following case study tells what happened in one of these regions.

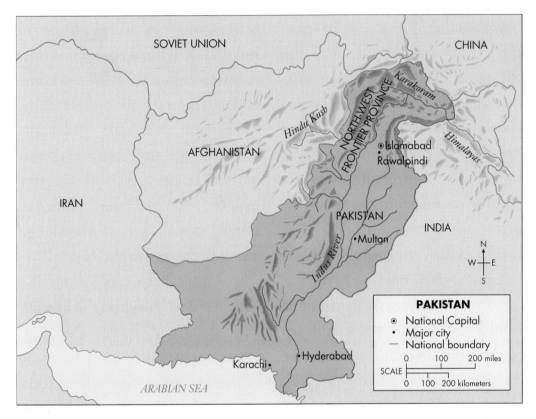

Replanting Trees in Pakistan
Look at the map of Pakistan. Now find the North-West Frontier Province, or NWFP for short. Why do you think it was given that name?

The NWFP is a zone that is important to the entire Indus River valley. The region is a **catch basin** for the melting snows of the Himalayas. The basin also catches heavy rains that arrive each year. From the catch basin, the water flows into the Indus River. For thousands of years, the Indus has been a "river of life" for people living downstream. Today, as in the past, they depend on the

257

Indus for water to irrigate crops and to use for drinking, washing, and cooking.

In recent times the NWFP has gone through changes that endanger the whole river valley. The trouble started with the cutting down of forests that once covered the NWFP. To earn money for food and clothing, people in the NWFP began cutting and selling timber. They also cut wood to use for cooking and heating. As the population grew, more and more trees disappeared. Finally only shrubs were left to grow on the steep hillsides. The shrubs in turn were eaten by goats belonging to wandering herders.

When the yearly heavy rains came, the bare land could no longer hold water. Rainwater rushed down the slopes, carrying away soil. The rushing water left deep gullies in the land. With every rain more soil got washed downstream. In some places the buildup of **silt** — fine bits of soil — stopped up canals and reservoirs.

By the 1960's the Pakistanis knew something had to be done. The government took steps to try to slow down the damage. But the Pakistanis knew they could not solve the problem without help. Pakistan is a non-industrial country, and it is very poor. It did not have the resources to do the job alone.

The Pakistanis found that other countries were willing to help. The United States was one. It invited some Pakistanis to come and study ways to restore damaged land. These Pakistanis studied at a university and also worked in the field with forestry experts. When they returned home, they had new knowledge and skills to use in the NWFP.

Other help came from the World Food Program. Through this program more than 70 governments offer food to those in need. In the NWFP the food was sent to farmers in exchange for their work in restoring the land.

The farmers in the NWFP are building dams to slow the force of water rushing down the gullies. The dams also catch soil before it gets to the river. When a lot of this soil has built up, the farmers add it to their fields. In this way the soil goes back for growing crops.

The farmers are planting more and more trees on the hillside in the NWFP. It will take a long time for forests to grow again. But through cooperation, the land will slowly be restored.

People Helping People

Look at the three symbols shown below.

No doubt you recognize the one on the left. You might even belong to the organization it stands for. More than 60 million young people around the world are members. This organization offers many services. It gives instruction in swimming, boating, and lifesaving. It provides ambulance, rescue, and blood bank services. Suppose there is a flood, hurricane, earthquake, or other disaster somewhere in the world. Volunteers from this organization are on the scene to help. What is its name?

All of these symbols actually stand for the same organization. The symbol and name that you know it by is most likely "the Red Cross." The Red Cross is probably the largest **people-to-people** program on Earth. Today more than 200 million persons in over 100 countries are members. Members who live in Islamic countries use the Red Crescent as their symbol. An exception is Iran, where the Red Lion and Sun is the symbol.

Through the International Red Cross, millions of people volunteer their services to those in need. This vast people-to-people program came into being because of what one person did more than a hundred years ago. Read how it happened.

Red Cross workers handing out food and clothing to victims of the 1989 San Francisco earthquake.

Memories of Solferino A Swiss businessman named Henri Dunant was traveling in Italy in 1859 while a war was going on. He happened to arrive in the town of Solferino the day after a terrible battle. More than 40,000 soldiers lay dead or dying on the battlefield.

Dunant was sickened by what he saw. He decided to do what he could to help the victims of both sides. He gathered some townspeople and gave them jobs to do. He turned churches, barns, and homes into hospitals. Under his direction, men, women, and children did what they could to comfort the wounded. They made beds, prepared bandages, hauled water, cooked, and nursed. Dunant himself worked day and night.

When Dunant returned to his home in Geneva, Switzerland, he couldn't stop thinking about his experiences in Solferino. He wrote about them in a booklet. Its title in English would be *Memories of Solferino*. In his book Dunant described the horrors of war. He had the book printed at his own expense and gave copies away.

Dunant's book caused a great stir. Teachers and religious leaders read it. So did kings and queens and other leaders of nations — including the President of the United States. People began asking each other the same questions Dunant put in his book:

"If we human beings can't
or won't stop wars, can't
we at least try to ease
the pain we cause others?
Why wait for govern-
ments to act? Why can't
people just help people?"

Why not, indeed! thought one of Dunant's friends. This friend, Gustave Moynier, took the next step. He formed a **committee** of five, including Dunant and himself. The group met in Geneva to see if it could come up with a plan.

The committee did come up with a plan. It developed the idea of the Red Cross. That idea has kept growing ever since — as people continue to help people through this worldwide organization.

Opposite page:
Center, A Red Cross shelter for people left homeless after the 1989 San Francisco earthquake.
Top right, Henri Dunant, founder of the Red Cross.
Lower left, A Red Cross center supplying food during a 1930 drought in Arkansas.

CHECK UP

- What are two ways in which people around the world are cooperating to solve problems?

- How has the chopping down of forests damaged land in the North-West Frontier Province and other areas of the world? What has been done to repair the damage in the NWFP? In what way was this an international effort?

- How and why was the Red Cross started? Why is it called a people-to-people program?

FOLKTALES

BOOK 5

LONG·AGO
AND·FAR·AWAY

LONG AGO AND FAR AWAY

Grab the carpet fringe and hold on tight. Fly the magic carpet through the centuries to exotic places you've only dreamed of. Each stop on this magical journey will be a story first told long ago in a land far away. Fly to ancient China to watch an old widow weave a magic brocade. Explore the golden palaces and desert sands of the Sahara. And journey to the northern plains of America to a time when humans could speak to animals. Read these magic words and let the adventure begin:

"Long ago, in a land far to the east . . ."

CONTENTS

The Weaving of a Dream   266
retold and illustrated by Marilee Heyer

The Emir's Son   286
retold by Martin Ballard
illustrated by Gareth Floyd

Her Seven Brothers   304
retold and illustrated by Paul Goble

THE WEAVING OF A DREAM

RETOLD AND ILLUSTRATED BY

MARILEE HEYER

Long ago, in a land far to the east, there lived an old widow who had three sons. The eldest was Leme, the second was Letuie, and the youngest was Leje. They lived in a small cottage in a mist-filled valley at the foot of a high mountain.

Everyone for hundreds of miles around knew the old widow, for she had a special gift. She could weave beautiful brocades that seemed to come alive under her fingers. The flowers, plants, birds, and animals she wove almost moved with the breeze. Her weaving was in constant demand at the marketplace in the village nearby. It was used to make dresses and jackets, curtains and coverlets. With the money she earned, the old widow supported her family, although the boys helped by chopping wood and selling it.

One day, while she was at the market selling some new weavings, she saw a most wondrous painting hanging in a stall nearby. It showed a large palace surrounded by beautiful flower gardens. There were vegetable gardens, too, fruit trees, pastures where cattle grazed, lovely birds, and even a fish pond. A river ran in front of the palace, and the whole painting was warmed by a great red sun. Everything she had always dreamed of was in the painting. She gazed at every detail, and her heart filled with happiness.

 Although she knew she should not, she traded her brocades for the painting. I should be buying rice for my sons, she thought, but she could not help herself.

Three times on the way home she stopped to unroll the painting and gaze at it. "If only we could live in that palace," she whispered to herself.

When she got home she showed the painting to her sons and told them of her dream.

"It's lovely, Mother," said Leme and Letuie. "But where is the rice you went to buy?" They didn't understand her desire to live in the picture palace.

"It's a silly dream, Old Mother," they said.

She turned to Leje, her youngest son, with a sadness in her eyes he had never seen before.

"Leje, I know that *you* will understand. I feel I must live in this lovely place or I will die," she sighed.

"Don't be sad, Mother. I will think of something."

As he comforted her an idea came to him.

"Why don't you do a weaving of the painting? Your weavings are so lifelike that, as you work on it every day, it will be almost like living there."

"You are right, Leje," she said with a smile. "It is the closest I will ever come to this lovely place."

She set to work by candlelight that very evening.

Once she started weaving she didn't stop. For days and months she worked, her shuttle flashing through the threads.

Leme and Letuie became very upset with their mother. One evening they even pulled her hands away from the loom.

"You are no longer making brocades to sell, Old Mother. Now we must all live on the money we make chopping wood, and we are tired of working so hard."

Leje ran to stop them.

"Let Mother be. She must weave the beautiful palace, or die of grief. I will chop all the wood."

From then on, Leje chopped day and night, cutting wood to sell for food.

The old widow continued to weave every hour, on and on, never stopping. At night she worked by candlelight. The smoke burned her eyes and made them red and sore, but she didn't stop. After one year, tears began to drop from her eyes onto the threads, and they became part of the river and fish pond she was weaving. After two years, blood dripped from her eyes onto her hand. Down her hand onto the shuttle it ran, and the drops of blood were woven into the splendid red sun and glowing flowers.

On and on she worked. At last, during the third year, she was finished. What a beautiful brocade it was, the most magnificent ever seen. Mother and sons stared at it in wonder. Even Leme and Letuie couldn't take their eyes from it. The garden, the flowers, the beautiful

palace, songbirds of every kind, luscious fruits and vegetables ready to pick, all in the most perfect detail. Behind the palace were pastures for the fat sheep and cattle, and fields of maize and rice. The river sparkled in front, and the marvelous sun warmed every thread.

"Oh, Mother, how proud we are of your wonderful work!" whispered her sons.

The old widow stretched her tired back and rubbed her bloodshot eyes. A smile creased her wrinkled cheeks and slowly grew into a joyous laugh.

Suddenly, a great wind blew the hut door open with a crash! It raced through the room, knocking everything over. Then taking the wondrous brocade with it, it blew out the window and up into the sky to the east.

They all ran after it, screaming and waving their arms, but the brocade was gone. Vanished! When the boys turned, they saw their mother lying unconscious on the doorstep.

They carried her inside and laid her on the bed. Slowly she opened her eyes.

"Please, Leme, my oldest son," she said. "Go east, follow the wind, and bring my brocade back to me. It means more to me than my life."

Leme nodded, put on his sandals, took a few supplies, and headed east. Within a month's time he came to a mountain. When he reached the very top he saw a strange house made all of stone, with a stone horse standing by the door. The horse's mouth was open, as if it were trying to eat some of the red berries that were growing at its feet. On the front doorstep sat a white-haired old crone.

"And where are you headed, young man?" she croaked in a little-used voice.

"I'm going east," said Leme, "where the wind has carried off a beautiful brocade my mother spent three years weaving."

"Ah, that brocade," cackled the fortune-teller, for that is what she was. "The fairies of Sun Mountain sent the wind to bring it to them. They wish to copy its beautiful design. You may never find it. The way is very difficult."

"Please tell me how to get there," pleaded Leme.

"First, you must knock out your two front teeth and put them into the mouth of my stone horse. Then it will be able to move and eat the berries it has wanted for so long. When it has eaten ten berries, it will let you on its back and will carry you to Sun Mountain, but on the way you must first pass over Flame Mountain, which is constantly on fire. When the horse goes through the flames, you must not cry out, even if the pain is unbearable. Keep your cries to yourself, or you will immediately be burned to ashes.

"Next, you will come to the Sea of Ice. When you go through the ice, you must not cry out, though your whole body will become numb with cold. If you do cry out, you will sink to the bottom of the sea. If you pass through these places as I have told you, you then will see Sun Mountain and will be given your mother's fine brocade to carry home."

Leme ran his tongue over his front teeth. He thought of the burning fire and freezing ice, and he grew very pale.

The old fortune-teller saw his face and laughed. "You will not be able to endure it, young man, and after all, you need not. I will give you a box of gold; go home and live happily."

From inside the house she brought the box. Leme took it quickly and turned toward home. He had gone about a mile before he realized how much better it would be if he spent all the gold on himself instead of sharing it with his family. So, instead of going home, he headed south toward the big city.

Waiting for Leme's return, the old widow grew thinner and thinner. After two months she could wait no longer.

"Letuie, you must go east and find my brocade. It means my life," she told her middle son.

Letuie agreed. He put on his sandals, took some supplies, and headed east. Within a month's time he was standing at the door of the stone house, listening to the old fortune-teller tell him he must knock out his teeth and go silently through fire and ice. Letuie also grew very pale. He, too, received a box of gold and went to the big city with it instead of returning home.

Again, the old widow waited. She grew as thin as a piece of old firewood. Every day she spent lying in her bed, staring at the door, waiting for Letuie's return. Every day when he didn't come, she wept. Her old tired eyes finally went blind from weeping.

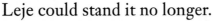

Leje could stand it no longer.

"Old Mother, please let me go look for the brocade. Perhaps Leme and Letuie have been injured. I will search for them, too. I will ask the neighbors to care for you while I'm gone."

After thinking for a long time the old widow agreed, but she hated to let Leje leave, for she loved her youngest son the best.

Leje put on his sandals and took some supplies. He threw back his shoulders and proudly started on his mission to the east. In half the time it had taken his brothers, he reached the top of the mountain. Again there was the old fortune-teller with her stone horse. She repeated the instructions a third time and watched Leje's face closely. It didn't grow pale as his brothers' had, and when she offered him the gold that his brothers had accepted, he refused it.

"I must bring back the brocade for my mother or she will surely die."

Immediately he picked up a stone, knocked out his front two teeth, and fed them to the stone horse. After the horse had eaten the ten berries, Leje jumped on its back, and clinging to its mane, kicked the horse with his heels. High into the air the wonderful horse jumped, and away they flew, as fast as the wind they were following.

For three days and three nights they flew across the sky. At last they reached Flame Mountain. Into the fire they dashed without a pause. The red flames hissed around Leje and stabbed at his skin, but he didn't cry out. With teeth clenched tight, he endured the pain, and in half a day's time he came out of the flames and stood on the shore of the Sea of Ice. Again, without hesitation, he sped on. Steam rose from his burning-hot body as it hit the ice-cold water. He felt his legs and arms grow numb and bleed from the sharp edges of the ice, but he uttered no sound. In half a day's time he came out of the Sea of Ice, and before him, glowing in golden light, shone beautiful Sun Mountain. The warmth of it soothed his body and eased his pain.

The loveliest palace he had ever seen stood on the top of the mountain, and from its windows came the sound of women's voices singing and laughing.

Up the mountain the stone horse flew, and soon they stood before the palace door. There two very strange creatures, unlike anything Leje had ever seen before, stood guard, but not even they could stop him now. Down from the horse he jumped, and straight through the door he marched. The creatures didn't blink, nor did he.

In front of him was a great hall filled with beautiful fairies, all weaving as fast as they could. In the very center of the hall, for them to copy, hung his mother's brocade.

Startled by the sight of Leje, the fairies stopped their weaving and sat as still as stones.

"Don't be afraid," he told them. "I have only come for my mother's brocade."

At the thought of losing the brocade, some of the fairies began to cry, but one fairy stood and said, "Very well, you may have the brocade in the morning. Just allow us one more night of weaving so that we can finish. You may stay here with us and rest for the night."

Leje agreed, and the fairies sent one of the creatures to prepare for him a most delicious dinner, after which Leje fell into a deep sleep.

When the sun set and the light in the hall began to grow dim, one fairy hung a shining pearl that filled the hall with light. They continued weaving through the night.

One beautiful fairy, dressed all in red, finished her weaving first. She had always been the finest and the quickest of the weavers, but when she held her weaving next to the old woman's, hers looked very poor by comparison, for the colors were not as bright nor the stitches so fine.

This brocade is so perfect, the fairy thought. Instead of trying to copy it, I wish I could become a part of it.

So while the other fairies worked on, the red fairy started to weave into the old widow's brocade a picture of herself sitting by the fish pond.

Late in the night Leje woke with a start.

Suppose the fairies will not give me the brocade in the morning, he thought. My poor mother has been ill so long. What will become of her?

As he looked around he saw that all the fairies had fallen asleep over their looms. There stood his mother's brocade, more lovely than ever by the light of the pearl. Quickly, Leje took down the brocade and ran to his waiting horse. Away into the moonlight they flew.

In three days and three nights they stood before the fortune-teller's house.

"Well done, my son," said the old woman. She took his teeth from the stone horse's mouth and put them back into Leje's mouth as if they had never been gone. The horse immediately froze into his old position.

"Quickly, my son, you must return home, for your mother is dying." From behind her back the old woman pulled a fine pair of embroidered boots and set them on the ground.

"Put these on; they will speed your way."

Hardly had Leje put the boots on than he was standing on his own doorstep. Inside, he saw his dear mother, now grown thinner than a splinter. At that very moment her heart was beating its last.

"No, Mother, don't die," cried Leje, running to her bedside. He pulled the brocade from his shirt and spread it over her. The warmth of its gleaming sun soothed her and pulled her back to life. She felt the delicate threads with her fingertips. Her eyes began to clear and her sight returned. She sat up in bed and gazed at the wonderful brocade that had taken three years from her and almost cost her her life.

"Oh, my most faithful son," she said, "help me take the brocade out of this dark hut into the sunlight, where we can see it better."

Outside they lovingly spread the brocade on the ground. Suddenly a soft, sweet-smelling breeze swept through the valley. It gently drew the brocade off the ground and spread it over the yard. Larger and larger and longer and wider it grew. Over the fence and over the house it spread, covering everything with its silken threads. The shabby hut disappeared, and in its place the brocade itself took on the very shape and form of the beautiful palace. Before their eyes the brocade was coming to life. The gardens, the fruit trees, the pasture — all became real. The colorful birds began to sing, the cattle grazed on the rich

281

pasture grass, and there, sitting by the fish pond, was the red fairy, as bright as the sun overhead.

The old widow was greatly astonished, for she knew she had not woven a fairy into her brocade. But she welcomed her and brought her to live with them in the beautiful palace. She asked all her neighbors to live with them too, for there was more than enough room and they had all been kind to her while Leje was away. Leje and the red fairy were married, and so the weaving of the dream was completed.

One day as Leje, the fairy, and his mother sat in the garden making toys for the new baby that would be coming soon, two beggars crept up and stared at them through the garden fence. They were Leme and Letuie. They had gone to the big city and lost all their gold, squandering it on themselves. Now they had nothing left. When they saw the happy scene before them, they thought of the terrible thing they had done. They were filled with grief and remorse, and they turned silently, picked up their begging sticks, and crept away.

DREAM WEAVING

When the old widow saw the beautiful painting hanging in the market, her only wish was to live in the world of the picture. Have you ever imagined what it would be like to live in another place or time? What would your place look like? Where would it be? Draw a picture of your dream. When you've finished, write a brief description of your dream under the drawing.

MARILEE HEYER

The Weaving of a Dream is Marilee
Heyer's first book. Before becoming an
author, Heyer worked as an illustrator and
designer. She helped design several cartoon
shows for television, including *The Lone
Ranger, Journey to the Center of the Earth, The
Hardy Boys*, and *The Archies*. More recently,
she worked as an artist for the movie *Return of
the Jedi*.

Heyer's second book, *The Forbidden Door*,
is about a mysterious world of evil hidden
behind a magic cellar door.

285

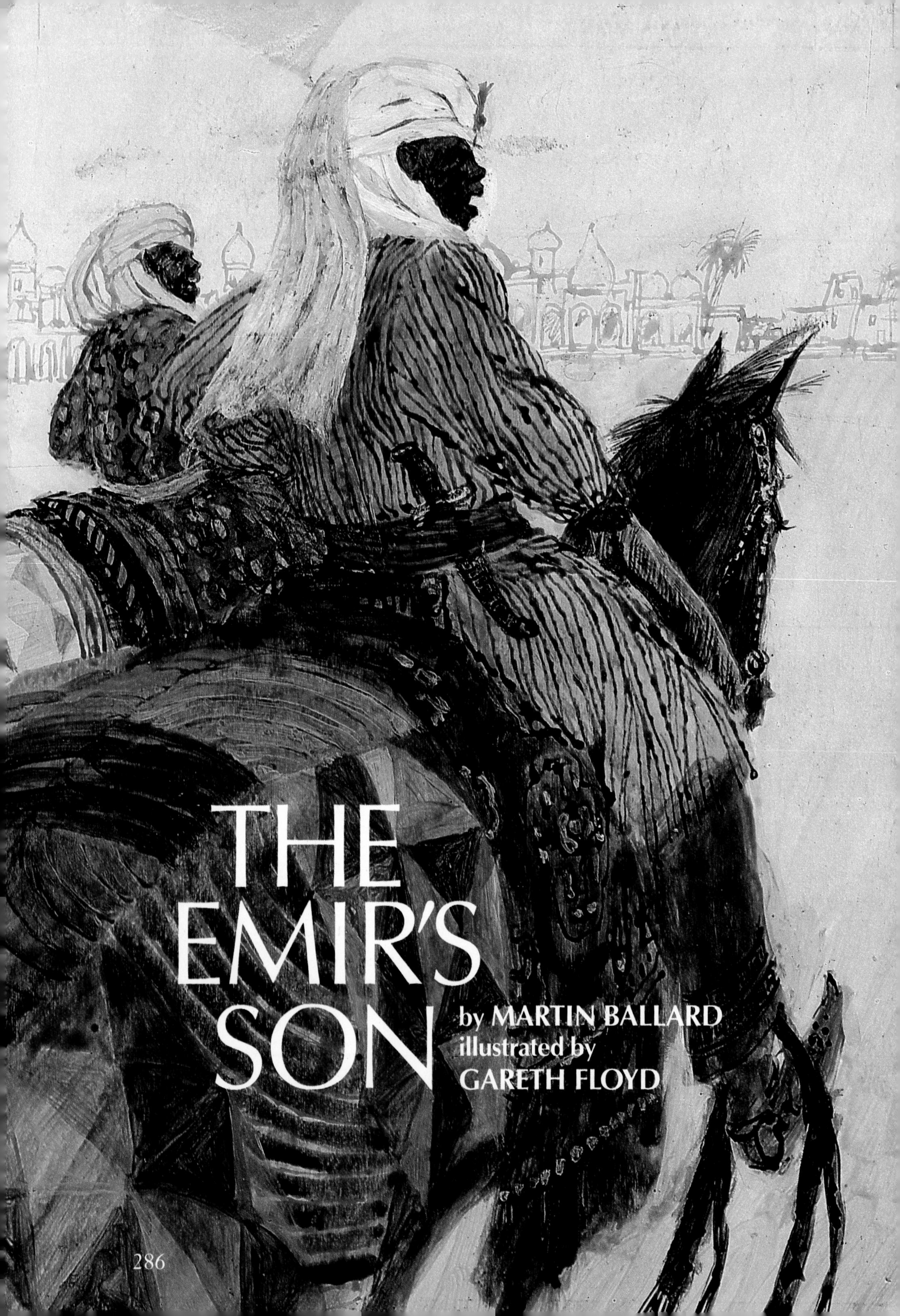

THE EMIR'S SON

by **MARTIN BALLARD**
illustrated by
GARETH FLOYD

The Emir's son lived in his father's palace. He had everything that a young man could wish for.

He had many fine robes woven in every shade of the rainbow.

He always ate the most delicious food. When his father's subjects sat down to their thin vegetable stew, he feasted from overflowing platters of roast venison.

He was rich and owned many cattle, and because he was rich he had many friends. Every young man in the land longed to be seen riding behind the Emir's son.

Out of all these young men he chose three special friends.

There was Audu.

There was Isa.

And there was Iakabu.

They were lively companions. They loved to wrestle and box, but none of them was strong enough to beat the Emir's son. They had fine, swift horses, but none could ride quite fast enough to outstrip the Emir's son. When he wanted to laugh and be gay, they were always ready to laugh with him.

The Emir's son thought that Audu, Isa, and Iakabu were the best friends in all the world. But when there was no one around to hear, the people of the land murmured together. They called them "the sons of the wind," because, like the wind, they stopped for no one and cared for no one. The people feared for the day when the old Emir would die and the sons of the wind would do as they wished.

One day, in the cool of the afternoon, the Emir's son called to his friends. "What shall we do to amuse ourselves today?" he asked.

They all thought for a minute, and then Audu said, "Let us wander through the palace. Perhaps we will find someone to laugh at."

The others liked this idea, so off they went together to visit every room in the palace. They burst into the kitchen where the cooks were working. Audu found some salt while Isa took a bowl of sugar. Then, onto the floor went the salt and sugar. They stirred and stirred until they were all mixed together, and then they called the kitchen boy.

"See this pile here," said the Emir's son. "You must separate every grain of salt and every grain of sugar and put each one back in its proper bowl. It must be finished tonight in time for you to serve them both at my table — and I warn you, let the sugar not taste of salt, nor the salt of sugar."

The four friends left the room, and they grinned at each other as they looked back at the boy crouched over his impossible task.

They went next to the room where the women of the palace were weaving cloth. Audu took his knife and slit the threads on the loom. Isa and Iakabu found a large ball of yarn and played football with it on the dusty floor.

The Emir's son leaned against the door and laughed at the antics of his friends.

On they went together until they had passed through every room of the palace, and they came out at last into the main courtyard. At once the four young men stopped laughing and their faces became serious, for there, in front of them, sat the Emir of the land, with his councillors on either side of him, holding his court. At his feet squatted two poor men who were arguing fiercely. Both their homes had been burned down in a fire. Now each of them was trying to put the blame on the other.

The Emir listened carefully to everything they had to say. He alone could be their judge, and he alone could settle their dispute. The Emir's son stood quietly while they argued. He wanted to find out how his father would decide the case, but after a few moments he felt Audu tug at his sleeve.

"Let's go," Audu hissed.

The Emir's son took one last look at the scene and then tiptoed after his friends, back into the palace. As soon as they were safely indoors, Audu, Isa, and Iakabu burst out laughing.

Iakabu imitated the Emir, leaning forward with his brow furrowed and his hand cupped round his ear.

Then Isa sat down in front of him and whined, "Oh Emir, the man next door has set fire to my house. I beg for justice."

Audu came up behind Isa and kicked him so that he fell over. Then he cried out, "That's what I give for you and your complaint, you silly old man."

When Isa had picked himself up, the sons of the wind laughed and laughed until they cried — and the Emir's son joined in and laughed with them.

"Ho, ho," gasped Audu. "Have you ever seen such a foolish old man as your father? He is the greatest in the land, and yet he sits, hour after hour, wasting his time like that. When you are Emir we will all feast and drink and make merry. You'll not sit in the courtyard, listening to fools' talk."

The sun had now set and there was nowhere else to go. The four friends said good-bye and returned to their own homes for the night.

Next day, in the cool of the afternoon, the Emir's son called to his friends once again. "What shall we do to amuse ourselves today, my friends?" he asked.

"There's nothing more to do in the palace," said Isa. "Let us ride out into the streets of the town and laugh at all the people we meet."

They called for their horses to be saddled and bridled and then the four young men cantered out of the palace gates. The streets were full of people. As the Emir's son rode past, they all dropped to their knees and bowed their foreheads to the ground. It was the custom of the land that they should greet their future ruler in this way, but Audu, Isa and Iakabu laughed loudly as they rode by.

At the outskirts of the town they came to the market-place. Here the friends stopped to look round them.

Everywhere there were people. There were people buying and people selling; there were children with no money to spend, who still loved playing in the market. The Emir's son smiled as he looked around him.

Then suddenly Audu reined in his horse and threw back his head. "Just watch me," he called as he lashed out with his whip and drove his spurs into his horse's flanks. At full gallop he shot forward, right into the midst of the market, with Isa and Iakabu hard on his heels.

The Emir's son paused for a moment, then he, too, set off after his friends.

The old women's bowls were upset, scattering their rice and spilling their milk.

The stalls were overturned and the cooking pots smashed.

The sheep and goats fled hither and thither, bleating in fear. The children crept into the corners to hide from the flying hoofs.

When the horsemen had gone, the people slowly picked up their belongings.

"It's Audu, Isa, and Iakabu," said one.

"Truly, they are the sons of the wind. They stop for no one and care for no one," said another.

"One day we will teach them a lesson."

"One day, yes — when they're not with the Emir's son."

The young men heard none of these murmurings. They rode back to the palace, where they spent the rest of the evening with songs and laughter.

On the third afternoon, in the cool of the day, the Emir's son called again to his friends. "What shall we do to amuse ourselves today?" he asked.

"The world is full of fools," cried Iakabu. "Let us this time ride out beyond the walls of the town. We can laugh at the women in the villages."

Again the horses were saddled, and again the young men rode out of the palace gates. But that day, when the people of the town saw the horsemen approach, they hurried back into their houses, leaving the

streets deserted as Audu, Isa, and Iakabu and the Emir's son swept through.

But the young men did not even pause to look around them as they rode on, past the empty market, through the town gate, and out into the open countryside beyond. The season of the rains had come, and in the fields the farmers were making furrows with their hoes to plant their seed in the damp earth.

As the Emir's son rode on, he felt the wind, cool on his face, and, excited, he cried to his friends that he would race them.

The horses' hoofs thundered over the sandy soil and gradually the Emir's son drew away from his friends, Audu, Isa, and Iakabu. On and on he rode, as the sound of their cries grew fainter and fainter behind him.

At last, when his horse had grown weary, he found himself in a little village of huts made of mud and thatched with straw. The women were preparing the evening meal outside their doorways and the goats

wandered in and out among them. The Emir's son sat back in his saddle to rest his horse, and, as he looked around him, he noticed a man in a distant field bending over his work.

The Emir's son trotted his horse towards him and, when he came near, saw that the man was indeed very old. His back was so bent that it would never be straight again.

"Old man," cried the Emir's son, "what are you planting?"

The old man was startled. Slowly and painfully he looked up and turned to face the speaker. When he saw that it was the Emir's son he bent his tired back once more and said, "May Allah preserve you, I am planting dates."

"Old man," cried the Emir's son, "what is your age?"

"May Allah preserve you, I have seen the time of planting and the time of reaping now these eighty-five years."

"Well then, do you not know that it will be fifteen years before any of these trees bear fruit? Do you expect to live to be a hundred so that you can taste their first harvest?"

"May Allah preserve you," replied the old one. "Others have planted and I have eaten. I, too, will plant so that others may eat."

The Emir's son stopped laughing and sat quiet on his horse.

He hardly noticed when Audu, Isa, and Iakabu rode up beside him.

Their horses' flanks were heaving after the long ride, but the three friends were still ready for a laugh, and, seeing the young date trees, Iakabu leaned out of his saddle to uproot one of them. In a moment he had jerked upright again as he felt the sting of a whip across the back of his hand.

The Emir's son, his whip still raised, frowned at Iakabu and then turned to the old man. "May Allah preserve you, father," he said. "And may Allah in his bounty give your trees a rich harvest."

So saying, he raised his hand in salute, turned his horse and rode back towards the town, with Audu, Isa, and Iakabu following behind.

The farmers were still working in the fields, dropping seeds into the long furrows and covering them carefully with earth.

He rode in through the town gates. In the market the women were waiting to sell the last of their milk before going home for the night. He came to the palace, left his horse and walked inside. He met the kitchen boy hurrying across the courtyard, carrying the evening meal. When he entered his room he found a fine new robe lying on his bed, woven for him by the women of the palace.

All through that evening the Emir's son thought long of the old man and his date trees. He remembered, too, the farmers planting their seed year after year so that he, who had never worked in a field, could eat. He remembered the herdsmen, far away with their cattle, whose wives came every day to market bringing milk for him to drink.

As he sat, clothed in his fine new robe, he thought for the first time of the many people whose lives were spent in his service. The more he

thought, the more clearly he realized that he would never be able to laugh at them again.

On the fourth day Audu, Isa, and Iakabu, the sons of the wind, went to look for the Emir's son.

They could not find him in his own room.

They thought he might have gone out riding, but his horse was still in the stable.

They looked for him in the kitchen, but he was not there.

They looked where the women were weaving, but he was nowhere to be seen.

Finally they went outside where the Emir sat in his usual place, holding his usual court. On either side of him stood two of his subjects — and there, at the Emir's feet, was his son.

Audu, Isa, and Iakabu finally caught the young man's eye. They grinned and pointed towards the open countryside. But the Emir's son shook his head and turned back to listen to the words of the complaint.

Sadly the three young men turned and walked away.

"Never mind," said Iakabu. "Let the three of us ride out together. We are sure to find some amusement."

But now it was a different story. No one bowed down as they rode past, and they were sped on their journey by jeers and stones.

"Perhaps the Emir's son will ride with us tomorrow," they said to each other.

The next day, however, they found their friend once more sitting at his father's feet, intent on the troubles of the people. One day, he knew, they would be his subjects. They would look to him for wisdom, as they now looked to his father.

As he listened, he felt happy in himself. Now he could say with the old one in the field: "Others have planted and I have eaten. I, too, will plant so that others may eat."

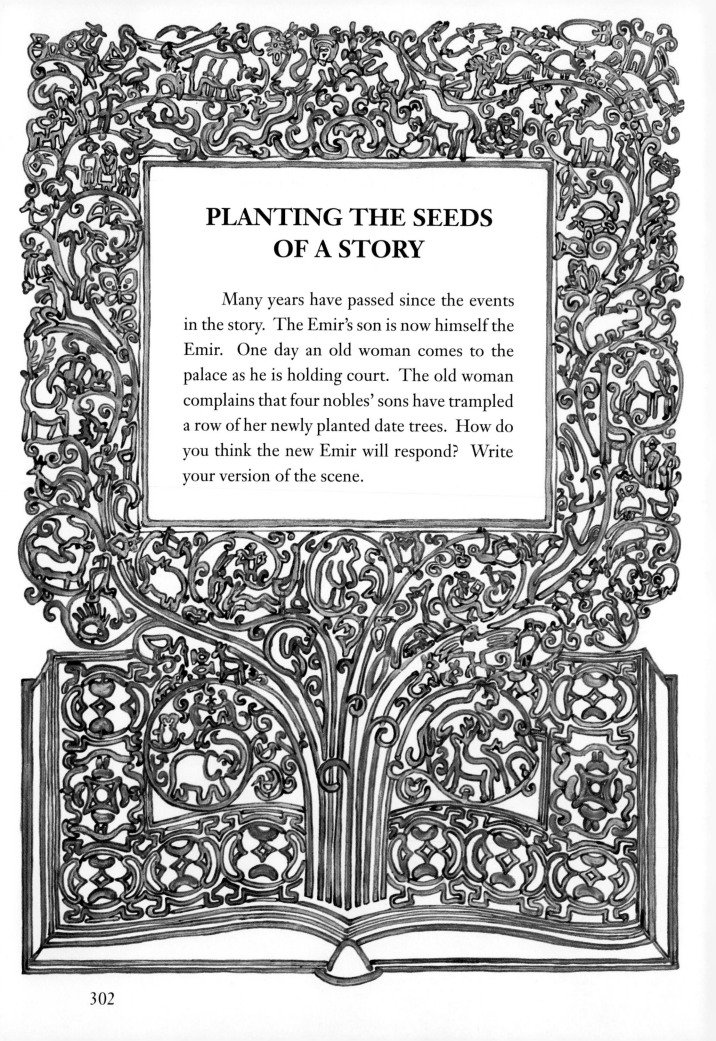

PLANTING THE SEEDS
OF A STORY

Many years have passed since the events in the story. The Emir's son is now himself the Emir. One day an old woman comes to the palace as he is holding court. The old woman complains that four nobles' sons have trampled a row of her newly planted date trees. How do you think the new Emir will respond? Write your version of the scene.

MARTIN BALLARD

After Martin Ballard finished college in England, he traveled to Africa where he first heard the story of *The Emir's Son*. He lived in the northern part of Nigeria, just below the Sahara. While he lived in Africa, Ballard loved listening to the people tell tales that had been handed down through the generations. Understanding their stories wasn't easy — he first had to learn how to understand Hausa, the language of northern Nigeria.

In English, the moral of *The Emir's Son* is "Others have planted and I have eaten. I, too, will plant so that others may eat." In Hausa, the moral is "Wani ya suka mini, ni na ci, ni kuma zan suka, a zo a ci."

A NOTE FROM PAUL GOBLE

The designs of the shirts and dresses and various other articles in this book are based on Cheyenne designs. These articles can be seen in many museums in both the United States and Europe. The designs of the painted tipis are taken from models that were made by Cheyennes about 1900 for the Field Museum of Natural History in Chicago.

The birds and animals, the flowers and butterflies share the earth with us, and so they are included in the pictures. Sometimes two of each are drawn; they, like us, enjoy each other's company. In other places many are drawn, reminding us of the Creator's generosity. They all live on the Great Plains, where this story takes place.

The illustrations are drawn with pen and India ink. When a drawing is finished, it looks much like a page from a child's painting book. The drawings are then filled in with watercolor, which is often applied rather thickly. Thin white lines are left, to try and achieve the brightness of Indian bead and quillwork, and to capture something of the bright colors that one sees in the clear air of the Great Plains.

304

HER SEVEN BROTHERS

retold and illustrated by

PAUL GOBLE

Stories were told after dark when the mind's eye sees most clearly. Winter evenings were best, when the children were lying under their buffalo robes and the fire was glowing at the center of the tipi. After the sounds in the camp had grown quiet and the deer had come out to graze, the storyteller would smooth the earth in front of him; rubbing his hands together, he would pass them over his head and body. He was remembering that the Creator had made people out of the earth, and would be witness to the truth of the story he was going to tell.

306

Do you know what the birds and animals say? In the old days there were more people who understood them. The Creator did not intend them to speak in our way; theirs is the language of the spirits. Yes, birds and animals, butterflies and beetles, stones and trees still speak to us; but we have to learn how to listen.

In those distant times there was a girl who lived with her parents. She did not have any brothers or sisters, but she was never alone because she could speak with the birds and animals. She understood the spirits of all things.

When the girl was quite young her mother taught her how to embroider with dyed porcupine quills onto deer and buffalo skin robes and clothes. She worked hard. In time she became very good at it. Her parents were proud when she gave away something she had made. People marveled at her skill and beautiful designs. They believed that Porcupine, who climbs trees closest to Sun himself, had spoken to the girl and given her mysterious help to do such wonderful work. While the girl worked, she kept good thoughts in her mind; she knew that she could not make anything beautiful without help from the spirits.

One day she started to sew clothes for a man: a shirt
and a pair of moccasins. She decorated them with porcupine quills in brightly colored patterns. Every design had a
meaning for her.

When the shirt and moccasins were finished, she did not give them
to anyone; she put them away and started on another set. Her parents
wondered why she did this when she had neither brothers nor young men
who were courting her. When a second set was finished and she was starting another, her mother asked her for whom she was making the clothes.

Her daughter replied: "There are seven brothers who live by
themselves far in the north country where the cold wind comes from. I
have seen them in my mind when I close my eyes. I am making the
clothes for them. They have no sister. I will look for the trail that leads
to their tipi. I will ask them to be my brothers."

At first her mother thought it was just a young girl's imagining, but
every day her daughter brought out her work. The months passed, and

she made six shirts and pairs of moccasins. And then she started with special care on a seventh set, smaller than the others, to fit a very small boy. Her mother was puzzled, and yet she sensed that her daughter had seen something wonderful. Even the wise men did not know, but they believed that the unseen powers had spoken to the girl.

Her mother said: "I will go with you. When the snow melts we will pack your gifts onto the dogs. I will help you guide them until you find the trail."

The geese brought back the springtime, and they set out for the north country. The way was green and beautiful with flowers; and loud with frogs and red-winged blackbirds calling by every pond. Two faithful dogs carried the bags of clothes. The girl had the little boy's clothes in a separate bundle on her back.

When the girl found the trail, she said to her mother: "This is where I will go on alone. Mother, do not be sad! You will be proud! Soon you will see me again with my brothers; everyone will know and love us!"

But her mother did cry. She called to the sun: "O Sun, look after my child!" She watched her daughter, leading a dog at either hand, walk away and fade slowly into the immensity of the blue distance.

The girl walked on for many days into the land of pine trees until she came at last to a tipi pitched close to a lake. It was painted yellow and had stars all over it. The door was partly open; she thought she could see bright eyes peering at her from inside.

She unpacked the bags from the dogs. After they had taken a drink at the lake, she thanked them. "Now go straight back home," she told them. "Keep to the trail, and do not chase rabbits."

A little boy ran out of the tipi and called to her: "I am glad you have come! I have been waiting for you! You have come looking for brothers. I have six older brothers. They are away hunting buffalo, but they will be back this evening. They will be surprised to see you; they do not have my power of knowing and seeing. I am glad to call you 'Sister.' "

The girl opened the bundle of clothes she had made for him. "Younger Brother," she said, "this is my gift to you."

The boy had never seen anything so beautiful; his clothes had always been plain, and often old. He put on his new shirt and moccasins and scampered down to the lake to take a look at himself in the water. The girl untied the other bags, and placed a shirt and pair of moccasins on each of the six beds around the tipi.

When the little boy heard his brothers returning, he ran out of the tipi to meet them. "Wherever did you get those fine clothes?" they asked.

The boy replied: "A girl made them for me. She came looking for brothers, and now I call her 'Sister.' She has made wonderful shirts for all of you. Come and see!"

The brothers were very proud of their sister and looked after her well. While they were out hunting, she stayed in the tipi with the little boy. He would take his bow and arrows to protect her if she went out for water or to gather firewood. She liked to have good meals ready for the hunters when they returned home.

They all lived happily together until a day when a little buffalo calf came to the tipi. He scratched at the door with his hoof. The boy went outside and asked: "What do you want, Buffalo Calf?"

"I have been sent by the chief of the Buffalo Nation," the calf said. "He wants your sister. Tell her to follow me."

"He cannot have her," the boy answered. "My sister is happy here. We are proud of her."

The calf ran away, but in a little while a yearling bull galloped up to the tipi and bellowed: "I have been sent by the chief of the Buffalo Nation. He insists on having your sister. Tell her to come."

"No! He will never have her," the boy answered. "Go away!"

It was not long before an old bull with sharp curved horns charged up and thundered: "The chief of the Buffalo Nation demands your sister *now*! She must come *at once*, or he will come with the whole Buffalo Nation and get her, and you will all be killed." He shook his mane and whipped his back with his tail in rage.

"No!" the boy shouted. "He will never have her. Look! There are my big brothers coming back. *Hurry*, or they will surely kill you!"

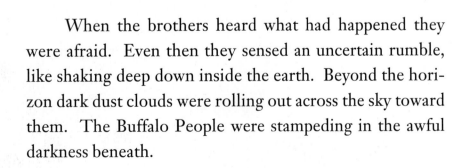

When the brothers heard what had happened they were afraid. Even then they sensed an uncertain rumble, like shaking deep down inside the earth. Beyond the horizon dark dust clouds were rolling out across the sky toward them. The Buffalo People were stampeding in the awful darkness beneath.

"Run!" shouted one of the brothers.

"Wait!" the little boy called out, and he ran into the tipi for his bow and arrows. He shot an arrow straight up into the air and a pine tree appeared, growing upward with the arrow's flight.

The girl quickly lifted her little brother onto the lowest branch and climbed up after him. All the brothers clambered after, just as the Chief of the Buffalo struck the tree a terrible blow, splintering it with his horns. He hooked at the trunk again and again and it was split into slivers. Dark masses of angry buffalo crowded around the tree, pawing the ground and bellowing. The tree quivered and started to topple.

"Hurry! You have power. Save us!" the brothers called to the little boy. He shot an arrow and the tree grew taller.

He shot another far into the sky and the tree grew straight upward, higher and higher, and they were carried far away up among the stars.

And there they all jumped down from the branches onto the boundless star-prairies of the world above.

The girl and her seven brothers are still there. They are the Seven Stars in the northern sky, which we call the Big Dipper. But look carefully and you will see that there are really eight stars in the Big Dipper; close to one of them there is a tiny star; it is the little boy walking with his sister. She is never lonely now. They are forever turning around the Star Which Always Stands Still, the North Star. It is good to know that they once lived here on earth.

Listen to the stars! We are never alone at night.

PAUL GOBLE

Paul Goble has been fascinated with Native American culture for as long as he can remember. He became so interested in studying and writing about Native American culture, Goble left his native country of England and now lives in the rugged Black Hills of South Dakota.

In 1959, Goble became a member of the Yakima and Sioux tribes and was given the Indian name "Wakinyan Chikala" or "Little Thunder."

Paul Goble has written many other books of Native American legends. Here is a list of some of them:
The Gift of the Sacred Dog is a Native American myth explaining how the Plains Indians tamed the horse.
Buffalo Woman is the tale of a man who marries a woman from the Buffalo Nation only to be banished from his tribe.
Iktomi and the Boulder is a Plains Indian trickster tale about Iktomi, a brave who tries to outsmart a clever boulder.

STORIES WRITTEN IN THE STARS

Many legends were created to explain the patterns of the stars. Because of their shapes, some of these patterns, or **constellations**, were named after ancient heroes or mythical animals.

Here are pictures of three star constellations. In small groups, choose one of the constellations. Explain why the constellation is in the sky and how it got there. As a group, tell your story to the rest of the class.

READING'S ENCHANTING SPELL

There is a land—
A marvelous land—
Where trolls and giants dwell;
Where witches
With their bitter brew
Can cast a magic spell;
Where mermaids sing,
Where carpets fly,
Where, in the midst of night,
Brownies dance
To cricket tunes;
And ghosts, all shivery white,
Prowl and moan.
There is a land
Of magic folks and deeds,
And anyone
Can visit there
Who reads and reads and reads.

Leland B. Jacobs

THE RIDE CONTINUES . . .

Vassilisa the Wise: A Tale of Medieval Russia

retold by Josepha Sherman

Will the beautiful and clever Vassilisa be able to rescue her husband from Prince Vladimir's dungeon?

Dawn

retold by Molly Bang

In this retelling of a Japanese folktale, a mysterious woman comes to help a shipbuilder shortly after he rescues an injured Canada goose.

The Shining Princess and Other Japanese Legends

retold by Eric Quayle

A lonely woodcutter discovers a tiny princess hidden inside a bamboo stalk in this book of ten traditional Japanese folktales.

The Enchanted Book: A Tale from Krakow

retold by Janina Porazinska

An evil enchanter lures three sisters to his magic castle. It's up to the youngest sister to learn the enchanter's secret and break the magic spell.

Seasons of Splendour: Tales, Myths and Legends from India

retold by Madhur Jaffrey

This collection of ancient Indian epics and fairy tales contains many of the thrilling stories Madhur Jaffrey heard as a child in India.

Where the Buffaloes Begin

retold by Olaf Baker

All of his life Little Wolf has longed to journey to the mystical lake where the Buffalo Nation was born.

NONFICTION

BOOK 6

JOURNEY INTO SPACE

This is Mission Control. Welcome aboard. Your mission is to study the effects of weightlessness, learn more about Mars, and decide what the next frontier in space will be. You have ten seconds to liftoff and counting. All systems go. Five. Four. Three. Two. One. We have ignition. Liftoff!

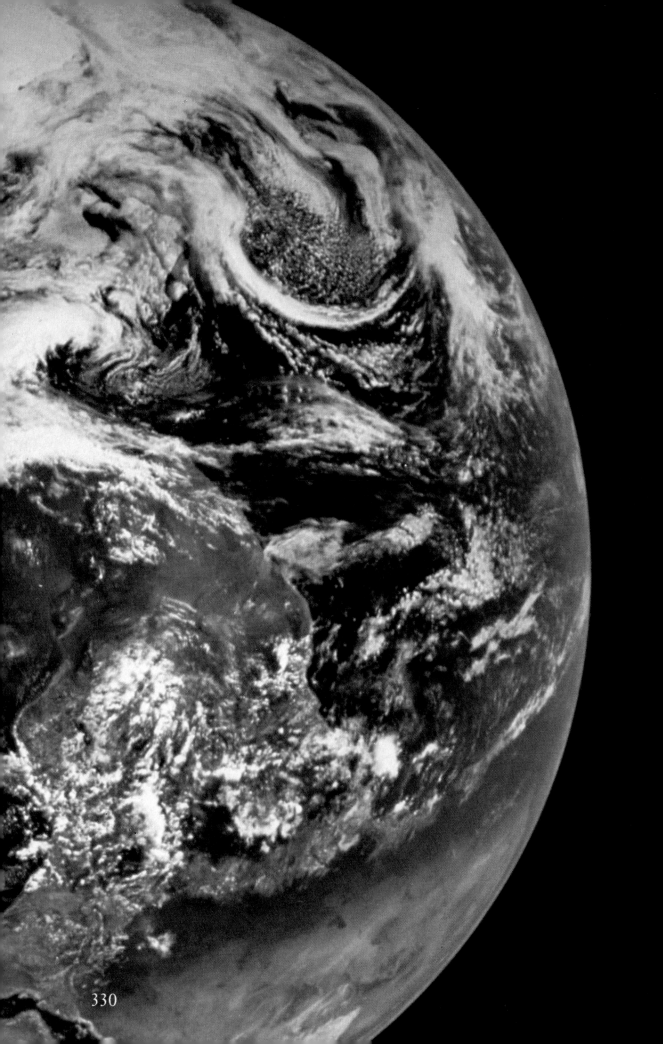

CONTENTS

332 To Space & Back
from the book by *Sally Ride* with *Susan Okie*

360 Mars
by *Seymour Simon*

378 Humans on Mars? Where Will the U.S. Space
Program Go Next?
by *Renée Skelton*

To Space & Back

from the book by Sally Ride with Susan Okie

In June 1983, Sally Ride became the first American woman to travel in space. With four other astronauts she spent a week orbiting Earth in the space shuttle *Challenger*. She made a second flight in October 1984. In this selection Sally Ride tells what it's like to live in space. The pictures you will see were taken by Ride and other space shuttle astronauts. Some were taken on Sally Ride's flights and some were taken on other space shuttle flights.

The book from which this selection is taken is dedicated to the seven astronauts who lost their lives when the *Challenger* exploded on January 28, 1986.

Floodlights brighten the early morning departure of an astronaut crew on their way to the launch pad.

LAUNCH MORNING.

6. . .5. . .4. . .

The alarm clock counts down.

3. . .2. . .1. . .

Rrring! 3:15 A.M. *Launch minus four hours.* Time to get up.

It's pitch black outside. In four hours a space shuttle launch will light up the sky.

Nine miles from the launch pad, in the astronaut crew quarters, we put on our flight suits, get some last-minute information, and eat a light breakfast.

Launch minus three hours. It's still dark. We leave the crew quarters, climb into the astronaut van, and head for the launch pad.

The space shuttle stands with its nose pointed toward the sky, attached to the big orange fuel tank and two white rockets that will lift it — and us — into space.

The spotlights shining on the space shuttle light the last part of our route. Although we're alone, we know that thousands of people are watching us now, during the final part of the countdown.

When we step out onto the pad, we're dwarfed by the thirty-story-high space shuttle. Our spaceplane looked peaceful from the road, but now we can hear it hissing and gurgling as though it's alive.

The long elevator ride up the launch tower takes us to a level near the nose of the space shuttle, 195 feet above the ground. Trying hard not to look down at the pad far below, we walk out onto an access arm and into the "white room." The white room, a small white chamber at the end of the movable walkway, fits right next to the space shuttle's hatch. The only other people on the launch pad — in fact, the only other people for miles — are the six technicians waiting for us in the white room. They help us put on our escape harnesses and launch helmets and help us climb through the hatch. Then they strap us into our seats.

Because the space shuttle is standing on its tail, we are lying on our backs as we face the nose. It's awkward to twist around to look out the windows. The commander has a good view of the launch tower, and the pilot has a good view of the Atlantic Ocean, but no one else can see much outside.

Launch minus one hour. We check to make sure that we are

Space shuttle *Discovery* poised on the launch pad.

strapped in properly, that oxygen will flow into our helmets, that our radio communication with Mission Control is working, and that our pencils and our books — the procedure manuals and checklists we'll need during liftoff — are attached to something to keep them from shaking loose. Then we wait.

The technicians close the hatch and then head for safety three miles away. We're all alone on the launch pad.

Launch minus seven minutes. The walkway with the white room at the end slowly pulls away. Far below us the power units start whirring, sending a shudder through the shuttle. We close the visors on our helmets and begin to breathe from the oxygen supply. Then the space shuttle quivers again as its launch engines slowly move into position for blast-off.

Launch minus 10 seconds. . .9. . .8. . .7. . . The three launch engines light. The shuttle shakes and strains at the bolts holding it to the launch pad. The computers check the engines. It isn't up to us anymore — the computers will decide whether we launch.

3. . .2. . .1. . . The rockets light! The shuttle leaps off the launch pad in a cloud of steam and a trail of fire. Inside, the ride is rough and loud. Our heads are rattling around inside our helmets. We can barely hear the voices from Mission Control in our headsets above the thunder of the rockets and engines. For an instant I wonder if everything is working right. But there's no more time to wonder, and no time to be scared.

In only a few seconds we zoom past the clouds. Two minutes later the rockets burn out, and with a brilliant whitish-orange flash, they fall away from the shuttle as it streaks on toward space. Suddenly the ride becomes very, very smooth and quiet. The shuttle is still attached to the big tank, and the launch engines are pushing us out of Earth's atmosphere. The sky is black. All we can see of the trail of fire behind us is a faint, pulsating glow through the top window.

Launch plus six minutes. The force pushing us against the backs of our seats steadily increases. We can barely move because we're being held in place by a force of 3 g's — three times the force of gravity we feel on Earth. At first we don't mind it — we've all felt much more than that when we've done acrobatics in our jet training airplanes. But that lasted only a few seconds, and this seems to go on forever. After a couple of minutes of 3 g's, we're uncomfortable, straining to hold our books on our laps and craning our necks against the force to read the instruments. I find myself wishing we'd hurry up and get into orbit.

Launch plus eight and one-half minutes. The launch engines cut off. Suddenly the force is gone, and we lurch forward in our seats. During the next few minutes the empty fuel tank drops away and falls to Earth, and we are very busy getting the shuttle ready to enter orbit. But we're not too busy to notice that our books and pencils are floating in midair. We're in space!

The atmosphere thins gradually as we travel farther from Earth. At fifty miles up, we're above most of the air, and we're officially "in space." We aren't in orbit yet, though, and without additional push the shuttle would come crashing back to Earth.

We use the shuttle's smaller space engines to get us into our final, safe orbit about two hundred miles above Earth. In that orbit we are much higher than airplanes, which fly about six miles up, but much lower than weather satellites, which circle Earth more than twenty-two thousand miles up.

The
Houston
area. The
circled spot
near the
bottom is
the NASA
Lyndon B.
Johnson
Space
Center,
which is
where I
work
most of
the time.

Anna Fisher, Rick Hauck, and Dave Walker floating, weightless.

Once we are in orbit, our ride is very peaceful. The engines have shut down, and the only noise we hear is the hum of the fans that circulate our air. We are traveling at five miles a second, going around the Earth once every ninety minutes, but we don't feel the motion. We can't even tell we're moving unless we look out the window at Earth.

We stay much closer to home than the astronauts who flew space capsules to the moon in 1969. When those astronauts stood on the moon, they described the distant Earth as a big blue-and-white marble suspended in space. We are a long way from the moon, and we never get far enough from Earth to see the whole planet at once.

We still have a magnificent view. The sparkling blue oceans and bright orange deserts are glorious against the blackness of space. Even if we can't see the whole planet, we can see quite a distance. When we are over Los Angeles we can see as far as Oregon; when we are over Florida we can see New York.

We see mountain ranges reaching up to us and canyons falling away. We see huge dust storms blowing over deserts in Africa and smoke spewing from the craters of active volcanoes in Hawaii. We see enormous chunks of ice floating in the Antarctic Ocean and electrical storms raging over the Atlantic.

Sunrises and sunsets are spectacular from orbit. Since we see one sunrise and one sunset each time we go around the Earth, we can watch sixteen sunrises and sixteen sunsets every twenty-four hours. Our sightseeing doesn't stop while we are over the dark side of the planet. We can see twinkling city lights, the reflection of the moon in the sea, and flashes of lightning from thunderstorms.

These natural features are not the only things we can see. We can also spot cities, airport runways, bridges, and other signs of civilization. When our orbit takes us over Florida, we are even able to see the launch pad at Cape Canaveral, where we crawled into the space shuttle just hours earlier.

THE BEST PART OF BEING IN SPACE IS BEING WEIGHTLESS. It feels wonderful to be able to float without effort; to slither up, down, and around the inside of the shuttle just like a seal; to be upside down as often as I'm right side up and have it make no difference. On Earth being upside down feels different because gravity is pulling the blood toward my head. In space I feel exactly the same whether my head is toward the floor or toward the ceiling.

When I'm weightless, some things don't change. My heart beats at about the same rate as it does on Earth. I can still swallow and digest food. My eyes, ears, nose, and taste buds work fine; I see, hear, smell, and taste things just as I do at home.

I *look* a little different, though — all astronauts do. Since the fluid in our bodies is not pulled toward our feet as it is on Earth, more of this fluid stays in our faces and upper bodies. This makes our faces a little fatter and gives us puffy-looking cheeks. We are also about an inch taller while in orbit because in weightlessness our spines are not compressed. Unfortunately (for me, anyway), we shrink back to normal height when we return to Earth.

During my first day in space, I had to learn how to move around. I started out trying to "swim" through the air, but that didn't work at all; air isn't dense, the way water is, and I felt silly dog-paddling in the air, going nowhere. Before long I discovered that I had to push off from one of the walls if I wanted to get across the room. At first I would push off a little too hard and crash into the opposite wall,

We use
cameras
constantly—
to take
pictures of
the Earth,
of experi-
ments, of
satellites,
and of
each other.

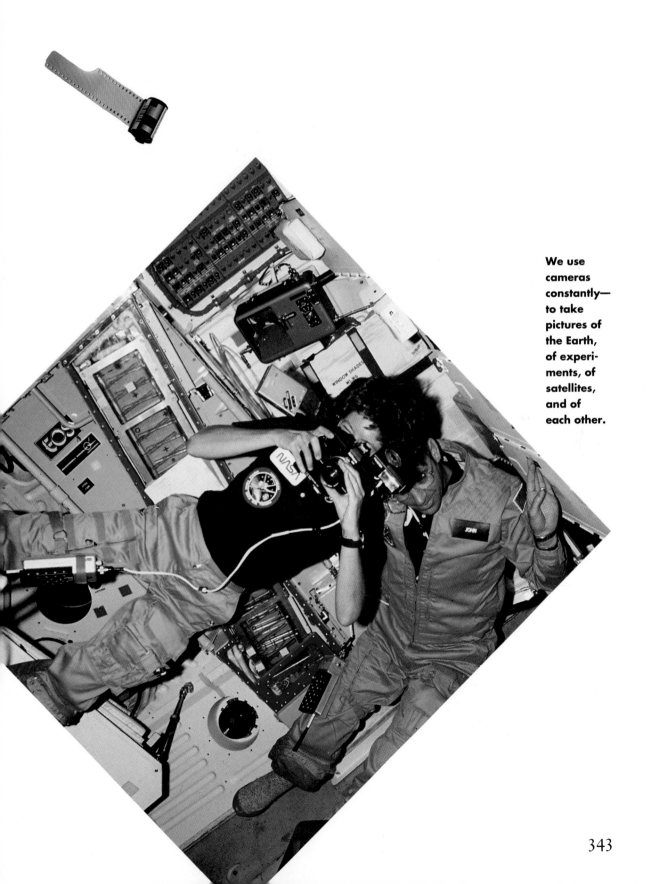

One person's upside down is another person's right side up. I'm coming down—head first—from the flight deck, while Kathy Sullivan is on her way up. The ladder that I have my hand on is completely useless in space.

but I soon learned to wind my way around with very gentle pushes.

In weightlessness the slightest touch can start an astronaut's body floating across the room or drifting over in a slow-motion somersault. The only way to stop moving is to take hold of something that's anchored in place. Early in my first flight I constantly felt that I was about to lose control, as though I were teetering on a balance beam or tipping over in a canoe. It's a strange, unsteady feeling that's difficult to describe, but fortunately it goes away. After a day or two I got the knack of staying still and could change clothes without tumbling backward.

Some astronauts are uncomfortable while their bodies are adjusting to weightlessness. Almost half of all shuttle crew members are sick for the first day or two. Space sickness is not like the motion sickness caused by bobbing on a boat or riding a roller coaster. It affects each person differently. A space-sick astronaut might feel nauseated or tired or disoriented or just strange. So far we haven't found out exactly what causes space sickness or how to cure it.

It's Dale Gardner's turn to fix lunch.

By the third day of a week-long shuttle flight, though, all the astronauts are feeling fine. Weightlessness is pure fun, once everyone gets the hang of it. The two rooms inside the shuttle seem much larger than they do on Earth, because we are not held down to the floor. We can use every corner of a room, including the ceiling. While one of us works strapped to a wall, another sits on the ceiling eating peanuts, and a third runs on a treadmill anchored to the floor. On Earth we need a ladder to climb from the mid-deck to the flight deck. In space we never use the ladder — we just float from one room to another.

For the first day or two in space, most astronauts are not as hungry as they would be on the ground. But by the third day, almost everyone has regained a normal appetite, and some — like me — actually eat a little more than usual.

Eating feels the same as it does on Earth. It's just as easy to swallow food and drink water in space, and everything tastes about the same as it would on Earth. Some of the food we carry on the space shuttle is like what we would eat at home: bread, tuna, canned pudding, apples, carrots,

345

peanuts, and cookies. We also have soups, vegetables, and main courses like chicken-and-noodle casserole, but these are freeze-dried and vacuum-packed in individual plastic cartons.

Astronauts eat three meals a day and take turns preparing food. Usually one or two astronauts make a meal for the whole crew.

To fix lunch, here's what an astronaut has to do:

1. Open the food locker and see what has been planned for lunch. How about hot dogs, macaroni and cheese, peanuts, and lemonade?

2. Get out the food trays. Each crew member has a tray that has slots to hold the cartons in place.

3. Attach the trays to the wall with Velcro so they won't float away.

4. Put one package of peanuts in each food tray.

5. Turn on the oven, open the oven door, and slide in the hot dogs in their sealed foil bags.

6. Fit the cartons of dehydrated macaroni and cheese, one at a time, into the water dispenser. The dispenser pushes a needle into the carton and squirts in the right amount of water.

7. Squeeze each macaroni carton to mix in the water, and then place it in the oven too.

8. Use the water dispenser to add water to each plastic carton of powdered lemonade. Slide a straw into each carton and put one lemonade carton in each tray.

9. Remove the hot food from the oven and put a carton of macaroni and a pouch of hot dogs in each tray.

10. Get out bread, butter, catsup, and mustard. Crew members have to make their own hot dog sandwiches; once a sandwich is made, it can't be put down because it would float apart.

**Sometimes
I ate
sitting on
the ceiling.**

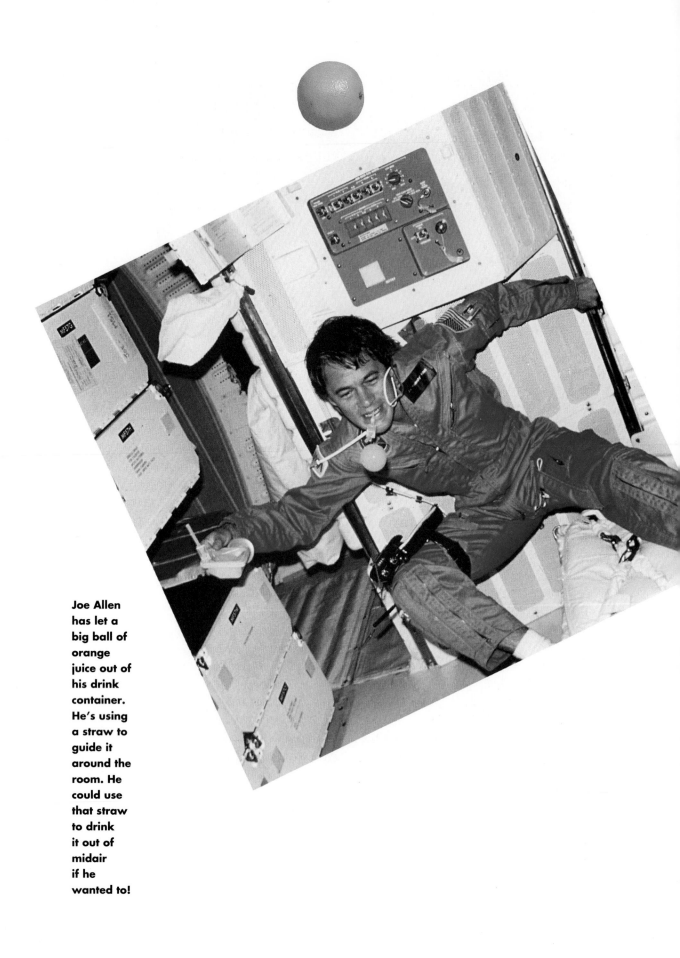

Joe Allen has let a big ball of orange juice out of his drink container. He's using a straw to guide it around the room. He could use that straw to drink it out of midair if he wanted to!

11. Call the rest of the crew to "come and get it."

We gather on the mid-deck to enjoy meals together like a family. The engineers at Mission Control try not to call us while we're eating, so we have some time to talk to one another and relax. But we don't look like a family sitting down to lunch on Earth. We don't eat at a table; our tables are the trays strapped to our legs. We don't sit in chairs. Each of us finds a comfortable spot — maybe floating near the ceiling, or upside down in the middle of the cabin.

We each have a knife and fork, but our most useful pieces of silverware are spoons and scissors. We need scissors to snip open the foil pouches of hot dogs, the packages of peanuts, and the plastic cartons of macaroni. Then we use spoons to get the food to our mouths. Most of our food is deliberately made sticky enough to stay on a spoon and not float away as we try to eat it. In fact, we can flip our spoons all the way across the cabin and the food won't come off — usually! Sometimes a blob of pudding escapes from a spinning spoon, and we have to catch it before it splatters on a wall.

A few foods, like scrambled eggs, are not quite sticky enough to stay on a spoon. I quickly learned to hold the carton close to my mouth and use my spoon to aim each bite of egg.

We don't have drinking glasses. If we tipped a glass of milk to drink from it, nothing would happen — the weightless milk would stay in the glass. We have to use straws to suck our drinks out of cartons.

We don't use salt shakers either, because grains of salt would float around the cabin instead of falling on the food. To solve this problem, we squeeze liquid salt into the cartons and then mix it with the food.

A peanut butter sandwich is simple to fix on Earth, but in space it takes two astronauts to prepare one. The first time I tried to make a peanut butter sandwich, I held the jar of peanut butter, unscrewed the top, and found I needed another hand. If I let go of either the lid or the jar, it would float away. So I tossed the lid to another astronaut and picked up a knife — but with the jar in one hand and the knife in the other, I had no way to reach for the bread! After that I asked someone else to hold the bread or the jar whenever I wanted a sandwich.

Astronauts can't always resist the fun of playing with weightless food. On one of my flights, we set a cookie floating in the middle of the room and then "flew" an astronaut, with his mouth wide open, across the cabin to capture it. We often share bags of peanuts because it gives us an excuse to play catch, floating peanuts back and forth into each other's mouths. We race to capture spinning carrots and bananas and practice catching spoonfuls of food in our mouths while they twirl in midair. These tricks are easy in space, but I don't recommend trying them on Earth.

After meals we clean up. We simply wipe off whatever utensils have been used and stow them in our pockets. Since each serving of food comes in its own carton, can, or pouch, "washing the dishes" really means disposing of the trash. We pack our empty food containers into garbage bags and bring all our trash back to Earth with us.

We don't have beds in the space shuttle, but we do have sleeping bags. Unlike the kind used on camping trips, each of these bags has a stiff pad for body support, a thin bag that can be unzipped from the pad and used by itself, and a pillow. During the day, when we're working, we leave the bags tied to the wall, out of the way. At bedtime we untie them and take them wherever we've chosen to sleep.

**Bob
Overmyer
eating—
no hands!**

On most space shuttle flights everyone sleeps at the same time. No one has to stay awake to watch over the spaceplane; the shuttle's computers and the engineers at Mission Control do that. If anything were to go wrong, the computers would ring an alarm and the engineers would call us on the radio.

On board the space shuttle, sleep-time doesn't mean nighttime. During each ninety-minute orbit the sun "rises" and shines brilliantly through our windows for about fifty minutes; then it "sets" as our path takes us around to the dark side of Earth. Forty minutes later the sun "rises" again as we return to the daylight side of the globe. So sunlight pours through the space shuttle windows more than half the time while we're trying to rest. To keep the sun out of our eyes, we wear black sleep masks, which we call Lone Ranger masks.

It is surprisingly easy to get comfortable and fall asleep in space. Every astronaut sleeps differently. Some sleep upside down, some sideways, some right side up. Some crawl into their sleeping bags and then tie them to anything handy, to keep them floating in one place. Others use the thin bags alone as blankets and wedge themselves into corners. Still others simply float in the middle of the cabin, sometimes cushioning their heads in case they drift gently against the ceiling — or another sleeping astronaut.

The first time I tried to sleep while weightless, I discovered that my arms and legs moved automatically into a "sleep position." Instead of hanging at my sides, as they would on Earth, my arms drifted out in front of me, motionless, at about shoulder height. It was strange to open my eyes and see my arms dangling in front of my face.

I also found that I couldn't turn over in space. There was no such thing as lying on my back, on my side, or on my stomach — it was all the same. No matter how much I twisted and turned, my body would go back to exactly the same natural sleep position as soon as I relaxed.

I don't use my pillow because I have discovered that my head will not stay on it unless I strap it there. I don't use the stiff pad, either — just the light bag. When it's time to sleep, I gather my bag, my sleep mask, and my tape player with earphones and float up to the flight deck. Then I crawl into the bag, zip it around me, and float in a sort of sitting position just above a seat, right next to a window. Before I pull the mask down over my eyes, I relax for a while, listening to music and watching the Earth go by beneath me.

You can find out more about everyday life in space and the special work done aboard a spacecraft by reading the rest of *To Space & Back* by Sally Ride with Susan Okie.

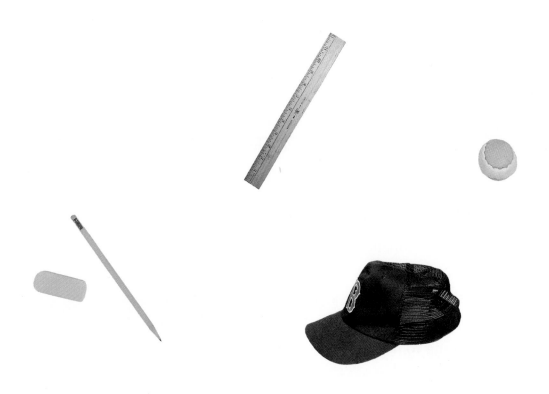

What on Earth!

Imagine a weightless day on Earth in your hometown. How would you get to school? How would you do your schoolwork? Could you play any games after school?

After you've thought about life without gravity, make two lists. In one, describe things it would be easier to do without gravity; in the other, describe things it would be almost impossible to do. Compare your lists with those of your classmates.

VOYAGER

In 1977 Voyager 1 and Voyager 2 were launched from Kennedy Space Center in Florida. Since their launch, the spacecraft have flown by four planets and transmitted photographs of them.

JUPITER

Voyager 1 took this photograph of Jupiter, the largest planet in our solar system, in 1979. Io and Europa, two of Jupiter's moons are also in the picture. Io is the moon floating above Jupiter's Great Red Spot located in the lower right portion of this picture.

SATURN

These photographs of Saturn were taken by Voyager 1 in 1980. Icy particles form the rings that circle the solar system's sixth planet. Tethys and Dione, two of at least twelve moons orbiting Saturn, are the two tiny white specks in the picture on the right.

URANUS

Uranus seems to be peeking over Miranda, one of Uranus's moons, in the picture below taken by Voyager 2 in 1986. Uranus is fourteen times larger than Earth.

358

NEPTUNE

Neptune is so far out
in the solar system, it
takes the planet 165
Earth years to make
a complete rotation
around the sun.
Neptune's rings were
discovered when
Voyager 2 flew by
the planet in 1989.

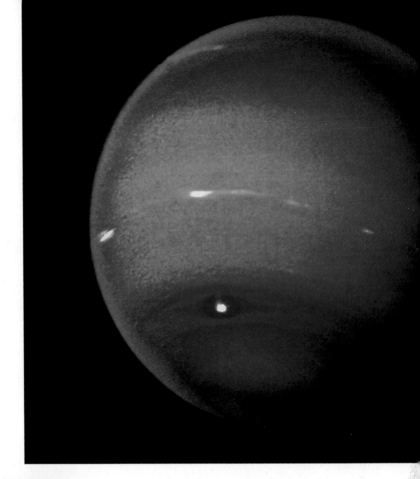

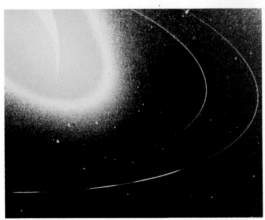

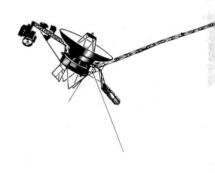

Voyager 1 and Voyager 2 are now traveling out of our solar system to
explore the space beyond. Attached to each Voyager is a "postcard
from Earth" with a message to other civilizations the spacecraft may
encounter. Included in the message are greetings to other forms of life
in fifty-four languages, Beethoven's Fifth Symphony, and Chuck
Berry's rock'n'roll song "Johnny B. Goode" — all recorded on a gold-
coated phonograph record. Each spacecraft also has a miniature slide
show with 117 pictures of Earth and its creatures.

MARS

by Seymour Simon

Mars looks like a bright star in the night sky. But Mars is a planet. Mars appears so bright because it is closer to us than any other planet except Venus.

Mars is sometimes called the "Red Planet" because it shines with a reddish or orange color. Two thousand years ago, the planet's red color made the Romans think of blood and war. So the Romans named it Mars, after their god of war.

Mars is the fourth planet from the sun, after Mercury, Venus, and our own planet, Earth. Mars is more than 140 million miles from the sun — 50 million miles farther away from the sun than Earth. It is also a smaller planet than Earth, 4,218 miles across. If Earth were hollow, seven planets the size of Mars could fit inside.

Earth and Mars travel around the sun in paths called orbits. Earth takes one year, 365 days, to orbit the sun. But Mars is farther away and takes longer to orbit the sun. A Martian year is 687 Earth days, almost twice as long as a year on Earth. A Martian day is only about half an hour longer than a day on Earth.

About one hundred years ago, an Italian astronomer named Giovanni Schiaparelli looked at Mars through his telescope. He thought he saw some straight, dark lines on the surface of the planet. He called them *canali*, the Italian word for channels.

People heard about the "canals" on Mars. They knew that canals are ditches dug by people to carry water from one place to another, so they decided that intelligent Martians must have built the canals. Some astronomers even drew maps of Mars showing long, straight canals crisscrossing the planet.

People began to imagine all kinds of living things on Mars. In 1898, author H. G. Wells's novel *The War of the Worlds* described tentacled, bug-eyed Martians that invade Earth to kill all the humans who live here. Later, many other monsters from Mars were featured in books, science fiction magazines, movies, and television programs.

Until recent years, no one knew whether Martians really existed because details on Mars could not be seen clearly through telescopes from Earth. But in the 1970's, four *Mariner* and two *Viking* spacecraft reached Mars. They found no canals on Mars, no cities, no intelligent Martians, and no life at all on the planet.

This view of Mars was sent back to Earth from one of the *Viking* spacecraft. It shows that the Martian surface has craters, mountains, volcanoes, plains, and valleys — but no straight lines. No one knows what the earlier astronomers were seeing when they thought they saw "canals." At the bottom of the photo, you can see the curving line of Mars's biggest valley, Valles Marineris. Four times as deep as the Grand Canyon of Arizona, it stretches for almost three thousand miles, about the distance from coast to coast across the United States.

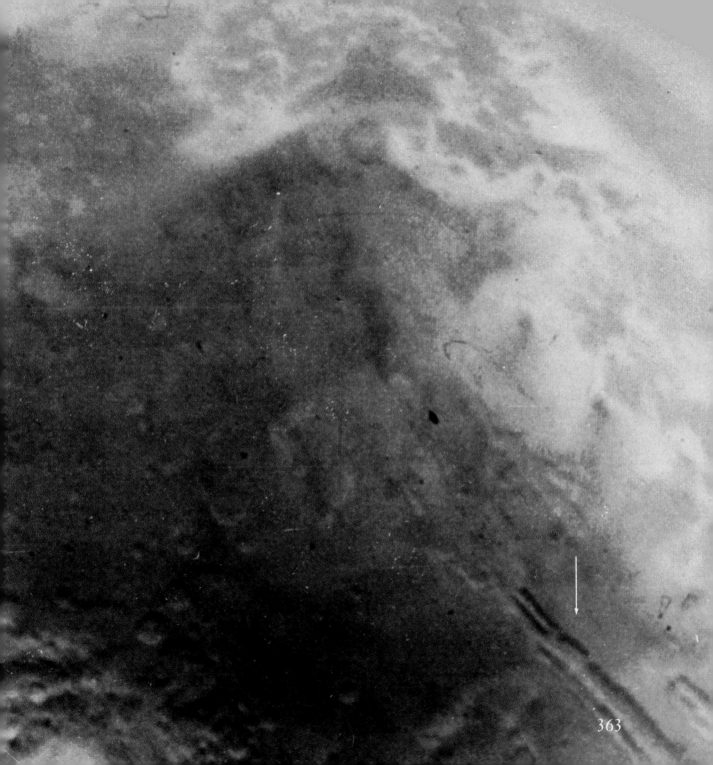

364

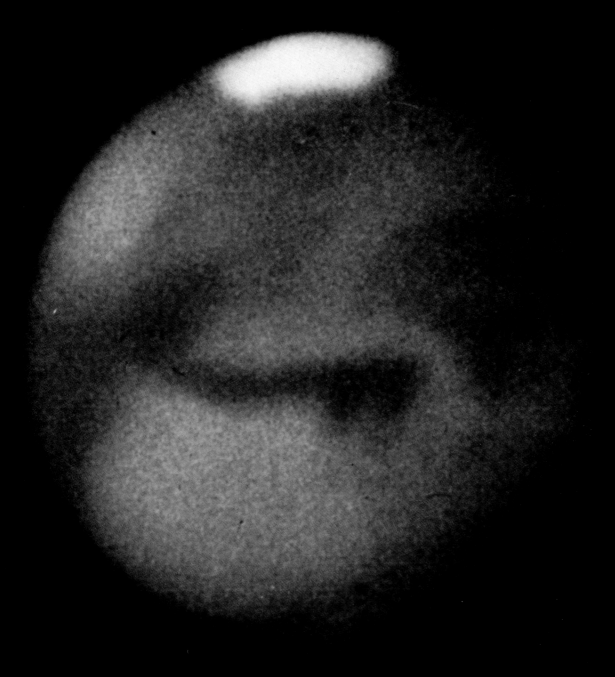

This photograph of Mars shows a polar ice cap and several large dark areas that appear greenish against the paler red surface. These dark areas grow in size during the Martian summer. Once it was thought that the green areas were covered by some kinds of plants that grew in the warmer weather. But the *Viking* space probes have shown that this is not so. There do not seem to be plants of any kind on Mars. The changes in color are the result of dust storms that hide or reveal darker materials on the surface.

Mars is a dusty planet. Its surface is covered by orange-red, dusty soil that is often moved from one spot to another by the wind. When *Mariner 9* first arrived and went into orbit around Mars, a heavy dust storm hid most of the planet. The storm raged for more than thirty days. Gradually, the dust settled down and the highest peaks poked through the haze. The black-and-white photograph shows some of the dust dunes that cover large parts of Mars.

The color photograph shows places where light-colored dust conceals the darker underlying rock.

Mars may look dry as dust, but water once flowed over the surface. Millions of years ago when Mars was a young planet, it may even have had oceans. The oceans are gone, but some of the water remains hidden in large underground reservoirs. Some scientists believe that if this water came to the surface it could flood the entire planet to a depth of one thousand feet.

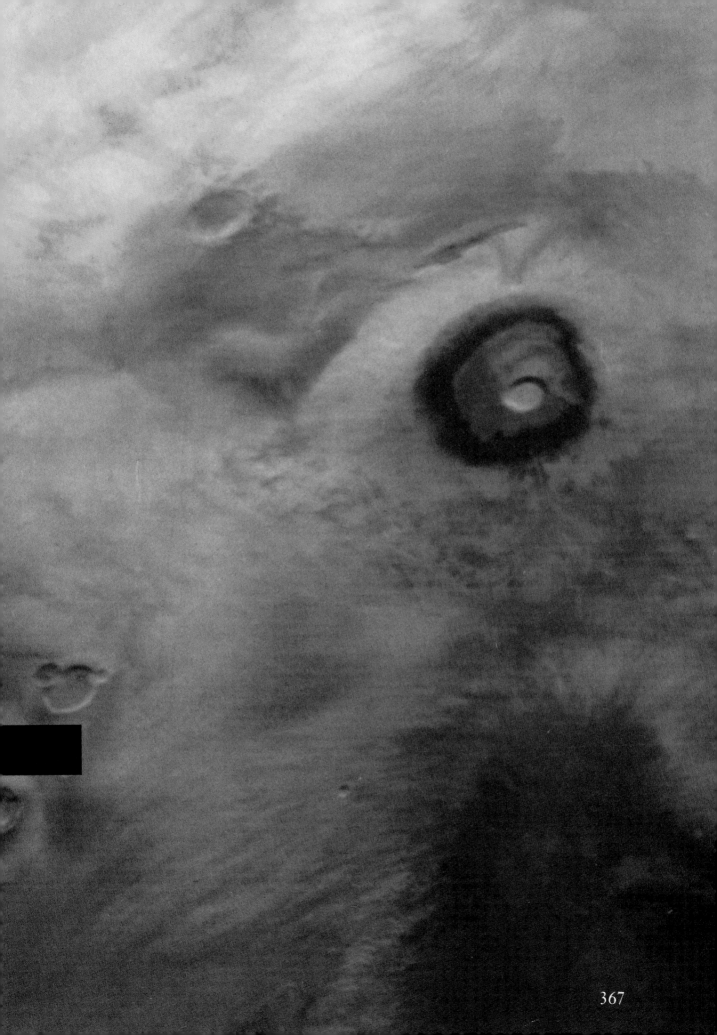

Many of the channels on Mars look like dry riverbeds. Some of the channels cut right through meteorite craters, showing that the craters formed first. Other channels are broken by craters, showing that the craters formed later.

Even though there is no liquid water on its surface, there is lots of ice on Mars. The polar ice caps are covered by a thin layer of ice and dust. The north pole is mostly frozen water, while the south pole is ice mixed with frozen carbon dioxide, sometimes called dry ice.

This frosty scene is near Mars's north pole. Where the white ice ends and the red land begins (top part of photo) are steep cliffs about fifteen hundred feet high. The black-and-white photograph shows a close-up of some of these great ice-covered cliffs.

For many years, astronomers wondered why the Martian polar caps grew larger during part of the year. Now they know that the ice caps on Mars change with the seasons, like Earth's. The southern half of Mars has short, hot summers and long, cold winters. Seasons in the north are less extreme.

Mars spins on an angle as it journeys around the sun. The part that is tilted toward the sun has summer while the other part has winter. As the seasons change, the advances and retreats of the ice caps tell us about the changing climate of Mars.

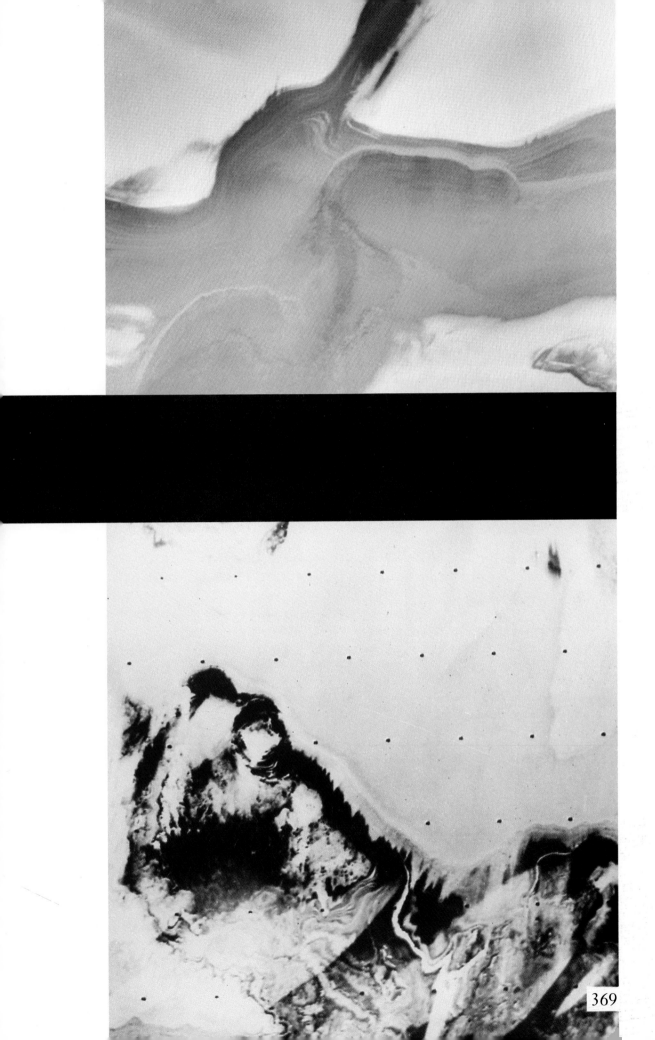

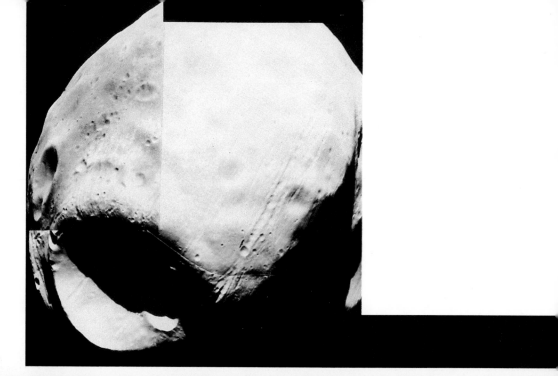

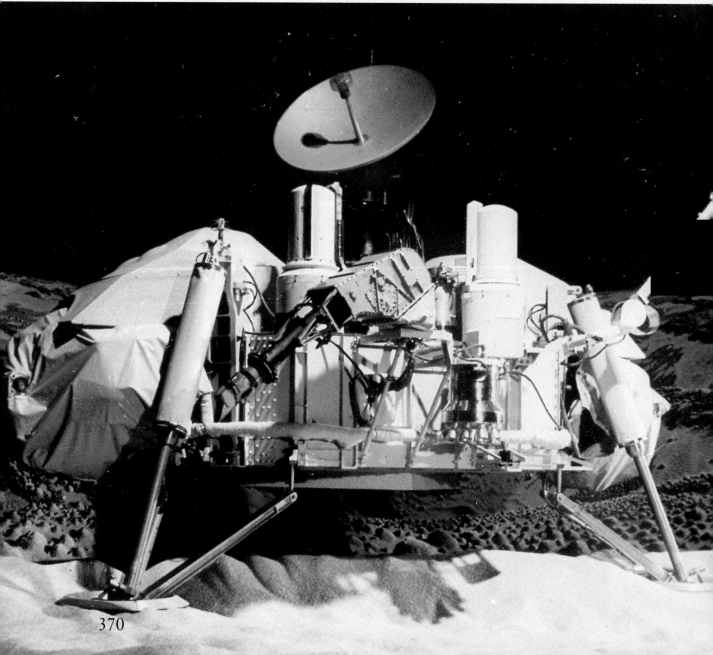

Mars has two small moons, Phobos and Deimos. They are named after the two sons of Ares, the Greek god of war. Phobos (FO-bos) is the larger of the two moons and nearer to Mars. Phobos is about seventeen miles long and twelve miles wide. It races around Mars in only seven and one-half hours, at a distance of about 3,000 miles from the planet. If you were an observer on Mars, Phobos would look several times brighter than a very bright star does from Earth.

The close-up photo of Phobos shows large meteorite craters and deep scratches across the surface.

Deimos (DIE-mos) is slightly smaller than Phobos, about nine miles long by seven miles wide. Deimos takes a bit longer than thirty hours to orbit Mars and is about 12,500 miles away from the planet. From the surface of Mars, Deimos would look as bright as the planet Venus does from Earth.

Viking 1 and *Viking 2* were launched two weeks apart in August and September of 1975. Each *Viking* carried an orbiting craft and a lander.

This was the United States's first attempt to land a spacecraft on another planet. The photograph shows a lander in a test site designed to look like Mars.

Traveling at tens of thousands of miles an hour, the *Viking* spacecraft took about ten months to reach Mars. The orbiters circled Mars
for another month before the decision to land was made.

The *Viking 1* lander weighed 2,633 pounds. Yet it had to come
down as lightly as a feather to avoid damaging delicate instruments.
The *Viking 1* landing was a lucky one. Scientists had thought that the
landing area was smooth and safe. But the field had many boulders

nearly as large as the lander itself. If *Viking 1* had set down on a boulder, it would have overturned and been damaged.

The day after it landed, *Viking 1* took this color photograph of the field on which it rested. The orange-red color is due to the chemical iron oxide, also called rust, in the dusty soil and rocks. Over the years, the *Viking* orbiters and landers sent back more than fifty thousand photos of Mars.

Mars is a harsh planet for human life. The pressure of the atmosphere is so low that your blood would boil if you stepped out on the surface unprotected. You'd also have to dress very warmly. The distant sun doesn't send very much heat. The temperatures around the landers ranged from 190 degrees (F) below zero at night to 45 degrees (F) below zero in midafternoon, much colder than a deep freeze.

On the other hand, the low gravitational pull on the surface of Mars would make it easy for you to walk around in a heavy space suit. If you weigh 100 pounds on Earth, you would weigh only 38 pounds on Mars.

Is there life on Mars? The *Viking* landers were supposed to find out. Each lander had a small biology laboratory on board. Soil was scooped up by mechanical arms and brought into the lab. Three different experiments were designed to look for any traces of life in the soil. The experiments were performed several times by both landers.

Scientists are still arguing about the results of the experiments. Many scientists think the experiments show that there is no life on Mars. But other scientists believe the results are not clear. They say that while we have not discovered life on Mars, life may still exist on the planet. Perhaps Martian life is very different from life on Earth, and the landers performed the wrong kind of experiments. Or perhaps we were looking in the wrong places. Much of Mars is unexplored, and it may be quite different from the two *Viking* landing sites. Some kind of life may exist in one of these unexplored places. Just now, no one knows for sure.

Mars Made Easy:
A Guide for First-Time Visitors

Work with a partner to put together a guidebook for visitors to Mars. What kinds of adventures can visitors expect to have there? What kinds of sights and activities are waiting for them? Be sure that your guidebook will make visitors feel welcome to Mars. Include illustrations if you wish.

INVASION FROM MARS

On October 30, 1938, the night before Halloween, people across the United States were in a panic. Thousands called the police. Others phoned their local newspapers. Families in New Jersey tied wet cloths over their faces, jumped into their cars, and jammed traffic for miles. Why was all this happening?

A 23-year-old producer named Orson Welles broadcast a radio play based on H. G. Wells's novel *War of the Worlds*. The story was presented as a series of special news bulletins that described an invasion by Martians. It was so believable people thought an invasion was actually taking place.

THIRD STOP: Beyond
MISSION: Consider the Next Frontier

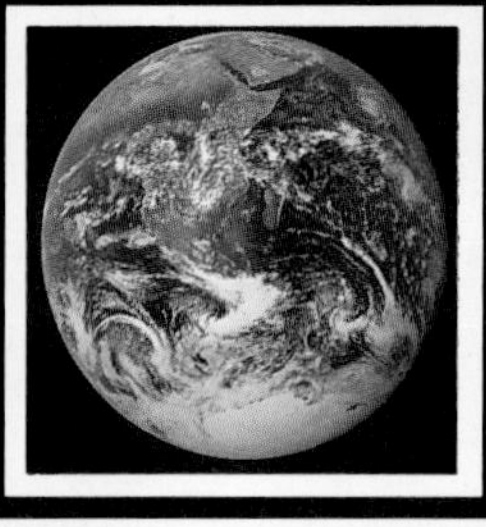

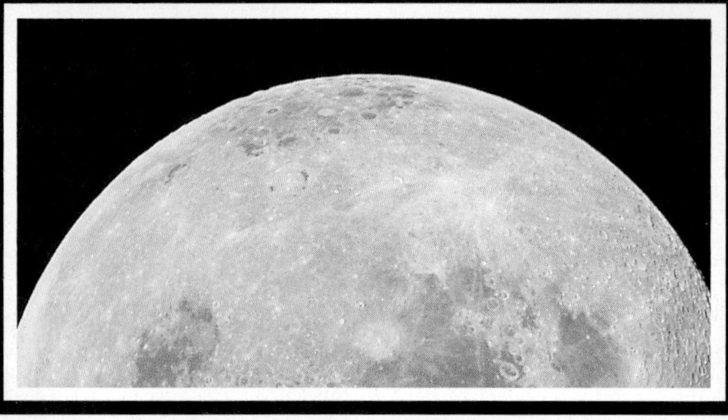

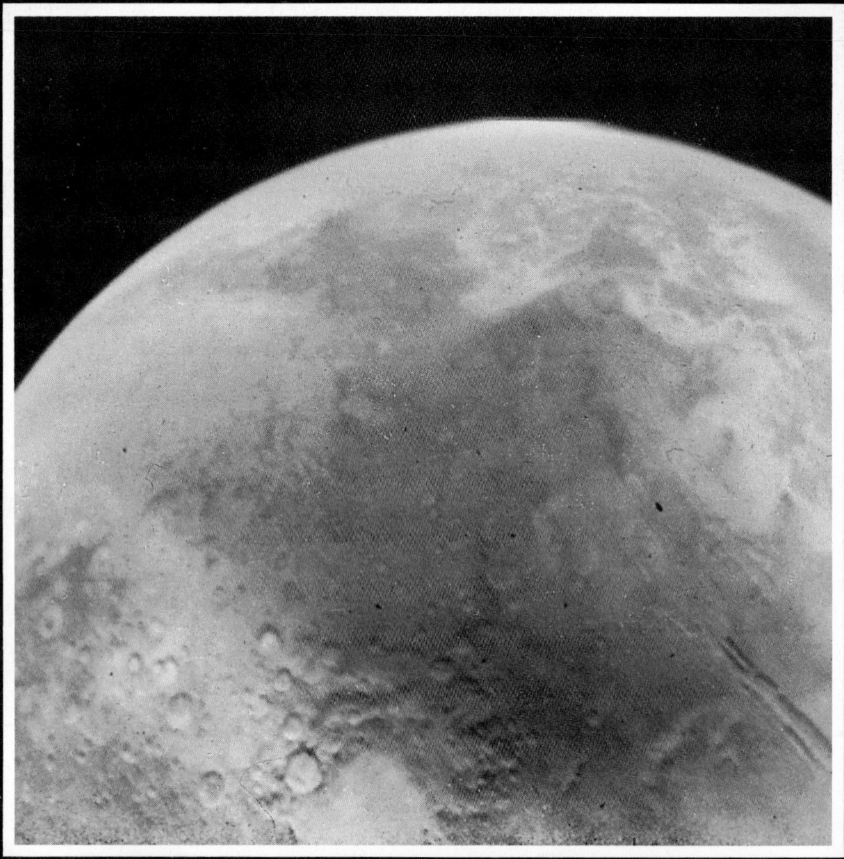

Humans on Mars? Where Will the U.S. Space Program Go Next?

by Renée Skelton

People first walked on the moon in 1969. Since then, the United States has tried other kinds of space exploration. NASA, the U.S. space agency, has launched mechanical space explorers to take photos of Jupiter, Saturn, and Uranus. And NASA has tested the space shuttle — a spacecraft that will one day be used for trips between Earth and nearby space stations.

Now scientists at NASA are making plans for future space exploration. But what to explore? Where to go? The moon? Mars? Even a mission to study Earth from space is a possibility. It's not an easy choice. Here's a look at what NASA is up to.

Moon Base

Even though humans have been to the moon, there are plenty of reasons to go back. For one thing, the moon is nearby. U.S. astronauts could be moonwalking by the year 2000 if NASA decides to try for a return trip.

"The moon gives astronauts experience living and working in space," says NASA's Alan Ladwig. "We can use the moon as a launching point to Mars. And there are resources on the moon that future space explorers can use."

What kind of resources? Astrofuel, for one. Astrofuel is a substance that's also called helium-3. It's rare on Earth, but there's plenty of it in moon soil. Some scientists believe it could become a major source of energy. It could power a lunar base. It might power rockets to other parts of the solar system. It might even provide energy here on Earth.

Other materials in moon soil could be used by astronauts to build the moon base itself. That means building materials wouldn't have to be shipped from Earth. Mines on the moon might provide materials to build an orbiting space station.

In past moon missions, astronauts stayed only a few days, then returned to Earth. If the new plans go into action, people will spend more time on the moon — but not right away.

First of all, sometime in the 1990's, robot probes will scan the moon's surface, looking for the best landing site. Then people will follow. They'll bring supplies and machines.

These astronaut-explorers will prepare the area for a full-scale moon base. They'll build apartments and laboratories. They might even set up a machine that can collect oxygen from lunar soil. By the year 2010, there could be as many as 30 people on the moon, each staying for months.

The moon is the nearest source of resources other than Earth itself. This drawing shows a lunar mining operation.

The moon would be mined for oxygen, iron, and aluminum. Here a robot vehicle scoops up moon dirt rich in minerals.

On to Mars

Earth scientists are no strangers to Mars. Back in the 1970's, robot probes landed on the "Red Planet." They sent back TV pictures and weather reports. They studied soil samples, looking for signs of life — but they found none. NASA plans to continue exploring Mars with a robot probe called *Mars Observer*. It will make detailed maps of the Martian surface.

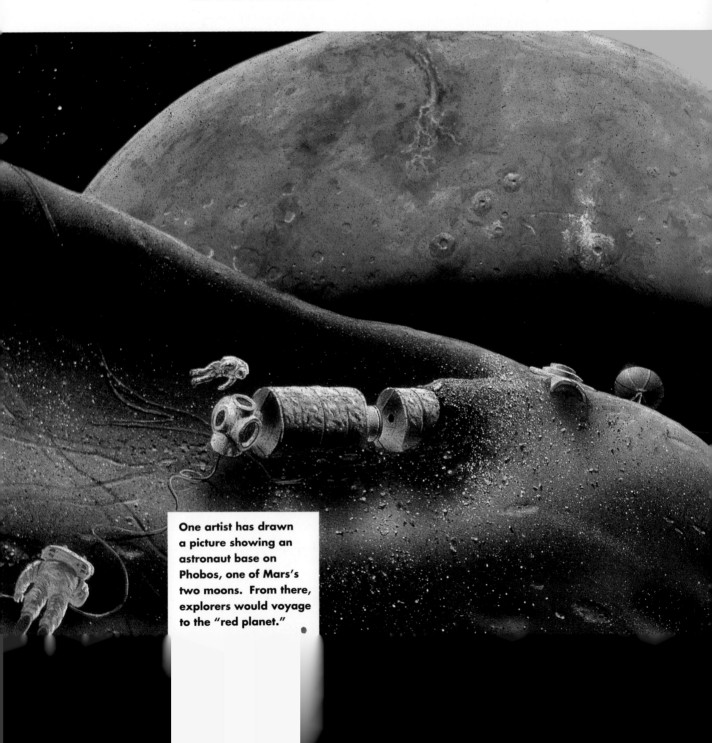

One artist has drawn a picture showing an astronaut base on Phobos, one of Mars's two moons. From there, explorers would voyage to the "red planet."

But when will people reach Mars? Some scientists say that a moon base has to come first. Others say the moon step isn't important. They say NASA should start now on a plan to send human explorers to Mars.

The moon is a three-day trip from Earth. A Mars trip would take seven months — a 49-million-mile voyage. That's quite a journey to plan. How would it happen?

The trip to Mars would start with robots. One robot ship would reach Mars in the late 1990's and start exploring. NASA scientists are already working on a robot vehicle, called a "rover," that could do the job.

The rover would collect information about the surface of Mars. It would study the Martian environment. It would also give clues to the most likely locations of underground water. All that data would help scientists on Earth choose a landing site for human visitors.

Meanwhile . . . Closer to Earth

While robots explored Mars itself, Mars travelers would prepare by spending months in a space station close to Earth. They would learn how to stay healthy and safe during the long journey to Mars. Astronauts from the U.S. and the Soviet Union might even work together to take one international trip to Mars.

More than a year before the humans start their voyage, NASA would launch a second robot ship. It would carry fuel and supplies for the astronauts. Its trip would last two years.

Once the robot ship was in Mars's orbit, six astronauts would set off from the space station. Three would land on Mars, while three stayed in their ship, orbiting the planet. The landing party would stay about a month. Then they'd return to the orbiting ship, fuel up with supplies from the robot ship, and head back to the space station.

After several Mars missions, humans might even set up a full-scale base on Mars. People would spend months at a time, living under a sort of dome. They would grow food in greenhouses. They would drill wells for water. They would set up a small power plant for electricity. All the while, they'd be working on experiments.

A Mars base would include green-houses for growing food and for storage.

Danger in Space

If all goes well, NASA could have a space station orbiting the Earth by the mid-1990's. That's the first step in the Mars plan. But why would astronauts headed for Mars need to spend months on a space station, getting ready for the trip? Why not leave straight from Earth?

Dr. Bevan French, a NASA scientist, explained: "The trouble with Mars is that it's such a long way away. We don't know what weightlessness might do to human beings over a long period of time. We don't know how humans would recover once they landed on Mars, which has lower gravity than the Earth does."

During months cooped up in a spacecraft, astronauts might lose control of certain muscles. Their bones might get weaker. They might be harmed by natural radiation in outer space. Scientists need to think about these possibilities. Maybe they're only imaginary problems. But if they're real, scientists need to find solutions.

This photo of Earth was taken from space. Our planet may be the next one to be explored from a unique place: space!

Mission to Planet Earth

A trip to Mars sounds thrilling. But some people at NASA think the next planet to explore from space should be — Earth!

As NASA's Alan Ladwig stated, "If we can use all these spacecraft to visit other planets, why not turn them toward cleaning up Earth and understanding what we are doing to *this* planet?"

This unusual plan is called "Mission to Planet Earth." The United States and several other nations would work together, launching satellites to study the Earth like never before. They would measure different chemicals in the air around Earth. They would study clouds and weather systems. They would examine vegetation growing on Earth. They would even look at the motion of the gigantic plates of rock beneath Earth.

Mission to Planet Earth would help scientists understand the way this planet works. It would teach about the Earth's environment and about the way people change the environment.

Whether the next step is a Mission to Planet Earth, to Mars or to the moon, space scientists have a lot of work ahead. For any of the plans, new spacecraft will need to be invented and built. And new robots will have to be designed. No matter what happens, though, it's going to be quite some time before ordinary people take a walk on Mars or the moon.

That doesn't mean it's a dream. Back in 1960, when a mission to the moon was first suggested, no human had ever been in space. Nine years later, an astronaut stepped onto the moon. Moonwalking — and Mars-walking — may not be for everybody very soon — but they may be for someone. They may even be for you!

Neighbors — Can We Pay a Visit?

Earth's Moon — We've been there already. It could be a base for trips deep into space.

Mercury — Probes have orbited Mercury and sent back photos, but don't look for a human landing. Mercury is too hot. And solar radiation would be dangerous.

Venus — Under Venus's thick blanket of clouds, temperatures reach 900 degrees F. Air pressure is 100 times that on Earth.

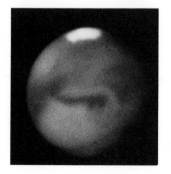

Mars — Mars is cold and frosty. Its air is mostly unbreathable carbon dioxide. Dust storms are frequent. But it's fairly close, and may have water underground. That's why it's worth a try.

Jupiter — Jupiter doesn't have a surface to land on! It's a huge ball of swirling gas above a deep, liquid ocean.

Saturn — Another ball of gas and liquid, like Jupiter. And it's farther away.

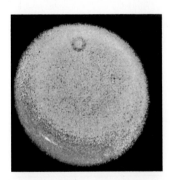

Uranus, Neptune, and Pluto — Too far. Too cold. Too dark. For the time being, it's impossible to think of visiting these "outer" planets.

As of yet, no photos of Pluto have been taken. This is an artist's view of how we think Pluto looks. The large planet in the upper left is Pluto. Pictured below Pluto is Charon, Pluto's moon. The star on the right is the Sun.

It's Up to You Now

What do *you* think? You have just read about possible future projects for the U.S. Space Program. What is your opinion? In a small group, discuss possible future projects for NASA.

MOON

by Myra Cohn Livingston

Moon remembers.

Marooned in shadowed night,

white powder plastered

on her pockmarked face,

scarred with craters,

filled with waterless seas

she thinks back

to the Eagle,

to the flight

of men from Earth,

of rocks sent back in space,

and one

faint

footprint

in the Sea of Tranquility.

AUTHORS

Sally Ride

Sally Ride hasn't always been an astronaut. In fact, she once played tennis so well that she ranked number eighteen among the nation's younger tennis players. Ride eventually gave up tennis to study physics and went on to earn her doctorate in physics from Stanford University. In all this time, however, she never dreamed of going into space. But when NASA put an advertisement in a Stanford newspaper, she applied for a job in the space program and wound up as the first American woman to go into orbit.

Susan Okie

Sally Ride and Susan Okie went to the same high school and have stayed close friends ever since, even though they have led very different lives. Okie studied biology at Radcliffe College and went on to earn a medical degree from Harvard University. She now works as a medical journalist for the *Washington Post*.

Seymour Simon

Seymour Simon likes to learn about science firsthand. He has written over sixty books on different subjects and says, "I like to try out the investigations and projects I write about. I've kept fishes, earthworms, gerbils, ants, crickets, and a host of other animals in my home." He taught science for over twenty years in New York City, and many of the ideas for his books came from questions that his students asked in class. Two of his many informative and enjoyable books are *Volcanoes* and *Icebergs and Glaciers*.

Renée Skelton

Renée Skelton has gone from making maps and doing geographical research to working for Children's Television Workshop (CTW) to writing. She continues to write for CTW's science magazine, *3–2–1 Contact*, from which the article in this book was taken. Skelton especially loves writing about the bits of science in everyday things, like "what makes a cake rise or why does it get windy before a thunderstorm?" Look for her articles in children's science magazines.

Go Into Orbit With These Books

Space Challenger:
The Story of Guion Bluford
by Jim Haskins and
Kathleen Benson

Guion Bluford's
experiences at NASA as
he trained for flight in the space
shuttle make this biography
exciting to read.

Journey to the Planets
by Patricia Lauber

Travel to the far corners
of space in this spectacular
book about the planets in
our solar system.

Galaxies
by Seymour Simon

Find out about the enor-
mous clusters of stars
known as galaxies, one
of the greatest wonders
in the universe.

Women in Space:
Reaching the Last Frontier
by Carole S. Briggs

Women from the United States,
the Soviet Union, Canada, and Japan
have gone to space. How were they
chosen and trained for
their missions?

Space Station:
Bold New Step Beyond Earth
by Charlene W. Billings

NASA has proposed build-
ing a permanent research
center in space. Learn
about the designs and what
everyday life may be like
there.

Danger on Apollo 13
by David Baker

The true story of the failed
mission of Apollo 13 makes
this book a gripping adventure of courage and survival
in space.

395

FICTION

BOOK 7

To Be Continued...

You pick up a book,
scan the cover,
and then turn to page one.
Before long, your eyes are locked
to a narrow track of words
that repeat a pattern of left to right
and then down. All of a sudden,
you're off in another world.

Has this ever happened to you?
Well, it's about to happen again,
because the stories you'll read next
are real page-turners —
full of action, adventure,
and mystery.
But a word to the wise:
just when you least expect it,
you'll come to the words

To Be Continued. . .

When this happens,
there's only one way to find out
what happens next —
read the books from which
these stories were taken.

Contents

The Voyage of the *Dawn Treader*   401
from the book by C. S. Lewis
with illustrations by David Small

The Blossoms Meet the Vulture Lady   419
from the book by Betsy Byars
with illustrations by Jacqueline Rogers

The Mouse and the Motorcycle   445
from the book by Beverly Cleary
with illustrations by Louis Darling

C. S. Lewis

The Voyage of the Dawn Treader, the story you are about to read, was almost never written.

Clive Staples Lewis never planned to write a whole series of books about a land called Narnia. However, his first book, *The Lion, the Witch and the Wardrobe*, became so popular that he decided to write six more books about Narnia.

Lewis wrote *The Lion, the Witch and the Wardrobe* for his goddaughter, Lucy Barfield. This letter from Lewis to Lucy appears on the dedication page of that book.

My dear Lucy,

I wrote this story for you, but when I began it I had not realized that girls grow quicker than books. As a result you are already too old for fairy tales, and by the time it is printed and bound you will be older still. But some day you will be old enough to start reading fairy tales again. You can then take it down from some upper shelf, dust it, and tell me what you think of it. I shall probably be too deaf to hear, and too old to understand a word you say, but I shall still be

your affectionate Godfather,
C. S. Lewis

From the book by C. S. Lewis

The Voyage of the *Dawn Treader*

Illustrated by David Small

Chapter 1: **The Picture in the Bedroom**

There was a boy called Eustace Clarence Scrubb, and he almost deserved it. His parents called him Eustace Clarence and his schoolmasters called him Scrubb. I can't tell you how his friends spoke to him, for he had none. He didn't call his father and mother "Father" and "Mother," but Harold and Alberta. They were very up-to-date and advanced people. They were vegetarians, non-smokers and teetotallers and wore a special kind of underclothes. In their house there was very little furniture and very few clothes on the beds and the windows were always open.

Eustace Clarence liked animals, especially beetles, if they were dead and pinned on a card. He liked books if they were books of information and had pictures of grain elevators or of fat foreign children doing exercises in model schools.

Eustace Clarence disliked his cousins, the four Pevensies — Peter, Susan, Edmund and Lucy. But he was quite glad when he heard that Edmund and Lucy were coming to stay. For deep down inside he liked bossing and bullying; and, though he was a puny little person who couldn't have stood up even to Lucy, let alone Edmund, in a fight, he knew that there are dozens of ways to give people a bad time if you are in your own home and they are only visitors.

Edmund and Lucy did not at all want to come and stay with Uncle Harold and Aunt Alberta. But it really couldn't be helped. Father had got a job lecturing in America for sixteen weeks that summer, and Mother was to go with him because she hadn't had a real holiday for ten years. Peter was working very hard for an exam and he was to spend the holidays being coached by old Professor Kirke in whose house these four children had had wonderful adventures long ago in the war years. If he had still been in that house he would have had them all to stay. But he had somehow become poor since the old days and was living in a small cottage with only one bedroom to spare. It would have cost too much money to take the other three all to America, and Susan had gone. Grown-ups thought her the pretty one of the family and she was no good at school work (though otherwise very old for her age) and Mother said she "would get far more out of the trip to America than the youngsters." Edmund and Lucy tried not to grudge Susan her luck, but it was dreadful having to spend the summer holidays at their aunt's. "But it's far worse for me," said Edmund, "because you'll at least have a room of your own and I shall have to share a bedroom with that record stinker, Eustace."

The story begins on an afternoon when Edmund and Lucy were stealing a few precious minutes alone together. And of course they were talking about Narnia, which was the name of their own private and secret country. Most of us, I suppose, have a secret country but for us it is only an imaginary country. Edmund and Lucy were luckier than other people in that respect. Their secret country was real. They had already visited it twice; not in a game or a dream, but in reality. They had got there of course by magic, which is the only way of getting to Narnia. And a promise, or very nearly a promise, had been made them in Narnia itself that they would some day get back. You may imagine that they talked about it a good deal, when they got the chance.

They were in Lucy's room, sitting on the edge of her bed and looking at a picture on the opposite wall. It was the only picture in the house that they liked. Aunt Alberta didn't like it at all (that was why it was put away in a little back room upstairs), but she couldn't get rid of it because it had been a wedding present from someone she did not want to offend.

It was a picture of a ship — a ship sailing nearly straight towards you. Her prow was gilded and shaped like the head of a dragon with wide open mouth. She had only one mast and one large, square sail which was a rich purple. The sides of the ship — what you could see of them where the gilded wings of the dragon ended — were green. She had just run up to the top of one glorious blue wave, and the nearer slope of that wave came down towards you, with streaks and bubbles on it. She was obviously running fast before a gay wind, listing over a little on her port side. (By the way, if you are going to read this story at all, and if you don't know already, you had better get it into your head that the left of a ship when you are looking ahead, is *port*, and the right is *starboard*.) All the sunlight fell on her from that side, and the water on that side was full of greens and purples. On the other, it was darker blue from the shadow of the ship.

"The question is," said Edmund, "whether it doesn't make things worse, *looking* at a Narnian ship when you can't get there."

"Even looking is better than nothing," said Lucy. "And she is such a very Narnian ship."

"Still playing your old game?" said Eustace Clarence, who had been listening outside the door and now came grinning into the room. Last year, when he had been staying with the Pevensies, he had managed to hear them all talking of Narnia and he loved teasing them about it. He thought of course that they were making it all up; and as

he was quite incapable of making anything up himself, he did not approve of that.

"You're not wanted here," said Edmund curtly.

"I'm trying to think of a limerick," said Eustace. "Something like this:

"Some kids who played games about Narnia
  Got gradually balmier and balmier — "

"Well, *Narnia* and *balmier* don't rhyme, to begin with," said Lucy.

"It's an assonance," said Eustace.

"Don't ask him what an assy-thingummy is," said Edmund. "He's only longing to be asked. Say nothing and perhaps he'll go away."

Most boys, on meeting a reception like this, would either have cleared out or flared up. Eustace did neither. He just hung about grinning, and presently began talking again.

"Do you like that picture?" he asked.

"For Heaven's sake don't let him get started about Art and all that," said Edmund hurriedly, but Lucy, who was very truthful, had already said, "Yes, I do. I like it very much."

"It's a rotten picture," said Eustace.

"You won't see it if you step outside," said Edmund.

"Why do you like it?" said Eustace to Lucy.

"Well, for one thing," said Lucy, "I like it because the ship looks as if it was really moving. And the water looks as if it was really wet. And the waves look as if they were really going up and down."

Of course Eustace knew lots of answers to this, but he didn't say anything. The reason was that at that very moment he looked at the waves and saw that they did look very much indeed as if they were going up and down. He had only once been in a ship (and then only as far as the Isle of Wight) and had been horribly seasick. The look of the waves in the picture made him feel sick again. He turned rather green and tried another look. And then all three children were staring with open mouths.

What they were seeing may be hard to believe when you read it in print, but it was almost as hard to believe when you saw it happening. The things in the picture were moving. It didn't look at all like a cinema either; the colours were too real and clean and out-of-door for that. Down went the prow of the ship into the wave and up went a great shock of spray. And then up went the wave behind her, and her stern and her deck became visible for the first time, and then disappeared as the next wave came to meet her and her bows went up again. At the same moment an exercise book which had been lying beside Edmund on the bed flapped, rose and sailed through the air to the wall behind him, and Lucy felt all her hair whipping round her face as it does on a windy day. And this was a windy day; but the wind was blowing out of the picture towards them. And suddenly with the wind came the noises — the swishing of waves and the slap of water against the ship's sides and the creaking and the over-all high, steady roar of air and water. But it was the smell, the wild, briny smell, which really convinced Lucy that she was not dreaming.

"Stop it," came Eustace's voice, squeaky with fright and bad temper. "It's some silly trick you two are playing. Stop it. I'll tell Alberta — ow!"

The other two were much more accustomed to adventures, but, just exactly as Eustace Clarence said "Ow," they both said "Ow" too. The reason was that a great cold, salt splash had broken right out of the frame and they were breathless from the smack of it, besides being wet through.

"I'll smash the rotten thing," cried Eustace; and then several things happened at the same time. Eustace rushed towards the picture. Edmund, who knew something about magic, sprang after him, warning him to look out and not to be a fool. Lucy grabbed at him from the other side and was dragged forward. And by this time either they had grown much smaller or the picture had grown bigger. Eustace jumped to try to pull it off the wall and found himself standing on the frame; in front of him was not glass but real sea, and wind and waves rushing up to the frame as they might to a rock. He lost his head and clutched at the other two who had jumped up beside him. There was a second of struggling and shouting, and just as they thought they had got their balance a great blue roller surged up round them, swept them off their feet, and drew them down into the sea. Eustace's despairing cry suddenly ended as the water got into his mouth.

Lucy thanked her stars that she had worked hard at her swimming last summer term. It is true that she would have got on much better if she had used a slower stroke, and also that the water felt a great deal colder than it had looked while it was only a picture. Still, she kept her head and kicked her shoes off, as everyone ought to do who falls into deep water in their clothes. She even kept her mouth shut and her eyes open. They were still quite near the ship; she saw its green side towering high above them, and people looking at her from the deck. Then, as one might have expected, Eustace clutched at her in a panic and down they both went.

When they came up again she saw a white figure diving off the ship's side. Edmund was close beside her now, treading water, and had caught the arms of the howling Eustace. Then someone else, whose face was vaguely familiar, slipped an arm under her from the other side. There was a lot of shouting going on from the ship, heads crowding together above the bulwarks, ropes being thrown. Edmund and the stranger were fastening ropes round her. After that followed what seemed a very long delay during which her face got blue and her teeth began chattering. In reality the delay was not very long; they were waiting till the moment when she could be got on board the ship without being dashed against its side. Even with all their best endeavours she had a bruised knee when she finally stood, dripping and shivering, on the deck. After her Edmund was heaved up, and then the miserable Eustace. Last of all came the stranger — a golden-headed boy some years older than herself.

"Ca — Ca — Caspian!" gasped Lucy as soon as she had breath enough. For Caspian it was; Caspian, the boy king of Narnia whom they had helped to set on the throne during their last visit. Immediately Edmund recognized him too. All three shook hands and clapped one another on the back with great delight.

"But who is your friend?" said Caspian almost at once, turning to Eustace with his cheerful smile. But Eustace was crying much harder than any boy of his age has a right to cry when nothing worse than a wetting has happened to him, and would only yell out, "Let me go. Let me go back. I don't *like* it."

"Let you go?" said Caspian. "But where?"

Eustace rushed to the ship's side, as if he expected to see the picture frame hanging above the sea, and

perhaps a glimpse of Lucy's bedroom. What he saw was blue waves flecked with foam, and paler blue sky, both spreading without a break to the horizon. Perhaps we can hardly blame him if his heart sank. He was promptly sick.

"Hey! Rynelf," said Caspian to one of the sailors. "Bring hot drinks for their Majesties. You'll need something to warm you after that dip." He called Edmund and Lucy their Majesties because they and Peter and Susan had all been kings and queens of Narnia long before his time. Narnian time flows differently from ours. If you spent a hundred years in Narnia, you would still come back to our world at the very same hour of the very same day on which you left. And then, if you went back to Narnia after spending a week here, you might find that a thousand Narnian years had passed, or only a day, or no time at all. You never know till you get there. Consequently, when the Pevensie children had returned to Narnia last time for their second visit, it was (for the Narnians) as if King Arthur came back to Britain as some people say he will. And I say the sooner the better.

Rynelf returned with the hot drink steaming in a flagon and four silver cups. It was just what one wanted, and as Lucy and Edmund sipped it they could feel the warmth going right down to their toes. But Eustace made faces and spluttered and spat it out and was sick again and began to cry again and asked if they hadn't any Plumptree's Vitaminised Nerve Food and could it be made with distilled water and anyway he insisted on being put ashore at the next station.

"This is a merry shipmate you've brought us, Brother," whispered Caspian to Edmund with a chuckle; but before he could say anything more Eustace burst out again.

"Oh! Ugh! What on earth's *that*! Take it away, the horrid thing."

He really had some excuse this time for feeling a little surprised. Something very curious indeed had come out of the cabin in the poop and was slowly approaching them. You might call it — and indeed it was — a Mouse. But then it was a Mouse on its hind legs and stood about two feet high. A thin band of gold passed round its head under one ear and over the other and in this was stuck a long crimson feather. (As the Mouse's fur was very dark, almost black, the effect was bold and striking.) Its left paw rested on the hilt of a sword very nearly as long as its tail. Its balance, as it paced gravely along the swaying deck, was perfect, and its manners courtly. Lucy and Edmund recognized it at once — Reepicheep, the most valiant of all the Talking Beasts of Narnia and the Chief Mouse. It had won undying glory in the second Battle of Beruna. Lucy longed, as she had always done, to take Reepicheep up in her arms and cuddle him. But this, as she well knew, was a pleasure she could never have: it would have offended him deeply. Instead, she went down on one knee to talk to him.

Reepicheep put forward his left leg, drew back his right, bowed, kissed her hand, straightened himself, twirled his whiskers, and said in his shrill, piping voice:

"My humble duty to your Majesty. And to King Edmund, too." (Here he bowed again.) "Nothing except your Majesties' presence was lacking to this glorious venture."

"Ugh, take it away," wailed Eustace. "I hate mice. And I never could bear performing animals. They're silly and vulgar and — and sentimental."

"Am I to understand," said Reepicheep to Lucy after a long stare at Eustace, "that this singularly discourteous person is under your Majesty's protection? Because, if not — "

At this moment Lucy and Edmund both sneezed.

"What a fool I am to keep you all standing here in your wet things," said Caspian. "Come on below and get changed. I'll give you my cabin of course, Lucy, but I'm afraid we have no women's clothes on board. You'll have to make do with some of mine. Lead the way, Reepicheep, like a good fellow."

"To the convenience of a lady," said Reepicheep, "even a question of honour must give way — at least for the moment — " and here he looked very hard at Eustace. But Caspian hustled them on and in a few minutes Lucy found herself passing through the door into the stern cabin. She fell in love with it at once — the three square windows that looked out on the blue, swirling water astern, the low cushioned benches round three sides of the table, the swinging silver lamp overhead (Dwarfs' work, she knew at once by its exquisite delicacy) and the flat gold image of Aslan the Lion on the forward wall above the door. All this she took in in a flash, for Caspian immediately opened a door on the starboard side, and said, "This'll be your room, Lucy. I'll just get some dry things for myself" — he was rummaging in one of the lockers while he spoke — "and then leave you to change. If you'll fling your wet things outside the door I'll get them taken to the galley to be dried."

Lucy found herself as much at home as if she had been in Caspian's cabin for weeks, and the motion of the ship did not worry her, for in the old days when she had been a queen in Narnia she had done a good deal of voyaging. The cabin was very tiny but bright with painted panels (all birds and beasts and crimson dragons and vines) and spotlessly clean. Caspian's clothes were too big for her, but she could manage. His shoes, sandals and sea-boots were hopelessly large but she did not mind going barefoot on board ship. When she had finished dressing she looked out of her window at the water rushing past and took a long deep breath.

She felt quite sure

they were in

for a lovely time.

To Be Continued...

The adventures of Lucy, Edmund, Eustace, and Caspian have only begun. You will follow them on their travels when you read the rest of **The Voyage of the *Dawn Treader.***

Captain's Log

King Caspian is standing on the deck of the great ship *Dawn Treader*. Suddenly, he sees three children in the water and jumps in to save them. What an amazing day it has been! Write an entry in the *Dawn Treader*'s log book describing the strange day as Caspian would. Tell how he might feel about seeing his old friends Edmund and Lucy as well as the new passenger, Eustace.

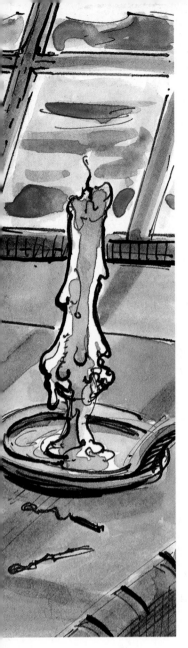

Explore the Land of Narnia

The Voyage of the Dawn Treader is the third of seven books that make up the Chronicles of Narnia. Here are the other books in the series:

Lucy leads her brothers and sister through the magical wardrobe in *The Lion, the Witch and the Wardrobe*.

Caspian battles his evil uncle in *Prince Caspian*.

Caspian launches a search for his missing son in *The Silver Chair*.

Shasta warns Narnia of impending doom in *The Horse and His Boy*.

The secret of the wardrobe is revealed in *The Magician's Nephew*.

The final confrontation of good and evil explodes in *The Last Battle*.

Betsy Byars

With more than twenty books to her credit, Betsy Byars is one of the most popular authors for young people today.

Because she likes to write about young people, Byars says that her own four children are her best source of story ideas. Her children are also her biggest critics. When they were younger and still living at home, they would read her manuscripts. Whenever a page bored them, they would draw little arrows pointing down.

Their instincts must have been good, because Byars has received high praise for her books, including the 1971 Newbery Medal for *The Summer of the Swans*.

From the book by Betsy Byars

The Blossoms Meet the Vulture Lady

Illustrated by Jacqueline Rogers

Mom is a rodeo star, Grandpa Pap collects cans, and Junior is a would-be scientist inventing who-knows-what next. Vern, Maggie, and Mud, the dog, make up the rest of the clan.

Meet the Blossoms. You're just in time for their latest disaster.

"And nobody's seen Junior?" Vicki Blossom said for the third time. Her eyes swept around the table.

Maggie answered. "I told you, Mom. The last time I saw him he was in the barn, under the tarp."

"Me too," said Vern.

"I ain't seen him since breakfast," Pap said.

The Blossom family was at supper. They had been answering this same question since the meal started, but like a detective hoping for a new clue, Vicki Blossom kept asking it.

Now there came a long silence. Vicki Blossom looked out the window. Her hand was pressed against her mouth as if she were trying to hold back a cough.

Under the table Mud chewed a flea on his leg. Mud made a lot of noise when he went after a flea. Then he watched the wet spot of fur for a moment to see if the flea had survived. When he didn't feel anything move beneath the fur, he licked the fur back into place. Then he dropped his head onto his paws.

Maggie dished up a spoonful of popcorn. Monday nights the Blossoms always ate popcorn with milk on it. As she chewed she said, "Vern and I think he went in the woods," she paused to swallow, "to set his trap."

"I thought about that," their mom said. "But that was hours and hours ago."

"So it was a coyote trap, that thing Junior was making?" Vern asked.

"Yes." Vicki Blossom sighed. "He heard Pap say something last night about a reward for a coyote, and he saw himself collecting it." Every time she finished speaking she put her hand against her mouth.

"They thought they caught the coyote," Pap said, "did I tell you?" He paused with a spoonful of popcorn in front of his mouth, the milk dripping back into his bowl. "A motorist claimed he hit it on Route ninety-one. He went to the police station to collect his hundred dollars. He went in carrying the coyote in his arms."

Pap grinned. "Turned out it was a collie he'd hit. Mr. Frank R. Roswell's prize collie. This man hadn't even noticed that his so-called coyote was wearing a collar and dog tags." He wagged his head. "Now he's got to pay for the collie, and prize collies ain't cheap." He shoveled the spoonful of popcorn into his mouth.

Vicki Blossom was still looking out the window.

"Junior will be all night setting that trap, making sure every leaf is just right, every piece of wire in place. Mom, you know how he is," Maggie said. "Junior's a . . ." She paused to spring a new word on the Blossoms. "Perfectionist."

"I know he is, but it's not like him to miss Monday-night supper no matter what he's doing. Popcorn and milk's his favorite."

Nobody could deny that.

There was a sudden roll of thunder, and they all lowered their spoons and looked toward the window. The sun was behind the clouds, and the afternoon had turned dark.

"Storm's coming," Pap said.

"Anyway, I'm not hungry," Maggie said. She threw down her spoon. It clattered on the table.

And as if this were the signal they had been waiting for, the others threw down their spoons, too, and got up from the table.

Junior had only been in the coyote trap six minutes, but the six minutes had been so long and confusing and terrible, he couldn't think straight.

When the trapdoor had first clicked behind him, his mouth had fallen open as if it were connected to the same device. He stared at the door in disbelief. Then he sat back hard and rested his back against the hog-wire side.

"No problem," he told his sinking heart. He closed his eyes and took a deep breath. "No prob-lem."

He pushed against the hog wire with his back. It was just as tight, just as secure as when he had crawled in during its construction and said gleefully, "Nobody could get out of this — not even me, the inventor!"

Well, maybe the hog wire was secure. It had to be to hold hogs. Hogs were strong.

He didn't even want to think of how many nails he had used to secure the superstrong wire — all he had, that's how many, every single nail he could get his hands on. And he had pulled the wire high on the top.

He slid his fingers through the wire mesh and felt the top. He had pulled the wire so tight that he could not even reach the nails. He tried to inch his stubby fingers forward. The wire cut the soft flesh between his fingers, and still he couldn't feel the end.

He pulled his hand in and poked it out at the corner. He could feel the screws at the top, the huge screws that held the four corner supports. He could reach those, but that did him no good. His heart sank lower. The screwdriver was back in the barn.

There was only one answer. He would have to go out the way he had come in: through the door. He licked his dry lips and bent low to inspect the latches.

The door was latched on either side — double latches, and both of them had caught. It hurt him to remember how happy he had been at finding two latches in Pap's junk box. "Double security," he had cried in the dusty empty barn. He had even danced a little around his invention.

He slipped one dirty finger through the hog wire and tried to jiggle the latch. It was firm. He tried the other side. It was caught firmly too. And the only way to open them, he remembered, was with the blade of a knife. You slipped the knife in and flipped up the latch.

"Piece of cake," he had cried when he flipped them open, a hundred years ago, back in the Blossom barn.

The knife was back at the barn, too, lying on the ground beside the screwdriver.

Junior glanced at his watch: 3:05. Junior shook his head. He guessed that he had been in the trap about twenty-five hours. Tears filled his eyes.

Actually it had only been six minutes, time enough to realize that he was not going to get out of the trap without outside help.

He spent the next six minutes yelling "Help! Will somebody please let me out of this thing! Please!" at the top of his lungs.

He spent the next two minutes listening for sounds of help on the way.

He spent the next two minutes weeping, bent over his knees, his tears rolling down his dusty legs.

A bee buzzed in from the blackberry bushes, and Junior batted it away. "Haven't I got enough trouble without you?" he sobbed.

Junior heard a noise. His head snapped up. His swollen eyelids opened.

He swirled around, prepared to meet the glint of wild, golden coyote eyes. For the first time the cage wasn't such a terrible place to be.

There was really only one place where the coyote could sneak up on him. The sides and back of the trap were covered with blackberry bushes; only the front faced a clearing.

And just beyond the clearing, standing behind a tree, watching through the low branches, was Mud. Relief flooded Junior's body like cool water. He had completely forgotten about Mud!

"Mud! Good dog! Come here, boy, come here, Mud. Good old Mud."

Mud flexed his legs and shifted his paws in the pine needles. He did not come.

"Mud, come on, boy! It's me — Junior!" His voice was high with fake good spirits and real despair. "I was just kidding back there in the woods when I told you to go home. I'm glad to see you, Mud. Come on, Mud."

Mud did not move.

Junior had a sudden inspiration. His head flew up so fast, it struck the ceiling of the trap. He didn't stop to rub it. He reached for the tin-can sandwich. He didn't have to bother about being careful with it now. He dangled it from the string like a yo-yo.

"You want some hamburger, Mud? You want some of this?" He waved it in the air to entice Mud. He said, "Hum-hum, is it good. Remember?"

He pinched off a piece, stuck it on the end of one finger, and poked it through the hog wire.

"Look, Mud. Look what I've got. You want some?"

He beckoned to Mud with the finger, luring him closer.

Mud's tail had started to wag. It was sweeping pine needles right and left.

"You do? Well, come on over. Come on, Mud. Good dog!"

Mud got up. Slowly he came across the clearing. He kept his eyes on the ball of hamburger meat, but he was not happy about himself. This whole trip with Junior had been wrong. As soon as he got over feeling bad about one thing, there was something else to feel bad about.

"Come on, Mud!" Junior tried to speed him along by putting extra enthusiasm in his voice. "Come on!"

Mud continued to walk in his slow, ashamed way, his eyes on the ball of pink meat stuck on the end of Junior's finger. Not until he was there, at the hog wire, did he lift his head.

"See?" Junior said. Junior allowed Mud to eat the meat from his finger, to lick his fingernail.

"Did you like that? Was it good? Want some more?"

Junior's plan was to get Mud right up against the hog wire and to grab him by the bandanna. Then he would hold Mud so tight that Mud would begin to howl. Mud always howled when he was held tight. "Don't hold the dog," Pap was always saying. "The dog's like me — he don't want to be held!"

So Junior would hold and Mud would howl — and Mud howled like something out of a horror movie. *Ahwooo-ooo-ooooo-ooooo.* It would raise goose bumps on your arms if you didn't know it was just a dog. Mud would

howl, and somebody would hear him, and somebody would come.

Mud's soft tongue licked Junior's finger one last time. Junior had a hard time not trying to go for the bandanna right then. He decided to wait. He said calmly, "You want another piece. Here you go."

He dug out another piece with one finger. This time Junior held it inside the hog wire. Mud could reach it with his tongue, and while he was reaching . . . that would be the time to . . . The tone of Junior's voice had made Mud suspicious. He backed away.

"Don't you want it?"

Junior got a bigger piece. "I'm not going to do anything to you," Junior said. "I'm not going to do anything even if it is your fault that I'm in here. If you hadn't poked your nose on my leg and scared me — Anyway, what can I do? Look at me. I'm locked up in a cage. Come on. I just want you to have this nice piece of meat. I know you like it."

Mud came forward. This time he stopped just out of Junior's reach. There was a long moment while Junior held the meat and Mud looked at it. Junior held it closer.

Mud came closer, but something told him not to go too close. He stretched out his neck.

"Here you go, good dog!"

Junior's fingers curved back toward the cage, bringing the meat away from the wire. His other hand was there, the fingers locked in the hog wire, waiting. His fingers flexed, ready to grab the bandanna when the opportunity came.

"Don't you want it?" Junior asked. Sweat was rolling down his face. His tongue flicked over his dry lips. "Take it!"

He had the ball of meat between his fingers now, scissorslike. He beckoned Mud closer.

Mud came.

This was the moment, the opportunity Junior had been waiting for. His fingers hooked into the bandanna, and he pulled Mud hard against the cage.

Mud bucked like a horse. He twisted and pulled and yelped. He threw himself into the air. He tried to duck under the collar and slip his head out.

Junior held on tight. Finally Mud stopped fighting and rested against the cage. His wild eyes were rolled in Junior's direction.

"See, now you just have to howl until somebody comes," Junior said. He was out of breath from excitement. He tried to swallow, but his throat was too dry.

Beneath his fingers he could feel Mud trembling. "I'm sorry," he gasped. "But I can't let you go yet."

Mud began to whine.

Good, Junior thought. Mud always whined a little before he howled.

Junior's fingers were beginning to hurt. The wire was cutting them. He switched fingers very carefully. Then those fingers began to hurt.

Junior got the inspiration of his life. He would tie the bandanna to the cage. The ends were just long enough. He

would take the ends of the bandanna and slip them through the hog wire and knot them.

Getting the ends through the hog wire was easy, but he was having a hard time tying the knot with one hand. Maybe he could let go of the bandanna just long enough to take the ends. There, it worked. Junior had one end of the bandanna in each hand. He bent to make the knot.

At that moment Mud flung himself back so hard that the cage rocked. Junior thought it was going to topple. He let go just long enough to keep from hitting his head.

The next thing Junior saw was Mud's tail disappearing into the woods.

"Come back, come back!" he cried. But Junior knew Mud would not return. He gave one final plea: "Mud, at least show them where I am." But he didn't think Mud would do that either.

Mud was gone for good, and Junior cried for an hour with helpless frustration. At the peak of his misery he rocked back and forth, hitting his head against the cage and not even feeling it. Then he stopped for a while, then he cried again.

The afternoon dragged on. Bees droned in and out of the cage. The sun beat down on his head. His eyes were so swollen from all the crying that he could hardly see. His

nose had somehow swollen, too, inside, so he had to breathe through his mouth.

Finally, to ease the pain in his crooked back, he curled up in a small ball. As he lay there on the hard wood, he realized he was nothing like that coyote on Saturday-morning cartoons. That coyote was always ending up the victim of his own traps, too, but then he got right back out.

The unfairness of it brought new tears of misery to his swollen eyes.

I —, he thought — this was his last unhappy thought before he slept — *I don't make a very good coyote.*

The Blossoms were on the front porch of the house. Vicki Blossom was giving orders. Pap, Vern, Maggie, and Mud were taking them. Supper was over, and the search for Junior was about to get under way.

Overhead, thunder rolled again in the western sky. This time the sound was louder. The storm was coming closer.

"All right now, what we're looking for is wheelbarrow tracks. If we can follow those, we'll find Junior. There's about — " She broke off and looked up at the threatening sky. "There's about three hours before night. We've got to find Junior before then."

She looked at them, one by one, as if to impress on each one the seriousness of the situation. They didn't need her looks to tell them that. Since supper an uneasy feeling had come over all of them. This was not one of Junior's usual absences. This time Junior was absent — each one knew this — because he could not help being absent. Something had happened to Junior.

Pap was the only one who spoke. "I sure do hate it when somebody's missing." He shook his head slowly, back and forth. "It leaves a hole."

In the silence that followed, Mud moved closer to Pap and leaned against his leg. Pap stepped aside, catching Mud off balance.

Mud straightened and looked longingly at Pap. He had the feeling that there was an enormous distance between him and Pap instead of the few inches that actually separated them.

Ever since Pap had come home from can collecting and said, "Well, where were you when I needed you?" in a certain accusing tone, Mud had known he was out of favor. It was the first can collection he had ever missed.

"Go on, I don't want to pet you." Pap had gone into the house and shut the door in Mud's face.

"I'll pet you, Mud," Maggie had said, but Maggie's hugs only made him struggle harder to get to the screen door so he could scratch on it and follow Pap inside.

And even after Maggie let him in, all Pap said was "I said I don't want to pet you."

Mud could not bear being out of favor with Pap. In the past hour he had done everything he could to make up to Pap for his desertion.

First he had pushed his head into Pap's hand, giving Pap the chance to scratch his nose. Pap had not. Then he

had poked his head under Pap's hand. Pap's hand had been like a cap on his head for a brief, satisfactory moment, and then Pap had moved it. Then Mud had rested his chin on Pap's leg during supper. Pap had shrugged him off. Now Mud moved closer to Pap for another try at leaning against his leg. Pap said, "Let's go."

Pap went down the steps so heavily, the boards bowed beneath his weight. Mud went behind him, staying close, hoping to hear Pap speak his name or touch him in the old pal-to-pal way.

The five of them followed the wheelbarrow tracks into the woods. Junior had taken a curving, weaving route, skirting trees and large rocks. It was easy to follow because Junior had been in a hurry and had torn up the moss and pine needles.

"Junior!" Vicki called. "Oh, Junior!"

No answer.

They tracked him through the creek. The wheel had been stuck briefly in the mud. It had apparently taken Junior three separate tries to get it up the bank.

"Junior! Oh, Junior!"

Still no answer.

At the edge of the old wheat field they ran into trouble. The ground was hard, and the old wheat so broken, they couldn't find a single mark.

"Here's where we split up," Vicki said. "Fan out and if you see anything, holler!"

With their eyes on the ground they proceeded slowly across the old field. Every now and then Vicki would pause to call Junior and to say in a worried way, "He ought to be able to hear me by now. Why doesn't he answer?"

"Now, Vicki," Pap would answer from across the rows of stubble. To calm himself he muttered, "We'll find him. We'll find him."

"Here's the track! He went this way!" Pap called suddenly. Being the one to spot the wheelbarrow tracks, particularly after a long time of looking, gave Pap a good feeling. "Over here!" he called. Pap's voice sounded so good that Mud bounded over the wheat field to him.

"Come on, Mud, let's find him," Pap said. He reached out with one hand and brushed Mud's head.

Mud happily took the lead. As he bounded to the woods his tail began to wag.

Mad Mary stopped with her hand reaching for some low blackberries. Her hand dropped to her knee.

"Well, look at that. Somebody put a little child in a cage."

She knelt. Her ragged skirts flared out around her. Mad Mary had not changed her clothes in five years.

When one skirt wore out, she just put another one on top of it. She had layers of rags now, some so old and colorless, even she did not know what the cloth had once looked like.

As she bent forward, her boots dug into the dust Junior had piled against the trap. Her socks bagged around her thin white ankles. She leaned her weight against her cane.

She watched Junior's curled figure for a moment, shaking her head, making little clicking sounds with her

mouth. *Tsk, tsk, tsk.* It was the sound she used to make a lot when she was living around people. She made it every time she saw an example of man's cruelty to his fellow man. Since she had started living by herself, she had not had to make the sound one single time.

Junior lay on his side. His thumb was beneath his chin, as if it had just fallen out of his mouth. His eyes were red and swollen. When he breathed in and out, unspilled tears rattled in his throat.

Mad Mary reached out her freckled hand and unlocked one latch, then the other. She didn't need a knife blade. Her fingernails were long, tough, and sharp. She could puncture a can of condensed milk with them.

She lifted the door silently and got it out of the way by tying it to the tree limb overhead. She knotted the fishing line with one hand, without looking up.

She brushed a bee aside as if it were a fly.

"Now let's get you out of here before whoever done this to you comes back," she said.

She leaned in the trap and, with surprising gentleness, pulled Junior toward her. He did not stir. She scooped him into her arms.

Junior was so worn out with trying to get free and with crying and with the pain of being a caged animal that he felt nothing. If this was what it was like to be in a trap — he had thought this at least a hundred times during the endless afternoon — if this was what it was like, he would never make another trap as long as he lived.

Mad Mary braced him against her knee for a moment and then lifted him. Years of living on her own in the woods had made her strong. Nothing bothered her. As she stood, Junior's head rolled into a comfortable curve of her shoulder.

"There you go," she said.

He moaned.

"You sleep," she told him.

She adjusted him so she would have the use of her walking cane. She needed that. The cane poked into the dust, leaving a sharp indentation by her feet.

"When you wake up, all your bad dreams will be over. You'll be safe. Nobody can get you in Mary's cave. Nobody even knows where Mary's cave is."

With long mannish strides Mad Mary bore Junior away deeper into the forest.

"And that," she said to the trees and the storm breeze and the darkening sky, "is a fact."

Mud was running wildly through the trees. His long ears flared out behind him. Now he remembered Junior in the bushes. He remembered the hamburger. He knew exactly where they were going and why.

He turned, barked over his shoulder, and then ran back in a frenzy to make sure the Blossoms were following him. He barked again to speed them up and then ran deeper into the woods.

"Mud knows something," Pap said, panting.

"Sure! He was with Junior!" Vern called over his shoulder.

"That's right! He was, Pap!"

At that, Maggie began running faster. She caught up with Vern and they ran together like forest creatures, jumping over briar bushes, slipping through the narrow spaces between trees, sliding down banks.

Their mom tried to keep up with them for a while, but she had to fall back when she lost one of her sandals. She slid her foot in again and ran forward, calling, "We're coming, Junior!"

Behind them, Pap could not keep up no matter how hard he tried. He was thrashing through the forest like a wounded moose. He was desperately trying to catch the others, but it was impossible. He watched them disappear, one by one, into the trees. His sense of frustration deepened.

The forest itself seemed to be fighting him. He pushed aside branches and they came back to slap him in the face. Briars caught his clothes and tore them. His shoelace got busted, and a loose stone turned his ankle onto its side.

"Wait for me!" he called, staggering to a stop. No one even heard him.

Pap tested his throbbing ankle by walking three steps to a tree. He held on to the tree as if it were his last friend. Then, as he leaned there, he suddenly felt old and useless. He put his weight on the tree.

Above his own ragged breathing he could hear Mud's joyful barking in the distance. It seemed to be in one place now. Mud had found Junior.

Well, that was good. Pap imagined Vern and Maggie and Vicki catching up. He imagined them running into the clearing, hugging each other, being happy and young. He wished he could be there.

It's terrible being old, he thought, terrible. His despair returned. He put his hand on his hip for support and bent his knees. He was going to sit down on a stone.

Suddenly in the distance he heard Vicki's voice. She was calling him. "Pap!" she cried. It was the voice she used when something bad had happened, the voice she had used on the phone the night she'd called to tell him his son, Cotton, had been killed by a steer. He had heard that cry enough to know it in his sleep. Her saying his name in that way turned his blood cold every time.

Pap's knees were bent so he could sit down, and it was hard for him to get his knees to realize they were going to have to straighten up instead and take him on through the forest.

He gave each knee a gentle nudge with his fist, and they popped back. He began his awkward push through the forest, favoring his bad ankle.

"I'm coming," he called, hobbling toward them. "I'm coming."

Pap came into the clearing with one hand over his pounding heart. "What?" he gasped. "What's happened?"

Vicki pointed to the cage set back in the blackberry bushes. Pap stumbled forward. He squinted. His hand clutched the bib of his overalls.

"What?" he said again. He didn't see anything, so he guessed he must not be looking in the right place. His head snapped this way and that. His neck bones creaked in protest.

"There, Pap," Maggie said. She pointed too.

"I don't see nothing."

"Exactly!" Vicki Blossom's voice wavered with tears.

"Junior's gone.

There is the cage

and Junior's gone!"

To Be Continued...

Where is Mad Mary taking Junior? Will the other Blossoms be able to find him? For the answers to these and other questions, read the rest of **The Blossoms Meet the Vulture Lady.**

In the Next Episode . . .

With three of your classmates, act out what might
happen now that the Blossoms have found the empty cage.
Will they continue their search for Junior? Will they find
him with Mad Mary? You and your classmates decide.

The Blossoms Continue to Blossom

The Blossoms aren't just an ordinary family, and the things that happen to them aren't ordinary happenings either. Read the further adventures of the Blossoms in these three books.

Pap gets into trouble for disturbing the peace in *The Not-Just-Anybody Family*.

Junior's latest invention is an unidentified flying object in *The Blossoms and the Green Phantom*.

Preparations go forth for the launching of Vern's home-made raft in *A Blossom Promise*.

Beverly Cleary

You probably already know Henry, Beezus, and Ramona. They're some of Beverly Cleary's best-known characters. Cleary first became famous for writing about real children. Before writing *The Mouse and the Motorcycle*, the story you will read next, Cleary had never written a fantasy story.

"I probably would not have written fantasy if I had not had a fourth-grade son who was disgusted with reading, who wanted to read about motorcycles but found all the books too hard, and who happened to run a high fever in the middle of the night when we were staying in a strange hotel," Cleary says. "*The Mouse and the Motorcycle* was the result."

From the book by Beverly Cleary

The Mouse and the Motorcycle

Illustrated by Louis Darling

1. The New Guests

Keith, the boy in the rumpled shorts and shirt, did not know he was being watched as he entered room 215 of the Mountain View Inn. Neither did his mother and father, who both looked hot and tired. They had come from Ohio and for five days had driven across plains and deserts and over mountains to the old hotel in the California foothills twenty-five miles from Highway 40.

The fourth person entering room 215 may have known he was being watched, but he did not care. He was Matt, sixty if he was a day, who at the moment was the bell-boy. Matt also replaced worn-out light bulbs, renewed washers in leaky faucets, carried trays for people who tele-phoned room service to order food sent to their rooms, and sometimes prevented children from hitting one another with croquet mallets on the lawn behind the hotel.

Now Matt's right shoulder sagged with the weight of one of the bags he was carrying. "Here you are, Mr. Gridley. Rooms 215 and 216," he said, setting the smaller of the bags on a luggage rack at the foot of the double bed before he opened a door into the next room. "I expect you and Mrs. Gridley will want room 216. It is a corner room with twin beds and a private bath." He carried the heavy bag into the next room where he could be heard opening windows. Outside a chipmunk chattered in a pine tree and a chickadee whistled *fee-bee-bee*.

The boy's mother looked critically around room 215 and whispered, "I think we should drive back to the main highway. There must be a motel with a *Vacancy* sign some-place. We didn't look long enough."

"Not another mile," answered the father. "I'm not driving another mile on a California highway on a holiday weekend. Did you see the way that truck almost forced us off the road?"

"Dad, did you see those two fellows on motorcycles — " began the boy and stopped, realizing he should not interrupt an argument.

"But this place is so *old*," protested the boy's mother. "And we have only three weeks for our whole trip. We had planned to spend the Fourth of July weekend in San Francisco and we wanted to show Keith as much of the United States as we could."

"San Francisco will have to wait and this is part of the United States. Besides, this used to be a very fashionable hotel," said Mr. Gridley. "People came from miles around."

"Fifty years ago," said Mrs. Gridley. "And they came by horse and buggy."

The bellboy returned to room 215. "The dining room opens at six-thirty, sir. There is ping-pong in the game room, TV in the lobby, and croquet on the back lawn. I'm sure you will be very comfortable." Matt, who had seen guests come and go for many years, knew there were two kinds — those who thought the hotel was a dreadful old barn of a place and those who thought it charming and quaint, so quiet and restful.

"Of course we will be comfortable," said Mr. Gridley, dropping some coins into Matt's hand for carrying the bags.

"But this big old hotel is positively spooky." Mrs. Gridley made one last protest. "It is probably full of mice."

Matt opened the window wide. "Mice? Oh no, ma'am. The management wouldn't stand for mice."

"I wouldn't mind a few mice," the boy said, as he looked
around the room at the high ceiling, the knotty pine walls,
the carpet so threadbare that many of its roses had almost
entirely faded, the one chair with the antimacassar on its
back, the washbasin and towel racks in the corner of the
room. "I like it here," he announced. "A whole room to
myself. Usually I just get a cot in the corner of a motel
room."

His mother smiled, relenting. Then she turned to
Matt. "I'm sorry. It's just that it was so hot crossing
Nevada and we are not used to mountain driving. Back on
the highway the traffic was bumper to bumper. I'm sure we
shall be very comfortable."

After Matt had gone, closing the door behind him, Mr. Gridley said, "I need a rest before dinner. Four hundred miles of driving and that mountain traffic! It was too much."

"And if we are going to stay for a weekend I had better unpack," said Mrs. Gridley. "At least I'll have a chance to do some drip-drying."

Alone in room 215 and unaware that he was being watched, the boy began to explore. He got down on his hands and knees and looked under the bed. He leaned out the open window as far as he could and greedily inhaled deep breaths of pine-scented air. He turned the hot and cold water on and off in the washbasin and slipped one of the small bars of paper-wrapped soap into his pocket. Under the window he discovered a knothole in the pine wall down by the floor and squatting, poked his finger into the hole. When he felt nothing inside he lost interest.

Next Keith opened his suitcase and took out an apple and several small cars — a sedan, a sports car, and an ambulance about six inches long, and a red motorcycle half the length of the cars — which he dropped on the striped bedspread before he bit into the apple. He ate the apple noisily in big chomping bites, and then laid the core on the bedside table between the lamp and the telephone.

Keith began to play, running his cars up and down the bedspread, pretending that the stripes on the spread were highways and making noises with his mouth — *vroom vroom* for the sports car, *wh-e-e wh-e-e* for the ambulance and *pb-pb-b-b-b* for the motorcycle, up and down the stripes.

Once Keith stopped suddenly and looked quickly around the room as if he expected to see something or someone but when he saw nothing unusual he returned to his cars. ***Vroom vroom. Bang! Crash!*** The sports car hit the sedan and rolled over off the highway stripe. ***Pb-pb-b-b-b.*** The motorcycle came roaring to the scene of the crash.

"Keith," his mother called from the next room. "Time to get washed for dinner."

"O.K." Keith parked his cars in a straight line on the bedside table beside the telephone where they looked like a row of real cars only much, much smaller.

The first thing Mrs. Gridley noticed when she and Mr. Gridley came into the room was the apple core on the table. She dropped it with a thunk into the metal waste-basket beside the table as she gave several quick little sniffs of the air and said, looking perplexed, "I don't care what the bellboy said. I'm sure this hotel has mice."

"I hope so," muttered Keith.

2. The Motorcycle

Except for one terrifying moment when the boy had poked his finger through the mousehole, a hungry young mouse named Ralph eagerly watched everything that went on in room 215. At first he was disappointed at the size of the boy who was to occupy the room. A little child, preferably two or even three children, would have been better. Little messy children were always considerate about leaving crumbs on the carpet. Oh well, at least these people did not have a dog. If there was one thing Ralph disliked, it was a snoopy dog.

Next Ralph felt hopeful. Medium-sized boys could almost always be counted on to leave a sticky candy-bar wrapper on the floor or a bag of peanuts on the bedside table, where Ralph could reach them by climbing up the telephone cord. With a boy this size the food, though not apt to be plentiful, was almost sure to be of good quality.

The third emotion felt by Ralph was joy when the boy laid the apple core by the telephone. This was followed by despair when the mother dropped the core into the metal wastebasket. Ralph knew that anything at the bottom of a metal wastebasket was lost to a mouse forever.

A mouse lives not by crumbs alone and so Ralph experienced still another emotion; this time food was not the cause of it. Ralph was eager, excited, curious, and impatient all at once. The emotion was so strong it made him forget his empty stomach. It was caused by those little cars, especially that motorcycle and the *pb-pb-b-b-b* sound the boy made. That sound seemed to satisfy something within Ralph, as if he had been waiting all his life to hear it.

Pb-pb-b-b-b went the boy. To the mouse the sound spoke of highways and speed, of distance and danger, and whiskers blown back by the wind.

The instant the family left the room to go to dinner, Ralph scurried out of the mousehole and across the threadbare carpet to the telephone cord, which came out of a hole in the floor beside the bedside table.

"Ralph!" scolded his mother from the mousehole. "You stay away from that telephone cord!" Ralph's mother was a great worrier. She worried because their hotel was old and run down and because so many rooms were often empty with no careless guests to leave crumbs behind for mice. She worried about the rumor that their hotel was to be torn down when the new highway came through. She worried about her children finding aspirin tablets. Ralph's father had tried to carry an aspirin tablet in his cheek pouch, the aspirin had dissolved with unexpected suddenness, and Ralph's father had been poisoned. Since then no member of the family would think of touching an aspirin tablet, but this did not prevent Ralph's mother from worrying.

Most of all Ralph's mother worried about Ralph. She worried because he was a reckless mouse, who stayed out late in the daytime when he should have been home safe in bed. She worried when Ralph climbed the curtain to sit on the windowsill to watch the chipmunk in the pine tree outside and the cars in the parking lot below. She worried because Ralph wanted to go exploring down the hall instead of traveling under the floorboards like a sensible mouse. Heaven only knew what dangers he might meet in the hall — maids, bellboys, perhaps even cats. Or what was worse, vacuum cleaners. Ralph's mother had a horror of vacuum cleaners.

Ralph, who was used to his mother's worries, got a good running start and was already halfway up the telephone cord.

"Remember your Uncle Victor!" his mother called after him.

Ralph seemed not to hear. He climbed the cord up to the telephone, jumped down, and ran around to the row of cars. There it was on the end — the motorcycle! Ralph stared at it and then walked over and kicked a tire. Close up the motorcycle looked even better than he expected. It was new and shiny and had a good set of tires. Ralph walked all the way around it, examining the pair of chromium mufflers and the engine and the hand clutch. It even had a little license plate so it would be legal to ride it.

"Boy!" said Ralph to himself, his whiskers quivering with excitement. "Boy, oh, boy!" Feeling that this was an important moment in his life, he took hold of the hand-grips. They felt good and solid beneath his paws. Yes, this motorcycle was a good machine all right. He could tell by the feel. Ralph threw a leg over the motorcycle and sat jauntily on the plastic seat. He even bounced up and down. The seat was curved just right to fit a mouse.

But how to start the motorcycle? Ralph did not know. And even if he did know how to start it, he could not do much riding up here on the bedside table. He considered pushing the motorcycle off onto the floor, but he did not want to risk damaging such a valuable machine.

Ralph bounced up and down on the seat a couple more times and looked around for some way to start the motorcycle. He pulled at a lever or two but nothing happened. Then a terrible thought spoiled his pleasure. This was only a toy. It would not run at all.

Ralph, who had watched many children in room 215, had picked up a lot of information about toys. He had seen a boy from Cedar Rapids throw his model airplane on the floor because he could not make its plastic parts fit properly. A little girl had burst into tears and run sobbing to her mother when her doll's arm had come out of its socket. And then there was that nice boy, the potato-chip nibbler, who stamped his foot because the batteries kept falling out of his car.

But this toy could not be like all those other toys he had seen. It looked too perfect with its wire spokes in its wheels and its pair of shiny chromium exhaust pipes. It would not be right if it did not run. It would not be *fair*. A motorcycle that looked as real as this one *had* to run. The secret of making it run must be perfectly simple if only Ralph had someone to show him what it was.

Ralph was not satisfied just sitting on the motorcycle. Ralph craved action. After all, what was a motorcycle for if it wasn't action? Who needed motorcycle riding lessons?

Not Ralph! He tried pushing himself along with his feet. This was not nearly fast enough, but it was better than nothing. He moved his feet faster along the tabletop and then lifted them up while he coasted. Feeling braver he bent low over the handlebars and worked his feet still faster toward the edge of the bedside table. When he worked up a little speed he would coast around the corner. He scrabbled his feet on the tabletop to gain momentum. In a split second he would steer to the left —

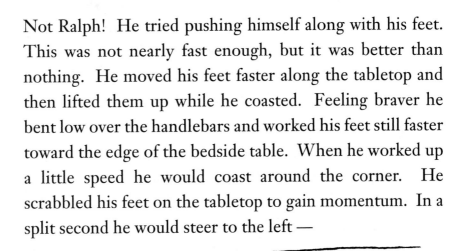

At that moment the bell on the telephone rang half a ring, so close that it seemed to pierce the middle of Ralph's bones. It rang just that half ring, as if the girl at the switchboard realized she had rung the wrong room and had jerked out the cord before the ring was finished.

That half a ring was enough. It shattered Ralph's nerves and terrified him so that he forgot all about steering. It jumbled his thoughts until he forgot to drag his heels for brakes. He was so terrified he let go of the handgrips. The momentum of the motorcycle carried him forward, over the edge of the table. Down, down through space tumbled Ralph with the motorcycle. He tried to straighten out, to turn the fall into a leap, but the motorcycle got in his way. He grabbed in vain at the air with both paws. There was nothing to clutch, nothing to save him, only the empty air. For a fleeting instant he thought of his poor old Uncle Victor. That was the instant the motorcycle landed with a crash in the metal wastebasket.

Ralph fell in a heap beside the motorcycle and lay still.

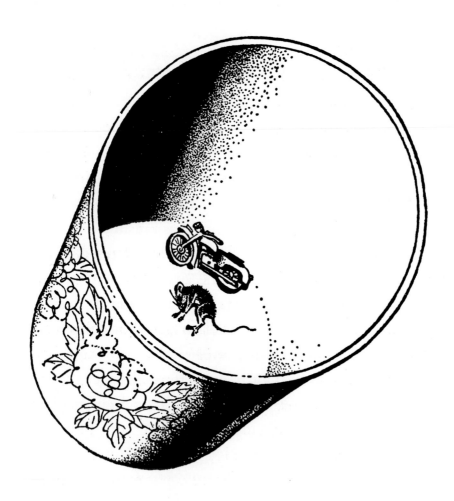

3. Trapped!

Even though Ralph woke up feeling sick and dizzy, his first thought was of the motorcycle. He hoped it was not broken. He sat there at the bottom of the wastebasket until the whirly feeling in his head stopped and he was able, slowly and carefully, to stand up. He stretched each aching muscle and felt each of his four legs to make certain it was not broken.

When Ralph was sure that he was battered but intact he examined the motorcycle. He set it upright and rolled it backward and forward to make sure the wheels still worked. One handlebar was bent and some of the paint was chipped off the rear fender, but everything else seemed all right. Ralph hoped so, but there was no way he could find out until he figured out how to start the engine. Now he ached too much even to try.

Wearily Ralph dragged himself over to the wall of his metal prison and sat down beside the apple core to rest his aching body. He leaned back against the side of the wastepaper basket, closed his eyes, and thought about his Uncle Victor. Poor nearsighted Uncle Victor. He, too, had landed in a metal wastepaper basket jumping there quite by mistake. Unable to climb the sides he had been trapped until the maid came and emptied him out with the trash. No one knew for sure what had happened to Uncle Victor, but it was known that trash in the hotel was emptied into an incinerator.

Ralph felt sad and remorseful thinking about his Uncle Victor getting dumped out with the trash. His mother had been right after all. His poor mother, gathering crumbs for his little brothers and sisters while he, selfish mouse that he was, sat trapped in a metal prison from which the only escape was to be thrown away like an old gum wrapper.

Ralph thought sadly of his comfortable home in the mousehole. It was a good home, untidy but comfortable. The children who stayed in room 215 usually left a good supply of crumbs behind, and there was always water from the shirts hung to drip-dry beside the wash basin. It should have been enough. He should have been content to stay home without venturing out into the world looking for speed and excitement.

Outside in the hall Ralph heard footsteps and Matt, the bellboy, saying, "These new people in 215 and 216, somehow they got the idea there are mice in the hotel. I just opened the window and told them the management wouldn't stand for it."

Ralph heard a delighted laugh from the second-floor maid, a college girl who was working for the summer season. "Mice are adorable but just the same, I hope I never find any in my rooms. I'm afraid of them." There were two kinds of employees at the Mountain View Inn — the regulars, none of them young, and the summer help, who were college students working during the tourist season.

"If you don't like mice you better stay away from that knothole under the window in room 215," advised Matt.

The sound of voices so close made Ralph more eager than ever to escape. "No!" he shouted, his voice echoing in the metal chamber. "I won't have it! I'm too young to be dumped out with the trash!"

In spite of his aches he jumped to his feet, ran across the wastebasket floor, and leaped against the wall, only to fall back in a sorry heap. He rose, backed off, and tried again. There he was on the floor of the wastebasket a second time. It was useless, utterly useless. He did not have the strength to tip over the wastebasket.

Ralph was not a mouse to give up easily. He considered his problem a moment before he rolled the motorcycle over to the wall of the wastebasket. Then he seized the apple core by the stem and dragged it over to the motorcycle. By putting his shoulder under the stem end, he managed to raise the core until it was standing on its blossom end, but when he put his front paws around it and tried to lift it, he found he could not. The core was too heavy to lift up onto the seat of the motorcycle. Ralph was disappointed but when he stopped to think it over, he saw that even if he could manage to get the apple core on top of the motorcycle, it still would not be high enough to allow him to climb out of the wastebasket.

Bruised and defeated, Ralph dropped the core and decided that he might as well be thrown out with the trash on a full stomach as an empty one. He took a bite of apple and felt a little better. It was the best food he had eaten for several days — juicy and full of flavor and much better than the damp zwieback crumbs the last guests had left behind. He took several more bites and settled down to a hearty meal, saving the seeds for dessert.

Two ant scouts appeared on the rim of the wastebasket.

"Go away," said Ralph crossly, because he did not like to eat food crawling with ants and because it embarrassed him to be seen in such a predicament. The ants left as silently as they had come.

When Ralph had eaten his fill of the apple he curled up beside the core. He only hoped that someone might happen to drop a tissue over him. It was bad enough to be carried to one's doom in a wastebasket, but to be carried to one's doom by a shrieking maid was unthinkable. There was one tiny ray of hope — if someone did happen to drop a tissue over him, he just might have a chance to jump and run when the maid tipped the basket up to empty it into the incinerator.

The thought that the boy was sure to miss his motorcycle and start looking for it kept Ralph tossing and turning behind the apple core until, stuffed and exhausted, he finally fell asleep.

4. Keith

Ralph did not know how much time had passed before he was awakened by the lamp on the bedside table shining down on him. He squeezed himself into the tiniest possible ball, wrapped his tail around his body, and tried to make himself as thin as the apple core.

"My motorcycle!" shouted the boy the very first thing. "Somebody stole my motorcycle!"

Oh-oh, thought Ralph. It won't be long now.

"Nobody stole your motorcycle," answered the boy's mother from 216. "It's around someplace. You just mislaid it. You can find it in the morning. You had better get ready for bed now."

"No, I didn't mislay it," insisted the boy. "I put it right here on the table beside my sports car."

"You'll find it someplace," said his mother, not much interested. Boys were always losing things.

While Ralph cowered behind the apple core, Keith opened the drawer of the bedside table and slammed it shut. He jerked back the bedspread, yanked the pillows off the bed, and threw them back. Then he got down on his hands and knees and looked under the bed and the table.

Ralph wrapped his tail more tightly around his body. Here it comes, he thought.

The boy's face appeared in the opening at the top of the wastebasket. Ralph's heart raced like a motor.

"Ha," said the boy to himself. "Here it is. I wonder how it got there." His hand came down into the wastebasket to seize the motorcycle and lift it out. Still leaning over the wastebasket, he examined the bent handlebar and the chipped paint. "That's funny," he remarked aloud. "It must have rolled off, but I don't see how it could."

The boy did the natural thing for a boy to do. He looked into the wastebasket again. Ralph closed both eyes tight and waited. He wished he had not eaten so much of the apple core. If he had not been so greedy, the core would have been thicker and he would have been thinner.

"Hey!" whispered the boy, obviously very much surprised. "How did you get in here?" He was careful to keep his voice lower than the sound of the breezes in the pines outside the window.

Ralph did not move. He was grateful to the boy for not touching the apple core even though it was really no protection at all.

"Psst!" whispered the boy. "Are you asleep?"

Still Ralph remained motionless except for a slight quiver of his whiskers which he was unable to control. The boy was silent, but the mouse could feel the rhythmic drafts of his breathing. The boy must be thinking, but what was he thinking? That was what was worrying Ralph. "No," said the boy to himself. "No, it couldn't be."

Couldn't be what? wondered Ralph, who was beginning to feel cramped from crouching behind the apple core.

"Hey, wake up," whispered the boy.

That was the last thing Ralph wanted to do.

"Come on," pleaded the boy. "I won't hurt you."

Ralph considered. After all, what did he have to lose? If he stayed in the wastebasket, he was almost certain to get dumped into the incinerator. He might as well come out from behind the core. If he did he might find some opportunity to escape. Cautiously he moved his head from his paws and opened one eye. The boy was smiling down at him. Encouraged, Ralph opened the other eye and lifted his head.

"That's the stuff," encouraged the boy. "Now come on. Tell me, did you or didn't you ride my motorcycle off the bedside table?"

This took Ralph by surprise. He had not expected the boy to guess what happened. "Well, yes. I guess you might say I did," confessed Ralph, rubbing his aching muscles.

"I thought so." Neither the mouse nor the boy was the least bit surprised that each could understand the other. Two creatures who shared a love for motorcycles naturally spoke the same language. "That must have been some accident. Did it hurt much?"

"Oh, some," answered Ralph with a display of bravado. "Anyway, I didn't exactly ride it. I really coasted off. The telephone rang and startled me. Now how about getting me out of here?"

"Just a minute," said the boy. "How did you get up here in the first place?"

"Climbed, stupid. On the telephone cord." Ralph instantly regretted his rudeness. He had better watch his tongue if he expected any help in escaping from the wastebasket.

"Oh, of course," said the boy apologetically. "I should have thought of that myself."

At that moment there came a quick knock on the door to room 215 and the rattle of a key.

"Help!" cried Ralph. "The maid! Don't let her see me!"

Before the boy could do anything, the maid burst into the room. "Oh — excuse me." She seemed surprised to see a boy kneeling by the wastebasket. "I've come to turn down the bed."

"That's all right," said the boy quickly. "I can do it myself. Thanks, anyway."

"Thank you," said the maid, backing out of the room. Ralph knew she was not anxious to waste time turning down the bed. As soon as she finished her duties she was going out to the parking lot to meet a busboy, a college boy whose job was clearing tables in the dining room.

"Whew! That was close." The boy seemed every bit as relieved as Ralph.

"I'll say," agreed the mouse.

"Keith," called his mother from 216. "Are you getting ready for bed?"

"Sort of," answered Keith.

"You'd better come in our bathroom and take a bath," said his mother.

"Aw, gee, Mom, do I gotta?" asked Keith.

"Yes, you do," said his father.

"And don't forget to brush your teeth," said his mother.

"I won't," promised Keith. Then he whispered to Ralph, "You just lie low. I'll hurry and take a bath and get into bed and turn out the light and after Mom comes and kisses me good night, we can talk some more."

Lie low indeed! Ralph was indignant. He couldn't lie much lower if he wanted to, and he certainly did not want to sit around waiting to talk. He wanted to get out of that wastebasket. Once he was out he would see about talking, but not before.

Ralph could hear the boy splashing in 216's bathtub and then hastily brushing his teeth in 215's washbasin. After this there was the sound of a suitcase being opened and clothes dropped on the floor. The boy hopped into bed and to Ralph's relief, the light was turned out. In a moment Mrs. Gridley came in to kiss her son good night.

"Night, Mom," said the boy, sounding as if he were already drowsy.

"Good night, Keith," said his mother. "It looks as if we are going to have to stay here for a few days. Your father refuses to budge."

"That's O.K.," muttered Keith, giving the impression he was almost asleep.

"Good boy," said his mother. "You're a good sport."

"Good night, Son," said the boy's father from the doorway between the two rooms.

Keith did not answer. Instead he breathed slowly and deeply and, as Ralph thought, a bit too noisily. There was no sense in overdoing things.

As soon as all was quiet in the next room, the boy swung his legs out of bed, fumbled around in his suitcase, and shone a flashlight into the wastebasket.

Almost blinded by the unexpected light, Ralph held his paws over his eyes. "Hey, cut that out!" He could not remember to be polite.

"Oh — sorry." The boy laid the flashlight on the bed where its beam shone across the wastebasket rather than into it.

"That's better," said Ralph. "Now how about getting me out of here?" As an afterthought he added, "Please."

The boy ignored the mouse's request. "How would you like to ride my motorcycle?" he asked.

Ralph's heart skipped a beat like a motor missing on one cylinder. The mouse-sized motorcycle really would run after all! And there was one thing certain. Since the motorcycle really would run, the boy could not expect him to ride around the bottom of a wastebasket. "Sure." Ralph tried to sound calm. The important thing was to get out of this prison. He braced himself, dreading the touch of the boy's hand on his fur.

To Ralph's surprise, the boy did not reach in and grab him. Instead, he slowly and gently tipped the wastebasket on its side, permitting Ralph to walk to freedom with pride and dignity.

"Thanks," said Ralph, genuinely grateful for this consideration. "I believe you're O.K."

"Sure I'm O.K.," said the boy, setting his motorcycle down beside Ralph. "Did you think I wasn't?"

"You never can tell." Ralph put his paw on the handlebar of the motorcycle. "It's a real beauty. Even with a bent handlebar. I'm sure sorry about that."

"Forget it," said the boy reassuringly. "It won't hurt much. The motorcycle will still run."

Ralph threw his leg over the motorcycle and settled himself comfortably in the seat.

"Perfect! Just perfect!" The boy was obviously delighted that his motorcycle was just right for a mouse.

Ralph could not have agreed more heartily. It *was* perfect — except for one thing. He did not know how to start it.

"Well, go on," said the boy. "Ride it."

Ralph was ashamed to confess his ignorance. "I don't know how to start it," he admitted. "It's the first motorcycle I have ever had a chance to ride."

Pb-pb-b-b-b

"You have to make a noise," the boy explained matter-of-factly. "These cars don't go unless you make a noise."

The answer was so obvious Ralph was disgusted with himself for not knowing without asking. He grasped the handgrips and, fearful lest his noise be too squeaky, managed a *pb-pb-b-b-b*. Sure enough, the motorcycle moved. It really and truly moved across the threadbare carpet. Ralph was so excited that he promptly forgot to make the noise. The motorcycle stopped. Ralph started it again. *Pb–pb-b-b-b*. This time he remembered to keep on making the noise. He sped off into a square of moonlight on the carpet and found a good threadbare spot without any bumps.

"Look out for your tail," said the boy. "Don't let it get caught in the spokes."

"Thanks for reminding me," said Ralph, causing the motorcycle to stop. He started it again and steered with one paw while he reached back with the other, caught up his tail and held the tip safely against the handlebar. It was a glorious sensation, speeding around on the carpet, freely and noisily and, most of all, fast. Ralph discovered that if he made the noise fast, the motorcycle speeded up. If he slowed the sound, the motorcycle slowed down. He promptly speeded up and raced around in the rectangle of moonlight, where he made another discovery. When he ran out of breath, the momentum of the motorcycle carried him on until he could take another breath.

"Gee, you're lucky," whispered the boy.

In order to answer, Ralph had to stop. "I am?" It had never occurred to him that a mouse could be luckier than a boy.

"You sure are." The boy spoke with feeling. "My mother would never let me ride a motorcycle. She would say I might break a leg or something silly like that."

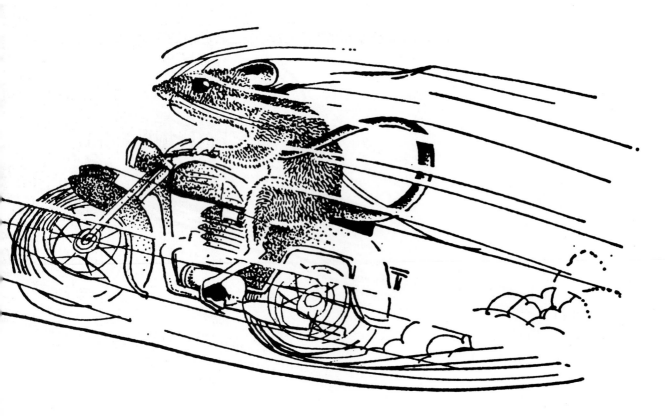

"Well, if you want to come right down to it," said Ralph, "I don't suppose my mother would be exactly crazy about the idea." He began to have an uneasy feeling that he really should be getting back to the mousehole.

"Anyway," said the boy gloomily, "it will be years and years before I'm old enough to ride a motorcycle, and then when I am old enough my mother won't let me."

Ralph really felt sorry for the boy, hampered as he was by his youth and his mother.

"Go on, ride it some more," said the boy. "I like to watch."

Pb-pb-b-b-b. Ralph started the motorcycle again and rode around in the moonlight once more, faster and faster, until he was dizzy from circling, dizzy with excitement, dizzy with the joy of speed. Never mind the danger, never mind what his mother thought. This was living. This was what he wanted to do. On and on and on.

"Lucky," whispered the boy with envy in his voice.

Ralph did not answer. He did not want to stop.

Pb-pb-b-b-b. . .

5. Adventure in the Night

When Ralph had mastered riding the motorcyle on the threadbare carpet, he went bumping over the roses on the less worn parts under the dresser and the bedside table. That was fun, too.

"Hey," whispered the boy. "Come on out where I can see you."

Pb-pb-b-b-b. Ralph shot out into the moonlight where he stopped, sitting jauntily on the motorcycle with one foot resting on the floor. "Say," he said, "how about letting me take her out in the hall? You know, just for a little spin to see how fast she'll go."

"Promise you'll bring it back?" asked Keith.

"Scout's honor," answered Ralph, who had picked up many expressions from children who had stayed in 215.

"O.K., I'll tell you what," said Keith. "You can use it at night and I'll use it in the daytime. I'll leave the door open an inch so you can get in. That way you can ride it up and down the hall at night."

"Can I really?" This was more than Ralph had hoped for. "Where do you want me to park it when I come in?" he asked.

"Someplace where the maid won't step on it," answered the boy.

"That's easy. Under the bed. She practically never cleans under the bed."

"Yes, I know," agreed Keith. "I looked. There are a lot of dust mice back there."

"Please — " Ralph was pained.

"Oh. Sorry," said the boy. "That's what my mother calls bunches of dusty fluff under the bed."

"*My* mother doesn't," said Ralph. "Now how about opening the door?"

The boy put his hand on the doorknob. "You won't let anything happen to my motorcycle, will you?" he asked.

"You know I wouldn't let anything happen to a beauty like this," said Ralph.

"See that you don't. And don't stay out too late." The boy opened the door and permitted Ralph to putt out into the dim light of the hall.

Ralph had a scary feeling

he was on the threshold

of adventure.

To Be Continued...

And he's off! But where's he going? You can find out by reading the rest of **The Mouse and the Motorcycle.**

Vrrrooom!

What kind of adventures can a mouse on a motorcycle
have in a hotel? Make a board game about Ralph's
adventures. Include the dangers and pitfalls he might
face. Remember, the object of the game should be to
return Ralph safely to his mousehole.

Take Off with Ralph

After he learns to ride a motorcycle, Ralph can't go back
to his quiet mousehole. He gets into many scrapes, which
you can read about in these two sequels to *The Mouse and
the Motorcycle*.

A vicious dog threatens mild-mannered Ralph at summer
camp in *Runaway Ralph*.

It's chaos in the classroom when Ralph attends school for
the first time in *Ralph S. Mouse*.

THE

Your reading adventures don't ever have to end. You can continue with the further adventures of Lucy, Eustace, the Blossoms, and Ralph. And then you can begin new adventures with these books.

The Mouse and the Motorcycle
by Beverly Cleary
Follow the rest of Ralph's adventures

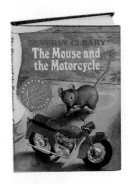

as he drives his motorcycle through some hair-raising scrapes with danger.

Henry Reed, Inc. *by Keith Robertson*
Grover's Corner is a quiet little town — until Henry Reed comes to visit one summer and teams up with Midge Glass to start a research business.

The Great Brain
by John D. Fitzgerald
Tom is always using his brain and money-loving heart to cook up wild schemes, while his brother is always trying to straighten him out.

Anne of Green Gables
by L. M. Montgomery
Anne comes to Green Gables with nothing more than a vivid imagination and bright red hair — and brings laughter to the lonely people who adopt her.

Misty of Chincoteague
by Marguerite Henry
This book is the first in an adventure series about wild ponies on islands off the coast of Virginia.

The Borrowers *by Mary Norton*
What happens to buttons, stamps, and other little things that "disappear" from your home? Meet the Borrowers — tiny people who borrow things from "human beans."

Glossary

Some of the words in this book may have pronunciations or meanings you do not know. This glossary can help you by telling you how to pronounce those words and by telling you the meanings with which those words are used in this book.

You can find out the correct pronunciation of any glossary word by using the special spelling after the word and the pronunciation key that runs across the bottom of the glossary pages.

The full pronunciation key opposite shows how to pronounce each consonant and vowel in a special spelling. The pronunciation key at the bottom of the glossary pages is a shortened form of the full key.

FULL PRONUNCIATION KEY

Consonant Sounds

b	**bib**	k	**c**at, **kick**, pi**que**	th	pa**th**, **th**in
ch	**church**	l	**l**id, need**l**e	*th*	ba**th**e, **th**is
d	**deed**	m	a**m**, **m**an, **mum**	v	ca**v**e, **v**al**v**e,
f	**f**ast, **f**i**f**e, o**ff**,	n	**n**o, sudde**n**		**v**ine
	phase, rou**gh**	ng	thi**ng**	w	**w**ith
g	**g**a**g**	p	**pop**	y	**y**es
h	**h**at	r	**r**oa**r**	z	ro**s**e, **s**i**z**e,
hw	**wh**ich	s	mi**ss**, **s**au**c**e, **s**ee		**x**ylophone,
j	**j**u**dg**e	sh	**d**i**sh**, **sh**ip		**z**ebra
		t	**t**igh**t**	zh	gara**g**e,
					plea**s**ure, vi**s**ion

Vowel Sounds

ă	p**a**t	î	d**ear**, d**eer**,	ou	c**ow**, **ou**t
ā	**ai**d, th**ey**, p**ay**		f**ie**rce, m**e**re	ŭ	c**u**t, r**ou**gh
â	**air**, c**are**, w**ear**	ŏ	p**o**t, h**o**rrible	û	f**ir**m, h**ear**d,
ä	f**a**ther	ō	g**o**, r**ow**, t**oe**		t**er**m, t**ur**n,
ĕ	p**e**t, pl**ea**sure	ô	**a**lter, c**au**ght,		w**or**d
ē	b**e**, b**ee**, **ea**sy,		f**or**, p**aw**	yo͞o	ab**u**se, **u**se
	s**ei**ze	oi	b**oy**, n**oi**se, **oi**l	ə	**a**bout, sil**e**nt,
ĭ	p**i**t	o͝o	b**oo**k		penc**i**l, lem**o**n,
ī	b**y**, g**uy**, p**ie**	o͞o	b**oo**t		circ**u**s
				ər	butt**er**

STRESS MARKS

Primary Stress′	Secondary Stress′
bi•ol•o•gy [bī ŏl′ə jē]	bi•o•log•i•cal [bī′ə lŏj′ĭ kəl]

a•ban•don (ə băn′dən) *v.* To leave, especially because of trouble or anger; to desert: *Because the seal's parents had not returned, the rescuers knew the seal pup had been **abandoned**.*

ad•vanced (əd vănst′) *adj.* Being beyond others in progress or development; advanced ideas: *The store has an **advanced** computer system that can read the name and price of the product with an electronic eye.*

a•muse (ə myo͞oz′) *v.* To give enjoyment to; to entertain pleasantly: *The audience was **amused** by the funny clown.* — **amusement**, *n.*

an•chor (ăng′kər) *v.* To hold in one place: *The controls kept the spaceship **anchored** in one place.* — *n.* A heavy metal device that is attached to a ship by a cable. When dropped overboard, an anchor keeps a ship from moving.

an•ti•bi•ot•ic (ăn′tē bī ŏt′ĭk) *n.* A substance, such as penicillin, that kills or slows the growth of such things as bacteria. Antibiotics help to treat and prevent disease.

an•tic (ăn′tĭk) *n.* An action that is odd or funny and makes no sense; a prank: *When my cousin put salt in the sugar jar, she was scolded for her **antic**.*

Arc•tic (ärk′tĭk) *adj.* Of or relating to the region surrounding the North Pole. Arctic animals are animals that live near the North Pole.

ar•rest (ə rĕst′) *v.* To seize and hold by authority of law: *The police **arrested** the criminals and took them to jail.*

as•tron•o•mer (ə strŏn′ə mər) *n.* A person who studies stars, planets, comets, and galaxies: *The **astronomer** looked through the telescope and saw the stars of the Milky Way.*

at•mos•phere (ăt′mə sfîr′) *n.* The gas that surrounds a body in space, especially the air that surrounds the earth: *Mars has no oxygen in its **atmosphere**.* — **atmospheric**, *adj.*

au•to•mat•ic (ô′tə măt′ĭk) *adj.* **1.** Capable of operating by or regulating itself; an automatic machine: *When the **automatic** dishwasher came, Sam no longer had to wash dishes by hand.* **2.** Done without thought or control. — **automatically**, *adv.*

ă pat / ā pay / â care / ä father / ĕ pet / ē be / ĭ pit / ī pie / î fierce / ŏ pot / ō go / ô paw, for / oi oil /

B

baf·fle·ment (băf'əl mənt) *n.* Confusing or difficult to understand or solve. "The farmer watched in bafflement" means the farmer could not understand what he was seeing.

ban·ner (băn'ər) *n.* A flag or similar piece of material with words or a special design on it: *The people carried huge banners with the words "Support Our Beautiful Town" written on them.*

ban·ty (băn'tē) *adj.* Small and wild or aggressive. A banty little man is a small man whose behavior is hard to predict.

bar·gain (bär'gĭn) *n.* **1.** Something offered or bought at a low price: *This coat is a bargain because it is half price.* **2.** An agreement between two sides, often involving payment or a trade; a deal.

base (bās) *n.* A starting point or central place: *A lunar base on the moon would be a central meeting place for the astronauts.*

bow¹ (bou) *n.* The front part of a ship or a boat.

bow² (bou) *v.* **1.** To bend the body, head, or knee to show such things as agreement, respect, or greeting: *At the end of the play, the performers bowed to the audience.* **2.** To give in: *They refused to bow to pressure.* — *n.* A bending of the body or head, as when showing respect or thanks.

bow³ (bō) *n.* **1.** A weapon for shooting arrows. **2.** A stick with horsehair stretched from end to end. A bow is used to play a string instrument, such as a violin. **3.** A knot tied with loops or something tied in such a knot: *Put a bow on that package.* **4.** Something that is bent or curved: *The river makes a bow around the mountain.*

break·er (brā'kər) *n.* A wave that breaks into foam when it reaches the shore: *The calm waves became white-capped breakers when the storm hit.*

bro·cade (brō kād') *n.* A heavy cloth with a rich, raised design woven into it: *The cloth of the drapes was a beautiful woven brocade of flowers and birds.*

buf·fet (bŭf'ĭt) *v.* To strike against with great force; batter: *When Miranda walked out into the storm, she was buffeted by the strong wind.*

bow¹

ōŏ book / ōō boot / ou **out** / ŭ **cut** / û **fur** / *th* **the** / th **thin** / hw **wh**ich / zh vision /
ə **ago**, item, pencil, atom, circus

ca·lam·i·ty (kə lăm′ĭ tē) *n., pl.* **calamities.** A state of severe distress or misfortune; a disaster: *When the bucking bull was set loose in the china shop, the owner declared the situation a real calamity.*

cap·tiv·i·ty (kăp tĭv′ĭ tē) *n.* The condition of being held as a prisoner or being kept under the control of another: *Bears living in captivity live in cages or enclosed pens instead of living in the wild.*

cat·walk (kăt′wôk′) *n.* A narrow platform or pathway, as on the sides of a bridge.

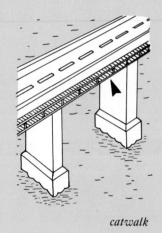

catwalk

chan·nel (chăn′əl) *n.* **1.** The part of a river or harbor deep enough for ships to pass through. **2.** A body of water that connects two larger bodies of water: *The English Channel connects the Atlantic Ocean with the North Sea.* **3.** A band of radio waves used for broadcasting, as on television.

chro·mi·um (krō′mē əm) *n.* A hard, steel-gray substance: *The shiny metal parts of the motorcycle were covered with chromium.*

clin·ic (klĭn′ĭk) *n.* A place that gives medical treatment to patients who are not ill enough to have to stay in a hospital: *When I was sick, my mother took me to the clinic to see a doctor.*

coast (kōst) *v.* To move or continue to move without use of power: *After pedaling my bike up the steep hill, I relaxed and coasted down the other side.* — *n.* The land next to or near the sea; seashore.

com·plaint (kəm plānt′) *n.* A statement or other act that expresses annoyance or unhappiness about something: *When the man was robbed by his neighbor, he took his complaint to the police.*

con·ceal (kən sēl′) *v.* To keep someone or something from being noticed or known; hide: *The thief concealed his face so that no one would recognize him.*

con·cen·tra·tion (kŏn′sən trā′shən) *n.* The act of fixing one's mind on something: *Because playing checkers takes a great deal of thought, concentration is required.*

con·struc·tion (kən strŭk′shən) *n.* The act or process of building: *The construction of a model airplane is easy if you follow the directions.*

ă pat / ā pay / â care / ä father / ĕ pet / ē be / ĭ pit / ī pie / î fierce / ŏ pot / ō go / ô paw, for / oi oil /

cor•al (kôr′əl) *n.* **1.** A substance, as hard as stone, that is formed by the skeletons of tiny sea animals. **2.** A yellowish-pink or reddish-orange color.

coun•cil•lor (koun′sə lər) *n.* A member of a group of persons called together to discuss or settle a problem: *The Emir and his* **councillors** *decided which man was telling the truth.*

cour•age (kûr′ĭj) *n.* The quality that makes a person able to face danger or difficulty with bravery: *Though she was afraid of Mr. Putterham, Beth had enough* **courage** *to complain to him.* — **courageous,** *adj.*

court (kôrt) *v.* To try to win the love of a person one wishes to marry. Courting is like dating. — *n.* A room or building in which legal cases are heard.

cour•te•ous (kûr′tē əs) *adj.* Considerate toward others; polite.

cramped (krămpt) *adj.* Small or confining; narrowed. A cramped space is a space that doesn't leave much room for movement.

cra•ter (krā′tər) *n.* **1.** A pit or hole in the ground created by an explosion or by the impact of a meteor. **2.** A hollow area shaped like a bowl at the mouth of a volcano or geyser.

creep (krēp) *v.* **crept, creeping.** **1.** To move slowly with the body close to the ground. **2.** To grow along the ground or a surface. **3.** To advance, move, or spread slowly or quietly. — **the creeps,** *n.* A feeling that things are crawling over the skin: *The scary old house gave him the creeps.*

cru•el•ty (krōō′əl tē) *n., pl.* **cruelties.** The quality or condition of liking to cause pain or suffering. Spreading lies that cause someone great pain is an example of cruelty.

D

deck (dĕk) *n.* **1.** One of the floors dividing a ship into different levels. **2.** A pack of playing cards.

deed (dēd) *n.* A legal document that shows the terms of an agreement, especially one transferring land from one owner to another: *The* **deed** *shows that this land is owned by my mother.*

de•fect (dē′fĕkt′) *n.* A lack of something necessary for perfection or completeness; a flaw: *A small crack was the mirror's only* **defect.**

de•sign (dĭ zīn′) *n.* An arrangement that forms a pattern: *The fabric had a checkerboard design.*

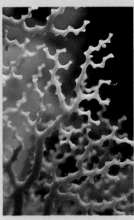

coral

COURAGE

Courage once meant "heart." People with courage act from the heart.

crater[2]

deck

---

o͝o book / o͞o boot / ou **out** / ŭ **cut** / û **fur** / *th* **the** / th **thin** / hw **which** / zh **vision** /
ə **ago,** it**em,** penc**il,** at**om,** circ**us**

de•spair (dǐ **spâr′**) *n.* Total lack of hope: *When he couldn't un-latch the cage after trying and trying, Junior felt total* **despair**.

de•tail (dǐ **tāl′** *or* **dē′**tāl′) *n.* A small part of a whole; an item: *The fish pond was just one of the many* **details** *in the painting of the garden.*

di•ges•tive sys•tem (dǐ **jĕs′**tǐv **sǐs′**təm) *n.* A group of bodily organs that work together to break food down into a form that is easily taken in and used by the body.

dis•may (dǐs **mā′**) *n.* A sudden loss of courage or confidence in the face of danger or trouble: *We thought we were winning the game but were* **dismayed** *to find out the other team was ahead.*

dis•pute (dǐ **spyo͞ot′**) *n.* An argument or quarrel; a fight: *Only a judge could settle the* **dispute** *between the two men.* — *v.* To argue about.

dis•turb•ing the peace (dǐ **stûrb′**ǐng *thə* pēs) *v.* To break the law by interrupting or endangering public security and order: *When the angry crowd pushed their way into the mayor's office, the police said they were* **disturbing the peace**.

dor•sal fin (**dôr′**səl fǐn) *n.* The main fin on the outer surface, underside, or back of fishes or certain sea mammals.

dorsal fin

ENDURE

Endure is an old word that originally meant "to make hard."

drain (drān) *v.* To use up completely: *The long-distance swim* **drained** *their strength and energy.*

em•broi•der (ĕm **broi′**dər) *v.* To decorate cloth by sewing on lines or shapes that form a pattern: *He used a needle and thread to* **embroider** *a picture of a rose on the cloth.*

en•dure (ĕn **do͞or′**) *v.* **1.** To put up with; to bear: *I can withstand almost any kind of pain, but I simply cannot* **endure** *a toothache.* **2.** To continue to exist; last.

en•er•gy (**ĕn′**ər jē) *n., pl.* **energies. 1.** Usable heat or electric power for doing work such as moving or lifting objects. Electricity is a form of energy. **2.** The ability to act, work, or put forth mental or physical effort.

en•vi•ron•ment (ĕn **vī′**rən mənt) *n.* The surroundings in which a plant or animal lives: *The* **environment** *on Neptune is too cold to support human life.* — **environmental,** *adj.*

ă pat / ā pay / â care / ä father / ĕ pet / ē be / ĭ pit / ī pie / î fierce / ŏ pot / ō go / ô paw, for / oi **oil** /

ex•er•cise (ĕk′sər sīz′) *n.* **1.** Physical activity for the good of the body: *To stay in shape, the athlete needed plenty of exercise.* **2.** The act of using or putting into practice. **3.** A lesson or problem designed to improve understanding or skill.

ex•er•tion (ĭg zûr′shən) *n.* Great physical effort; hard work: *Mike had never before had to crawl such a long distance. His muscles weren't used to that kind of exertion.*

ex•haust (ĭg zôst′) *v.* **1.** To make very tired; wear out: *Miranda worked so hard she was exhausted.* **2.** To use up; consume.

ex•haust pipe (ĭg zôst′ pīp) *n.* A pipe through which gases are released from an engine.

ex•pe•di•tion (ĕk′spĭ dĭsh′ən) *n.* **1.** A journey made for a definite purpose: *The scientists and researchers spent months preparing for an expedition to the North Pole.* **2.** The group making such a trip.

F

---

fend•er (fĕn′dər) *n.* A cover or guard mounted above and around a wheel, as on a car or bicycle.

flap (flăp) *v.* To move or cause to move wings or arms up and down: *The bird began flapping its wings.* — *n.* A flat piece attached along one side and hanging loose on the other, often forming a cover for an opening: *I licked the flap of the envelope.*

exhaust pipe

float (flōt) *v.* To be held up in or at the top of a liquid or air: *Astronauts float in space.*

flu•id (floo′ĭd) *n.* A substance, such as air or water, that flows easily and takes the shape of its container: *Milk is a fluid, but ice is not.*

fore•close (fôr klōz′) *v.* To deprive a person of the right to own land when the owner has failed to make payments on time. When Heck Jones tried to foreclose on the McBroom farm, he was trying to take the farm away from the McBrooms. — **foreclosure,** *n.*

fender

for•mu•la (fôr′myə lə) *n.* A liquid food for infants: *Constance gave Andy Bear a formula of evaporated milk and water to drink.*

frac•ture (frăk′chər) *n.* A break or crack, as in a bone. When a bone has fractures, it has been broken or cracked in several places.

---

oo **boo**k / oo **boo**t / ou **ou**t / ŭ **cu**t / û **fu**r / *th* **the** / th **th**in / hw **wh**ich / zh **vi**sion / ə **a**go, **i**tem, penc**i**l, at**o**m, circ**u**s

frus·tra·tion (frŭ strā'shən) *n.*
The condition of feeling puzzled,
helpless, or discouraged: *We felt
great **frustration** when our team
lost every game.*
— **frustrate,** *v.*

gadg·et (găj'ĭt) *n.* A small mechanical piece of equipment. A
can opener is a kitchen gadget.

grav·i·ty (grăv'ĭ tē) *n.* **1.** The
natural force that causes objects
to fall to the earth: *A ball tossed
in the air falls back to the
ground because of the pull of
gravity.* **2.** Great importance.

grief (grēf) *n.* Great sadness; deep
sorrow: *The man was over-
come with **grief** when his cat
died.*

hab·it (hăb'ĭt) *n.* An activity or
action done so often that a person
does it without thinking: *I have
a **habit** of washing my hands
before every meal.*

hab·i·tat (hăb'ĭ tăt') *n.* The place
where an animal or plant naturally lives and grows: *The polar
bear's **habitat** is the Arctic.*

GRIEF

Grief was origi-
nally a French
word that meant
"heavy." When
people are sad we
say they are
"heavy with
grief."

hand clutch (hănd klŭch) *n.* A
lever that operates the clutch.
The hand clutch connects and
disconnects the source of power
on a motorcycle.

har·mon·i·ca (här mŏn'ĭ kə) *n.*
A small bar-shaped musical instrument with a row of metal
reeds inside. A player blows
through holes along the front of
the harmonica to make the reeds
vibrate and produce musical
sounds.

hu·man na·ture (hyoo'mən
nā'chər) *n.* The basic character
or quality of people. When Beth
said Bonnie had no faith in human nature, she meant that
Bonnie did not trust people.

im·i·tate (ĭm'ĭ tāt') *v.* To copy
the actions, looks, or sounds of
something: *Parrots like to
imitate human sounds by re-
peating what they hear.*

im·men·si·ty (ĭ měn'sĭ tē) *n.*
Something very large: *The star
was just a tiny speck of light in
the **immensity** of the night sky.*

im·prove·ment (ĭm proov'mənt)
n. A change or addition that
makes something better: *A new
dishwasher, new silverware,
and new tables were just a few
of the **improvements** made in the
restaurant.*

ă pat / ā pay / â care / ä father / ĕ pet / ē be / ĭ pit / ī pie / î fierce / ŏ pot / ō go / ô paw, for /
oi oil /

in•cin•er•a•tor (ĭn sĭn′ə rā′tər) *n.*
A furnace for burning garbage:
*The janitor threw the trash in
the incinerator.*

in•cu•ba•tor (ĭng′kyə bā′tər) *n.*
A device in which an unusually
small newborn baby or some
other delicate living thing is kept
warm and safe while it develops:
*A chick that is hatched away
from its mother needs the
warmth and safety of an
incubator.*

in•spi•ra•tion (ĭn′spə rā′shən) *n.*
A sudden, original idea: *Junior
had an inspiration when he
thought of using his dog to help
him escape from the trap.*
— **inspirational,** *adj.*

in•su•lin (ĭn′sə lĭn) *n.* A medicine
taken for the treatment of diabe-
tes: *Because Buddy is a diabetic, he must take insulin
shots.*

in•tend (ĭn tĕnd′) *v.* To have in
mind as an aim or goal; to plan.

in•ven•tion (ĭn vĕn′shən) *n.* An
original device, system, or process: *Some people think the light
bulb is the greatest invention of
all time.*

in•ven•tor (ĭn vĕn′tər) *n.* A person who creates something for
the first time: *Thomas Edison
was the inventor of the light
bulb.*

L

la•bor sav•ing de•vice (lā′bər
sā′vĭng dĭ vīs′) *n.* Equipment
that is made to save time or
work. Washing machines,
dryers, and dishwashers are
labor saving devices.

la•goon (lə gōōn′) *n.* A shallow
body of water along a coast or
shore.

lagoon

lamp room (lămp rōōm) *n.* The
room at the top of a lighthouse
from which the warning lights
shine.

launch (lônch) *v.* **1.** To begin or
start something. **2.** To move or
set in motion with force; send
off: *to launch a rocket.* **3.** To
put a boat or ship into the water.

le•gal (lē′gəl) *adj.* Based on or
authorized by law: *After the
money was paid, we became
the legal owners of the house.*

life•like (līf′līk′) *adj.* Looking
alive or seeming very real: *The
people in the painting looked so
lifelike they seemed to be real.*

launch²

loop•hole (lōōp′hōl′) *n.* A way of
escaping a difficulty, especially
something left out or not clearly
stated in a contract or law: *The
loophole in the contract allowed
the man to get out of paying
the money.*

ōō **book** / ōō **boot** / ou **out** / ŭ **cut** / û **fur** / *th* **the** / th **thin** / hw **which** / zh **vision** /
ə **ago,** it**e**m, penc**i**l, at**o**m, circ**u**s

mast (măst) *n.* An upright pole that supports the sails and rigging of a ship or a boat.

mast

mer•chan•dise (mûr′chən dīz′) *n.* Things that are bought and sold; goods: *The store owner stocked his shelves with all kinds of* **merchandise**.

me•te•or•ite (mē′tē ə rīt′) *n.* A rock from outer space that reaches the surface of a planet: *The* **meteorite** *fell to earth in a ball of fire.*

mis•er•y (mĭz′ə rē) *n., pl.* **miseries.** Great pain or distress: *Junior was upset and in* **misery** *because he was trapped in the cage.*

mold¹ (mōld) *n.* A type of fungus that forms a fuzzy coating on the surface of damp or decaying substances: *Bread that has been left out too long will become covered with a fuzzy green* **mold**. — *v.* To become moldy.

mold² (mōld) *n.* **1.** A hollow container in which a liquid or soft substance, such as wax or plaster, can be shaped. **2.** Something shaped in a mold: *We had a gelatin* **mold** *for dessert.* — *v.* To shape or form in or as if in a mold.

mo•men•tum (mō mĕn′təm) *n.* The force or speed that something has when it moves: *Though the bicyclist squeezed the handbrakes, the* **momentum** *of the bike made it continue moving down the hill.*

moon (mo̅o̅n) *n.* A heavenly body that revolves around a planet; a satellite: *Phobos and Deimos are two small* **moons** *that revolve around Mars.*

muf•fler (mŭf′lər) *n.* **1.** A metal pipe that deadens the noise of a motor vehicle's engine: *Our car is very noisy because the* **muffler** *is broken.* **2.** A scarf worn around the neck for warmth.

o•be•di•ent (ō bē′dē ənt) *adj.* Doing what is asked, ordered, or required; willing to obey. An obedient servant is a servant who follows instructions.

o•blige (ə blīj′) *v.* To help; to do a favor for: *The neighbors were always glad to* **oblige** *anyone in need of help.*

or•phaned (ôr′fənd) *v.* To make or cause a child or animal to be without either parent: *When the mother seal did not return for her baby, it was left* **orphaned**.

ă pat / ā pay / â care / ä father / ĕ pet / ē be / ĭ pit / ī pie / î fierce / ŏ pot / ō go / ô paw, for / oi oil /

pac•i•fi•er (păs′ə fī′ər) *n.* A rubber or plastic nipple or teething ring for a baby to suck or chew on.

pan•ic (păn′ĭk) *n.* A sudden feeling of great fear. — *v.* To feel panic: *The thought of being trapped in the cave frightened Buddy so much that he began to panic.* — **panicky**, *adj.*

pat•tern (păt′ərn) *n.* **1.** The way in which shapes and colors are arranged; a design. **2.** A guide or model for something to be made: *a dress pattern.* **3.** A combination of events or qualities that always happen the same way or in the same order.

per•fec•tion•ist (pər fĕk′shə nĭst′) *n.* A person who sets very difficult goals and becomes disappointed when they are not met. A perfectionist does not like anything that is less than perfect.

per•suade (pər swād′) *v.* To cause to do or believe something, as by arguing; to convince: *Beth and her club persuaded people not to shop at Mr. Putterham's store.*

phos•pho•rus (fŏs′fər əs) *n.* **1.** A substance that glows in the dark. "The water is alive with phosphorus" means that the water is glowing. **2.** A poisonous chemical used in making matches, detergents, and fertilizers.

pick•et line (pĭk′ĭt līn) *n.* A line of people standing or marching outside a place of business to express their dissatisfaction with that business.

por•cu•pine (pôr′kyə pīn′) *n.* An animal covered with long, sharp spines called quills.

prank•ish (prăng′kĭsh) *adj.* Marked by playful, often naughty behavior: *The prankish man played tricks on everyone who came into the forest.* — **prank**, *n.*

pre•dic•a•ment (prĭ dĭk′ə mənt) *n.* A difficult or embarrassing situation: *My predicament is that I have promised to be in two different places at the same time.*

prof•it (prŏf′ĭt) *n.* The amount of money left after the costs of operating a business have been subtracted from the money earned: *I made a profit of five cents on every newspaper I sold.*

prow (prou) *n.* The pointed front of a ship; the bow.

pacifier

PANIC

Ancient Greeks were convinced the scary night sounds they heard in the forest were caused by Pan, the forest god. The fright they felt gives us the word *panic*.

PHOSPHORUS

Phosphorus comes from *phos*, the Greek word for "light."

porcupine

ŏŏ book / ōō boot / ou out / ŭ cut / û fur / *th* the / th thin / hw which / zh vision / ə ago, item, pencil, atom, circus

487

pur•sue (pər sōō′) *v.* To chase in order to catch: *The anteater* **pursued** *the ants all the way to the anthill.*

Q

quill (kwĭl) *n.* **1.** One of the sharp, hollow spines of a porcupine. **2.** A long, stiff feather. **3.** A writing pen that is made from a feather.

R

quill

re•ac•tion (rē ăk′shən) *n.* A response to something: *I had a bad* **reaction** *to the medicine and became very sick.*

re•ceipt (rĭ sēt′) *n.* **1.** A regional term for recipe. A receipt is a set of directions for making or preparing something, especially food. **2.** A written statement that money has been paid or that merchandise has been received: *When Beth paid for her shirt, the storekeeper gave her a* **receipt.**

reck•less (rĕk′lĭs) *adj.* Not careful or cautious: *Ralph was a* **reckless** *mouse because he risked getting caught playing outside his mousehole.*

re•cov•er (rĭ kŭv′ər) *v.* **1.** To return to a normal condition, as of health: *The seal* **recovered** *from the illness and was released back into the ocean.* **2.** To get back: **recover** *a lost ring.* **3.** To make up for: **recover** *lost time.*

reef (rēf) *n.* A strip or ridge of rock, sand, or coral that rises to or is close to the surface of a body of water.

re•flec•tor (rĭ flĕk′tər) *n.* A shiny surface or device that throws back light rays, heat, or sounds. A mirror is a reflector.

re•flex (rē′flĕks′) *n.* An automatic response. Blinking and sneezing are reflexes.

re•fund (rĭ fŭnd′) *v.* To pay back: *The store will* **refund** *your money for the damaged shirt.* — *n.* (rē′fŭnd′) **1.** The refunding of an amount of money. **2.** An amount refunded.

re•ha•bil•i•ta•tion (rē′hə bĭl′ĭ tā′shən) *n.* The process of being restored to a former state or condition, such as in health: *After the seal was nursed back to health, its* **rehabilitation** *was complete when it was released back into the ocean.*

re•morse (rĭ môrs′) *n.* Bitter regret for a past action: *The two brothers felt great* **remorse** *for the trick they'd played on their sister.*

ă pat / ā pay / â care / ä father / ĕ pet / ē be / ĭ pit / ī pie / î fierce / ŏ pot / ō go / ô paw, for / oi oil /

re•serve (rĭ zûrv′) *v.* To set aside for a special purpose or for later use: *The empty lot has been reserved for a new park.*

re•source (rĭ sôrs′) *n.* Something that is a source of wealth to a country. Natural resources include trees that can be used for lumber and paper.

rev•e•la•tion (rĕv′ə lā′shən) *n.* Something made known that had not been known or realized before: *Christopher Columbus's discovery of the New World was a revelation to Europeans.*

ruck•us (rŭk′əs) *n.* A noisy outbreak of disorder: *When the mouse ran through the classroom, it caused a ruckus among the students.*

rust•y (rŭs′tē) *adj.* **1.** Weaker, slower, or less skilled because of a lack of use or practice. When Lonesome John said his checker game was rusty, he meant he hadn't played checkers in a long time. **2.** Covered or coated with rust.

S

scan (skăn) *v.* To look at or examine something closely: *The astronauts scanned the planet for a safe place to land their spacecraft.*

shrink (shrĭngk) *v.* **shrank** or **shrunk, shrunk** or **shrunken.** To make or become smaller: *Sometimes shirts washed in hot water shrink to a smaller size.*

shut•tle (shŭt′l) *n.* A device used in weaving. The shuttle carries a thread that runs lengthwise over and under threads that run from top to bottom.

shuttle

sin•cere (sĭn sîr′) *adj.* Not lying or pretending; honest; genuine. When Beth said Mr. Putterham didn't have a sincere smile, she meant that he seemed to be only pretending to be pleasant.

slay (slā) *v.* **slew, slain, slaying.** To kill violently: *In many fairy tales, the hero has to slay a dragon.*

sleigh (slā) *n.* A vehicle on runners that is usually pulled by a horse over ice or snow.

slick•er (slĭk′ər) *n.* A shiny raincoat, especially one made of plastic or oilskin.

smoth•er (smŭ*th*′ər) *v.* To cause someone to die from lack of air or to make it difficult for a person to breathe: *When Mike felt like he was being smothered in the cave, he felt as if he couldn't breathe.*

slicker

ŏŏ **book** / ōō **boot** / ou **out** / ŭ **cut** / û **fur** / *th* **the** / th **thin** / hw **which** / zh **vision** /
ə **ago**, it**em**, penc**il**, at**om**, circ**us**

spoke

spe·cial·ist (spĕsh′ə lĭst) *n.* A person, such as a doctor, who is involved in a particular activity or branch of study. *Animal-care specialists are people who are experts in the field of animal health.*

spell¹ (spĕl) *n.* **1.** A word or group of words thought to have magic power: *The old man said he would cast a spell on anyone who tried to enter his garden.* **2.** A short period of time.

spell² (spĕl) *v.* To name or write the letters of a word in the correct order.

spir·it (spĭr′ĭt) *n.* **1.** A ghost: *A tree spirit is a ghost that lives in a tree.* **2.** A person's mood or state of mind. **3.** Enthusiasm, courage, or pep.

spoke (spōk) *n.* A rod or brace that connects the rim of a wheel to its hub.

stern (stûrn) *n.* The rear part of a ship or a boat.

stilt (stĭlt) *n.* One of a pair of long, slender poles each with a foot support, used to help a person walk high above the ground: *The stilts the clown wore made him appear to be walking twenty feet off the ground.*

stern

strug·gle (strŭg′əl) *v.* To make a great effort: *The pelican was so tired and sick, it barely struggled when Joel picked it up.*

sub·ject (sŭb′jĭkt) *n.* A person under the authority, rule, or control of another: *The king and queen ruled over all the subjects of the land.*

suf·fo·cate (sŭf′ə kāt′) *v.* **1.** To be hot and uncomfortable because of the lack of air: *Mike felt as if he were suffocating from the lack of air.* **2.** To die from lack of air.

surf (sûrf) *n.* The sport of riding the tops of waves before they break on a shore: *Surfing is a sport that requires a surfboard, big ocean waves, and balance.*

surge (sûrj) *v.* To rise and move forward with force: *The giant waves surged up and nearly rolled the boat over.*

sy·ringe (sə rĭnj′) *n.* A medical instrument used to inject medicine into the body. *Syringes are used to inject insulin into a diabetic person.*

tempt (tĕmpt) *v.* To appeal strongly to; attract: *The woman held the food in front of the seal to tempt it to eat.*

ă pat / ā pay / â care / ä father / ĕ pet / ē be / ĭ pit / ī pie / î fierce / ŏ pot / ō go / ô paw, for / oi oil /

thresh•old (thrĕsh′ōld′) *n.* **1.** The point where something begins. A threshold is the same as a beginning. **2.** The piece of wood or stone built into the floor of a doorway. **3.** An entrance.

tri•um•phant (trī ŭm′fənt) *adj.* Victorious; successful: *Miranda felt triumphant when she succeeded in keeping the lighthouse lamps lit during the storm.*

un•con•scious (ŭn kŏn′shəs) *adj.* Not being able to see, feel, hear, or understand what is happening for a time: *After the man fainted, he lay unconscious on the floor.*

un•pre•dict•a•ble (ŭn′prĭ dĭk′tə bəl) *adj.* Not able to tell about in advance: *Adult polar bears are unpredictable because it is difficult to tell how they will behave.*

up and com•ing (ŭp ănd kŭm′ĭng) *adj.* Marked for future success or popularity; showing promise: *The new restaurant was considered up and coming because every night long lines of people waited to get inside.*

val•iant (văl′yənt) *adj.* Acting with or showing courage: *The valiant captain was afraid of nothing.*

ven•ture (vĕn′chər) *n.* A task or an activity that is risky or dangerous: *Climbing a mountain is a risky venture.*

vet•er•i•nar•i•an (vĕt′ər ə nâr′ē ən) *n.* A doctor who is trained to treat animals: *When our dog was sick, we took him to the veterinarian.*

vol•ca•no (vŏl kā′nō) *n., pl.* **volcanoes** or **volcanos.** **1.** A mountain that is formed by the material released during a volcanic eruption. **2.** An opening in the earth's crust through which lava, dust, ash, and hot gases are released.

vow (vou) *n.* A promise: *Carlos made a vow to take care of his younger brothers and sisters.*

voy•age (voi′ĭj) *n.* A long journey to a distant place, made on a ship, an aircraft, or a spacecraft. When Lucy said she was used to a lot of voyaging, she meant that she had traveled a great deal.

vul•ner•a•ble (vŭl′nər ə bəl) *adj.* Easily affected by physical injury: *Turtles are less vulnerable to injury because they can withdraw into their hard shells.*

VOLCANO

Vulcan was the Roman god of fire. From his name came the word *volcano*.

ŏŏ book / ōō boot / ou **out** / ŭ **cut** / û **fur** / *th* **the** / th **thin** / hw **which** / zh **vision** /
ə **ago, item, pencil, atom, circus**

wick

weave (wēv) *v.* To make something, such as a cloth or a basket, by passing something, such as threads or twigs, over and under one another: *The woman used brightly colored threads to* **weave** *the cloth.*

weight•less (wāt'lĭs) *adj.* Experiencing little or no pull of gravity: *A* **weightless** *astronaut floats through space.*

wick (wĭk) *n.* A cord or piece of twisted thread in a candle or oil lamp. When it is lighted, the wick draws up the melted wax or oil to be burned.

wis•dom (wĭz'dəm) *n.* Intelligence and good judgment in knowing what to do and being able to tell the difference between good and bad and right and wrong.

ă pat / ā pay / â care / ä father / ĕ pet / ē be / ĭ pit / ī pie / î fierce / ŏ pot / ō go / ô paw, for / oi oil / o͝o book / o͞o boot / ou out / ŭ cut / û fur / *th* the / th thin / hw which / zh vision / ə ago, item, pencil, atom, circus

Acknowledgments

For each of the selections listed below, grateful acknowledgment is made for permission to excerpt and/or reprint original or copyrighted material, as follows:

Major Selections

"Andy Bear: A Polar Cub Grows Up at the Zoo," from the book by Ginny Johnston and Judy Cutchins. Copyright © 1985 by Ginny Johnston and Judy Cutchins. Reprinted by permission of the authors and Morrow Junior Books, a division of William Morrow & Co., Inc.

"The Blossoms Meet the Vulture Lady," from the book by Betsy Byars. Copyright © 1986 by Betsy Byars. Reprinted by permission of Delacorte Press, a division of Bantam, Doubleday, Dell Publishing Group, Inc.

"The Doughnuts," written and illustrated by Robert McCloskey, from *Homer Price*. Copyright © 1943, renewed © 1971 by Robert McCloskey. Reprinted by permission of Viking Penguin, a division of Penguin Books USA, Inc.

"Earth Is Our Address," from *Around Our World*, Houghton Mifflin Social Studies by Margaret Stimmann Branson. Copyright © 1980 by Houghton Mifflin Company. Reprinted by permission of Houghton Mifflin Company.

"The Emir's Son," by Martin Ballard, illustrated by Gareth Floyd. Text copyright © 1967 by Martin Ballard. Illustrations copyright © 1967 by Gareth Floyd (Constable Young Books Ltd., London). Reprinted by permission of Martin Ballard and Gareth Floyd.

"Fly Away Free," by Joan Hewett, photographs by Richard Hewett. Copyright © 1981 by Joan and Richard Hewett. Reprinted by permission of Joan and Richard Hewett.

"Ghost of the Lagoon," by Armstrong Sperry. Reprinted by permission of the author and the author's agents, Scott Meredith Literary Agency, Inc., 845 Third Avenue, New York, New York 10022.

"Her Seven Brothers," by Paul Goble. Copyright © 1988 by Paul Goble. Reprinted by arrangement with Bradbury Press, an imprint of Macmillan Publishing Company.

"The Hey Hey Man," by Sid Fleischman. Copyright © 1979 by Albert S. Fleischman. Reprinted by permission of Sid Fleischman, Inc.

"Humans on Mars? Where Will the U.S. Space Program Go Next?" by Renée Skelton from the September, 1988 issue of *3–2–1 Contact*. Copyright © 1989 by The Children's Television Workshop. Used courtesy of the *3–2–1 Contact* magazine.

"The Lighthouse Keeper's Daughter," by Arielle North Olson. Text copyright © 1987 by Arielle North Olson. Illustrations copyright © 1987 by Elaine Wentworth. Used by permission of Little, Brown and Company.

"Mars," by Seymour Simon. Text copyright © 1987 by Seymour Simon. Illustrations copyright © 1987 by William Morrow and Company, Inc. Used by permission of Morrow Junior Books, a division of William Morrow and Co., Inc.

"McBroom Tells the Truth," by Sid Fleischman. Copyright © 1966 by Sid Fleischman. Reprinted by permission of Sid Fleischman, Inc.

"The Mouse and the Motorcycle," from the book by Beverly Cleary, illustrated by Louis Darling. Copyright © 1965 by Beverly Cleary. Used by permission of Morrow Junior Books, a division of William Morrow and Co., Inc., and Hamish Hamilton Ltd., London.

"The Pretty Pennies picket," from *Philip Hall likes me. I reckon maybe.* by Bette Greene. Text copyright © 1974 by Bette Greene. Reprinted by permission of the publishers, Dial Books for Young Readers and Hamish Hamilton Ltd., London.

"The Scarebird," by Sid Fleischman. Text copyright © 1987 by Sid Fleischman, Inc., illustrations copyright © 1988 by Peter Sis. Reprinted by permission of Greenwillow Books, a division of William Morrow and Co., Inc.

"Sterling: The Rescue of a Baby Harbor Seal," by Sandra Verrill White and Michael Filisky. Copyright © 1989 by the New England Aquarium. Reprinted by permission of Crown Publishers, Inc.

"The Streets Are Free," a play by Kurusa, based on her book, *La Calle Es Libre*. Copyright © 1981 by Ediciones Ekare-Banco del Libro. Reprinted by permission of Ediciones Ekare-Banco del Libro.

"To Space and Back," from the book by Sally Ride with Susan Okie. Copyright © 1986 by Sally Ride with Susan Okie. Reprinted by permission of Lothrop, Lee & Shepard Books, a division of William Morrow & Co., Inc., and International Creative Management, Inc., New York.

"The Voyage of the *Dawn Treader*," from the book by C. S. Lewis. Copyright the estate of C. S. Lewis, 1952. Copyright © renewed by Geoffrey Bles. Reprinted by permission of William Collins Sons & Co., Ltd.

"The Weaving of a Dream," by Marilee Heyer. Copyright © 1986 by Marilee Heyer. All rights reserved. Reprinted by permission of the author, the author's agent, Toni Mendes, Inc. and Viking Penguin, a division of Penguin Books USA, Inc.

"Where's Buddy?" from the book by Ron Roy, illustrations by Troy Howell. Text copyright © 1982 by Ron Roy. Illustrations copyright © 1982 by Troy Howell. Reprinted by permission of Houghton Mifflin Company.

Poetry

"Bison" by Tonye Garter, from *Arrows Four: Prose and Poetry by Young American Indians*, edited by T. D. Allen. Copyright © 1974 by T. D. Allen. Used by permission of the author. All rights reserved.

"Buffalo Dusk," by Carl Sandburg, from *Smoke and Steel*. Copyright © 1920 by Harcourt Brace Jovanovich, Inc., and renewed 1948 by Carl Sandburg. Reprinted by permission of the publisher.

"A Chameleon," by Eve Merriam, from *Jamboree: Rhymes for All Times*. Copyright © 1962, 1964, 1966, 1973, 1984 by Eve Merriam. All rights reserved. Reprinted by permission of Marian Reiner for the author.

"Eagle Flight," by Alonzo Lopez, from *The Whispering Wind* by Terry Allen. Copyright © 1972 by The Institute of American Indian Arts. Used by permission of Doubleday, a division of Bantam, Doubleday, Dell Publishing Group, Inc.

"A Flea and a Fly in a Flue," author unknown, from *Laughable Limericks*. Copyright © 1965 by Sara and John E. Brewton (Harper & Row, Publishers, Inc.).

"Long Trip," by Langston Hughes, from *Selected Poems of Langston Hughes*. Copyright © 1926 by Alfred A. Knopf, Inc., renewed © 1954 by Langston Hughes. Reprinted by permission of Alfred A. Knopf, Inc. and Harold Ober Associates Incorporated.

"Moon," by Myra Cohn Livingston, from *Space Songs*. Published by Holiday House. Copyright © 1988 by Myra Cohn Livingston. Reprinted by permission of Marian Reiner for the author.

"A Mouse in Her Room Woke Miss Dowd," author unknown, from *Laughable Limericks*. Copyright © 1965 by Sara and John E. Brewton. (Harper & Row, Publishers, Inc.).

"On Reading: Four Limericks," by Myra Cohn Livingston, from *4-Way Stop and Other Poems*. Copyright © 1976 by Myra Cohn Livingston. Reprinted by permission of Marian Reiner for the author.

"The Passenger Pigeon," by Paul Fleischman, text only from *I Am Phoenix*. Copyright © 1985 by Paul Fleischman. Reprinted by permission of Harper & Row, Publishers, Inc. and Bill Berger Associates Inc.

"Reading's Enchanting Spell," by Leland B. Jacobs. Reprinted with permission of the publisher Early Years, Inc., Norwalk, Connecticut 06854. From the November/December 1985 issue of *Teaching/K-8* (formerly *Early Years/K-8*).

"Sea Calm," by Langston Hughes, from *Selected Poems of Langston Hughes*. Copyright © 1926 by Alfred A. Knopf, Inc. Renewed, 1954 by Langston Hughes. Reprinted by permission of Alfred A. Knopf, Inc. and Harold Ober Associates Incorporated.

"A Very Mean Man of Belsize," author unknown, from *Laughable Limericks*. Copyright © 1965 by Sara and John E. Brewton (Harper & Row Publishers, Inc.).

"Writing Limericks," from "Write Me a Verse," from *One At a Time*, by David McCord. Copyright © 1961, 1962 by David McCord. Reprinted by permission of Little, Brown and Company.

Quotations from Authors/Illustrators

Beverly Cleary, page 444, from "A National Heroine and an International Favorite," by Shirley Fitzgibbons, Winter, 1977, in *Top of the News*. Reprinted by permission of the American Library Association.

Judy Cutchins and Ginny Johnston, page 151, from *Contemporary Authors*, Vol. 127. Copyright © 1989 by Gale Research, Inc. Reprinted by permission of the publisher.

Robert McCloskey, page 251, from "Robert McCloskey, Master of Humorous Realism," in *Authors and Illustrators of Children's Books*.

Ron Roy, page 129, from *Something About the Author*, Vols. 40, 4. Copyright © 1985, 1973, respectively, by Gale Research, Inc. Reprinted by permission of the publisher.

Seymour Simon, page 393, from *Something About the Author*, Vols. 40, 4. Copyright © 1985, 1973, respectively, by Gale Research, Inc. Reprinted by permission of the publisher.

Armstrong Sperry, page 128, from *The Junior Book of Authors*, 2nd ed., edited by Stanley J. Kunitz and Howard Haycraft. Copyright © 1934, 1951 by the H.W. Wilson Company, New York. Reprinted by permission.

Additional Acknowledgments

"McBroom's Almanac," page 64, from the book by Sid Fleischman. Copyright © 1984 by Sid Fleischman. Reprinted by permission of Little, Brown and Company and Sid Fleischman, Inc.

"To Lucy Barfield," page 400, from *The Lion, the Witch and the Wardrobe*, by C. S. Lewis. Copyright © 1950 by C. S. Lewis Pte. Ltd. Copyright renewed. All rights reserved. Reprinted by permission of the publisher, William Collins Sons & Co., Ltd.

Theme Books

The Theme Books shown on Extended Reading pages are available from Houghton Mifflin Company and are reprinted with permission from various publishers. Jacket artists for these books are listed below.

The Kid in the Red Jacket, by Barbara Park. Cover art by Rob Sauber, copyright © 1987 by Rob Sauber.

A Lion to Guard Us, by Clyde Robert Bulla. Jacket art by Michele Chessare, copyright © 1981 by Michele Chessare.

The Mouse and the Motorcycle, by Beverly Cleary. Jacket art by Paul O. Zelinsky, copyright © 1989 by William Morrow & Co.

Saving the Peregrine Falcon, by Caroline Arnold. Photographs by Richard R. Hewett, copyright © 1985 by Richard R. Hewett.

Space Challenger: The Story of Guion Bluford, by Jim Haskins and Kathleen Benson. Photographs courtesy of the National Aeronautics and Space Administration.

Vassilisa the Wise: A Tale of Medieval Russia, retold by Josepha Sherman. Jacket art by Daniel San Souci, copyright © 1988 by Daniel San Souci.

The Whipping Boy, by Sid Fleischman. Jacket art by Peter Sis, copyright © 1986 by Peter Sis.

Additional Recommended Reading

Houghton Mifflin Company wishes to thank the following publishers for permission to reproduce their book covers in Extended Reading lists:

Arcade Publishing, a Little, Brown company:
The Shining Princess and Other Japanese Legends, by Eric Quayle. Jacket art by Michael Foreman, copyright © 1989 by Michael Foreman.

Atheneum Publishers, an imprint of Macmillan Publishing Company, Inc.:
Ice Swords: An Undersea Adventure, by James Houston. Jacket art by James Houston, copyright © 1985 by James Houston.

Clarion Books, a division of Houghton Mifflin Company:
How Many Days to America? A Thanksgiving Story, by Eve Bunting. Jacket art by Beth Peck, copyright © 1988 by Beth Peck; *The Way of the Grizzly*, by Dorothy Hinshaw Patent. Jacket art by William Muñoz, copyright © 1987 by William Muñoz.

Delacorte Press:
The Fox Busters, by Dick King-Smith. Jacket art by Richard Watson, copyright © 1988 by Richard Watson.

Frederick Warne and Co., Inc.:
Where the Buffaloes Begin, retold by Olaf Baker. Jacket art by Stephen Gammell, copyright © 1981 by Stephen Gammell.

Grosset & Dunlap:
Anne of Green Gables, by L. M. Montgomery. Jacket art by Jody Lee in association with Artists International, copyright © 1983 by Jody Lee.

Harcourt Brace Jovanovich, Publisher:
The Enchanted Book, by Janina Porazinska. Jacket art by Jan Brett, copyright © 1987 by Jan Brett.

Harper & Row, Publishers:
The Queen's Nose, by Dick King-Smith. Jacket art by Jill Bennett, copyright © 1983 by Jill Bennett; *The Explorer of Barkham Street*, by Mary Stolz. Jacket art by Emily Arnold McCully, copyright © 1985 by Emily Arnold McCully.

Houghton Mifflin Company:
Help! I'm a Prisoner in the Library, by Eth Clifford. Jacket art by George Hughes, copyright © 1979; *The Terrible Wave*, by Marden Dahlstedt. Jacket art by Charles Robinson, copyright © 1989; *The Luck of the Miss L.*, by Lee Kingman. Jacket art by Lee Kingman, copyright © 1986 by Mary Lee Natti.

Lerner Publications Company:
Women in Space: Reaching the Last Frontier, by Carole S. Briggs. Jacket photo courtesy of NASA, copyright © 1988.

J. B. Lippincott Company, subsidiary of Harper & Row Publishers, Inc.:
Whoppers Tall Tales and Other Lies, by Alvin Schwartz. Jacket art by Glen Rounds, copyright © 1975 by Glen Rounds; *Flapdoodle*, by Alvin Schwartz. Jacket art by John O'Brien, copyright © 1980 by John O'Brien. Published simultaneously in Canada by Fitzhenry & Whiteside Limited, Toronto.

William Morrow and Company, Inc.:
Dawn, by Molly Bang. Jacket art by Molly Bang, copyright © 1983 by Molly Bang.

Credits

Program design   Carbone Smolan Associates

Cover design   Carbone Smolan Associates

Design   12–67 Stockton & Associates;   68–131 Carbone Smolan Associates;   132–189 Martine Bruel;   190–253 Imprint;   262–325 Piotr Kaczmarek;   326–395 Summerford Design, Inc.;   396–475 Appleton Design Inc.

Illustrations   13 Frank Remkiewicz;   14, 29, 43, 65 Cynthia Brodie;   16–28 John Littleboy;   30–42 Peter Sis;   44–45 John Littleboy;   46–64 Stephen Osborn;   69–71 David Lombard;   72–84 Francesca Pelizzoli;   85 Kevin Hawkes;   86–102 Elaine Wentworth;   103 Kevin Hawkes;   105 Alexander Farquharson;   106–125 Troy Howell;   126 Kevin Hawkes;   127 Ken Longtemps;   128–131 David Lombard;   134–135 Anna Vojtech;   150 George Schill;   152–155 Anna Vojtech;   167–168, 185, 187 George Schill;   188–189 Anna Vojtech;   194–209 Floyd Cooper;   212–215 Rosenkrans Hoffman;   216–229 Brian Pinkney;   232–249 Robert McCloskey;   257 (map) Precision Graphics;   263–265 Piotr Kaczmarek;   266–283 Marilee Heyer;   284–285 Piotr Kaczmarek;   286–301 Gareth Floyd;   302–303 Piotr Kaczmarek;   304–320 Paul Goble;   321–325 Piotr Kaczmarek;   356 (top left) The Archambault Group;   376 Steve Fuller;   382 © Michael Carroll;   384–385 © Carter Emmart;   397–399 Kimberly Britt;   401–416 David Small;   417 Pauline Baynes, from *The Lion, the Witch and the Wardrobe*, courtesy of Collins Publishers;   419–443 Jacqueline Rogers;   445–472 Louis Darling;   473 Paul O. Zelinsky;   479, 481 (bottom), 486, 487, 490 (bottom) Cecile Duray-Bito;   480, 481 (top), 482, 483; 485, 487, 488, 490 (top), 492 Simon Galkin/Asciutto Art Representatives

Photography   14 Margaret Miller;   45 (top left) Pete Konzak; (top right) Courtesy of The Furrow, Deere and Company; (bottom left and bottom right) Peter Menzel;   104–105 (all) Collection of the Newport Historical Society;   128 Courtesy of Margo Burns;   129 (left) Courtesy of Clarion Books, imprint of Houghton Mifflin Company; (right) Clarence Olson;   133 Leslie Cowperthwaite;   136 Constance Noble;   139–141 (all) Judy Cutchins;   142 Constance Noble;   143 (top) Judy Cutchins/Fernbank Science Center; (bottom) Kathleen Flynn;   144–148, 151 (all) Constance Noble;   156 (top) Amy Burack; (bottom) Ingrid Bartinique;   157 Leslie Cowperthwaite;   158 (top) Bruce M. Wellman; (bottom) Animals Animals/© Caroline Kroeger;   159 (top) Andrew J. Martinez; (bottom) Leslie Cowperthwaite;   160 (top) Bruce M. Wellman; (bottom) Leslie Cowperthwaite;   161 (all) Leslie Cowperthwaite;   162–166 (all) Ken Mallory & Margaret Thompson/New England Aquarium;   168–169, 171–172, 175, 177–178, 180–183 (all) Richard R. Hewett;   191, 192–193, 210–211 Frank Wing;   211 Ken Rome;   230–231 Frank Wing;   231 Juan Santana;   250–251 Frank Wing;   251 Mary Velthoven, Courtesy of Viking Penguin Childrens Books;   252–253 Frank Wing;   255 NASA;   256 Victor Englebert;   259 Susan Kallewaard/American Red Cross;   260 (top right and bottom left) American Red Cross; (center) Susan Kallewaard/American Red Cross;   285 Roy H. Williams, courtesy of Viking Penguin Childrens Books;   303 Courtesy of Martin Ballard;   321 Janet Goble;   327 Comstock;   328 (top) NASA;   328–329 Comstock;   330 NASA;   332–333 (all) Ben Weaver;   334–336, 339 NASA;   340 (center) NASA;   343 (bottom) NASA;   344 (top) NASA;   345 (left) NASA;   347 (left) NASA;   348 (bottom) NASA;   351 (center) NASA;   354 (bottom) Lawrence Migdale/Stock Boston;   356 (top) NASA; (bottom) JPL/NASA;   357–359, 363–364 (all) JPL/NASA;   365 JPL/NASA, photo by Dr. Robert Leighton;   366–367, 369–370, 372–373, 375 (all) JPL/NASA;   377 (all) Culver Pictures;   378 (top and center) NASA; (bottom) JPL/NASA;   379 (all) JPL/NASA;   381 (all) NASA;   386 NASA;   388 (Moon and Mercury) NASA; (Venus) NASA/Taurus Photos; (Mars) JPL/NASA, photo by Dr. Robert Leighton;   399 (Jupiter and Neptune) NASA; (Saturn and Uranus) JPL/NASA; (Pluto) NASA/Taurus Photos;   390 (photo) © Copyright California Institute of Technology and Carnegie Institution of Washington; (logo) NASA;   392 (top) NASA; (bottom) Courtesy of Susan Okie;   393 (top) Courtesy of Seymour Simon; (bottom) Courtesy of Renée Skelton;   394–395 Steven Hunt/The Image Bank;   400 Arthur Strong, Camera Press/Globe Photos;   418 Edward Byars, courtesy of Viking Penguin Childrens Books;   444 Nancy Crampton;   481 Biological Photo Services;   483 Baron Wolman/Woodfin Camp & Associates, Inc.;   487 Tom Stack & Associates, Inc.;   489 William Strode/Woodfin Camp & Associates, Inc.;   489 Peter Vilms/Jeroboam, Inc.

End Matter layout design by Publicom, Inc.